THE MAZE OF INGENUITY

Ideas and idealism in the development of technology

Arnold Pacey

THE MAZE OF INGENUITY

Ideas and idealism in the development of technology

The MIT Press
Cambridge, Massachusetts, and London, England

Sixth printing, 1986
First MIT Press paperback edition, 1976

First published in 1974 by Allen Lane, A Division of Penguin Books Ltd,
London

ISBN 0 262 66030 X

Contents

Preface to the Paperback Edition

The maze revisited

Progress in technology follows a varying direction, with new twists and turns and fresh choices of route confronting each new generation. To achieve progress is to thread a maze, not to follow a straight highway.

But there are those who think that technical progress must always follow a single, forward direction, with each new development growing by an inevitable logic out of what has gone before, and with social change following in the wake of technical innovation as industries adopt new inventions and as changed lifestyles become possible or necessary.

The current debate about technology, in its fundamentals, is between people who hold this 'one-dimensional' view of technical progress and those who discern the possibility of different directions of advance, with occasional lateral shifts in the approach or the subject matter of technology. This 'lateral' view portrays technology as an integral part of human culture, developing in response to the pressures, purposes and practices of human society. Technical progress is therefore just one aspect of a wider progress or development within society, and changes in the direction of technical progress occur whenever the values and objectives of society change.

The one-dimensional view has been the conventional wisdom for a long time, but began to run into trouble during the decade of growing disillusion with technology which is discussed towards the end of this book – disillusion which began with a sense of 'alienation' from technological society felt by many young people and with the 'swing from science' in the mid-1960s (p. 305 ff.); and which culminated in 1972 with questions about resources and pollution raised by work done at M.I.T. (p. 307) for the Club of Rome.

The pessimism arising from these developments can all too

easily turn into fatalism and despair for those who take the one-dimensional view, because it can seem as if the only route for further progress is totally blocked. But the re-emergence of the lateral view very recently has been associated with a more hopeful outlook, because it means that there are now more people who are actively exploring alternative directions for technological and social development.

For example, there are some who are critical of the Club of Rome's efforts to extrapolate current trends into the future, who say that we have no need to drift with the trend, but should instead decide what we want the future to be like, and then work out if it is feasible, and how to get there. The most notable work of this kind has been done at San Carlos de Bariloche in Argentina, but the approach is shared in different ways by many of those who study 'futures' as an academic subject and, indeed, by some who have contributed to the Club of Rome's more recent reports.

Another exploration of new directions for development is that by Ralf Dahrendorf (see literature review at the end of this preface), who suggests that instead of growth measured in terms of quantity, we should seek a development in terms of quality which would make possible a widening of freedom and of educational opportunity with a more creative emphasis. Complementing this approach from a far more radical point of view are Ivan Illich's views on freedom, education and health within a 'post-industrial balance' in the modes of production.

A third kind of exploration of new directions for technical progress is represented by the alternative technology movement (which also uses such terms as 'people's technology', 'soft technology' and many others). All over the United States, the science weekly *Nature* reports, 'small groups of scientists, technologists, artists, children and plain people are forming communities built on small scale self-sufficiency technology. To them, this is innovation . . . with the old string and sealing wax approach. Except they understand optics and electronics and mechanical inventions as well. . . . Others are designing new health maintenance systems built on the premise that the body tends to heal itself and can be promoted to do so without heavy resort to medications. And no one up high notices them for the innovations they could represent. The worst offender is none other than the National Science Foundation, whose mission is to search out and fertilise the innovator'. (4 December 1975.)

The rapid development of all these activities, mostly since the text of this book was completed in 1972, provides an opportunity to explain the purpose of the book more clearly than was possible then. The book is in fact intended as a contribution to the lateral view of technological development – its aim is to use historical evidence to show how the direction of technical progress in Western culture has changed from time to time, and how in some periods, for example in the 17th century as well as in the 1970s, there is tension between two (or more) contrary directions of technical progress being explored simultaneously. It can be seen historically that when an impasse is reached in the development of technology (or in any other cultural movement), the difficulty is often avoided by a change of direction or by the exploration of a different opportunity for development. As Dahrendorf puts it, 'History proceeds by changing the subject'.

The decline of the one-dimensional view of progress has also altered the way in which the history of science and technology needs to be written. As long as historians believed that science could only go forwards and that the direction of technical progress was always the same, they interpreted the researches and inventions of previous generations as a struggle to lay the foundations of our present technological achievement. Now it is more easily possible to see that the thinkers and inventors of the past were making quite different explorations from ours into technological possibility and that they were promoting quite different directions for technical progress, motivated by the social priorities of their own time. Recent historical works by Raymond Williams and Charles Webster which explain and use this approach are noted in the literature review.

My own way of using this alternative view of the history of technology is to look at the development of technology as a series of movements, some of them lasting for as long as two centuries and each with its own characteristic goals and disciplines. In this book, I have tried to characterise these different movements and portray their goals in terms of specific types of objectives, classified as 'humanitarian and social', 'intellectual', 'symbolic' and 'economic'.

Thus the first five chapters of this book may each be read as a self-contained portrait of a specific technological movement, though there is a good deal of continuity between the first two, covering the period 1100–1350, and the second two, covering the

Renaissance and scientific revolution. Following this, there comes an episode in the 18th century, dealt with in chapters 6 and 7, which may be regarded as a movement for rational improvement in technology. It is typified by developments in agriculture (horse-hoes, seed drills, better crop rotations, animal breeding), and by the style and attitudes of such engineers as Perronet, Hell and Smeaton (pp. 206–7). In many ways, the theme of 'improvement' and of experimental practical science was taken over from the 17th century, but without the idealistic fervour and controversy of that period. Improvements achieved were measured against what the Romans were known to have done, against ideals of the public good, and according to notions of the perfectibility of man. And it was probably quite widely felt that changes then occurring tended towards stabilisation at an optimum condition of orderliness, plenty and cultural achievement.

The succeeding technological movement, that of industrialism, can be looked upon as replacing the ideal of *improvement* with one of *expansion* – expansion in the quantity of goods produced and expansion in the geographical outreach of Western trade. My intention in this book was originally to deal with the theme of expansion in three parts – first, quantitative expansion, beginning in the 1770s, as demonstrated by the graphs on pp. 217 and 230; second, changes in attitude, whereby generous and hopeful views of social progress gave way to a narrower view of industrial growth (chapter 8); and third, geographical expansion, and what this meant in terms of Western domination of Asian trade (chapter 9) and in terms of communications (steamships, railways, the electric telegraph of 1837, and so on).

It now seems to me that the necessarily selective account I gave of all these aspects of early industrialism was actually overselective. What Dickson calls the 'ideology of industrialisation' should have been given more emphasis, and so should the expansion of agriculture and the chemical industries – noting, for example, that by the 1840s grain yields in Britain were increasing, not least through the use of superphosphate fertiliser then being manufactured by a new chemical process.

The theme of geographical expansion could also have been amplified, especially by reference to the American experience of industrialisation and expansion into an (almost) empty continent. Prairie farming stimulated such inventions as McCormick's mechanical reapers (from 1834), which were imported by English farmers after the 1851 exhibition. And although Richard Roberts may have pioneered interchangeable parts in England (p. 267), the system came to be used more widely in America, because of different market conditions and a shortage of skilled labour. The principle was applied in numerous small water-powered factories in Connecticut which made clocks, machine tools, firearms and furniture. Owen's idealistic approach to industrialism had its American counterparts also, not just as a result of Owen's own transatlantic travels (p. 255), but through Francis C. Lowell, inventor of the first American power loom, who visited Owen at New Lanark and who later, in Massachusetts, demonstrated how a factory could be run without degrading labour.

One cross-current in 16th-century technology was an interest in agricultural improvement which began in parts of Italy rather before 1500 (and in the Venetian Republic around 1530; see p. 103) and which ultimately spread throughout Europe. By the end of the century, its influence was being felt in England. When Francis Bacon wrote about gardens and plant husbandry in 1625, there were already a number of English books on the subject; there were land drainage schemes afoot; and at some country houses and in Oxford University, there were botanic gardens where exotic and medicinal plants were grown.

Francis Bacon was the source of much inspiration for a movement in 17th century practical science which is described in chapter 5. Much new information about this movement has recently become available in Charles Webster's book *The Great Instauration*, and it seems to me that there is an interesting and instructive comparison to be drawn between this movement in the 17th-century and alternative technology in the 20th. Both movements represent alternatives to systematic and rather mechanistic philosophies of science and technology, and both show their reaction against the apparent sterility of over-developed rational systems by a tendency towards a mystical world view.

Bacon himself was critical of the excessive mysticism of the alchemical tradition in chemistry, in which the light of Nature, loudly proclaimed by Paracelsus, seemed to produce only 'empty delusions'. But the mysticism persisted, although accompanied by a rapidly improving experimental technique in chemistry, matching the careful, empirical methods now evident in the agricultural books being compiled by Hartlib and his associates.

It is interesting that in the alternative technology movement of the 1970s there is some occasional harking back to the alchemical tradition, as in the name of the New Alchemy Institute at Woods Hole, Massachusetts. There is, too, a homespun, 'back to nature' mysticism among advocates of organic farming and a widespread, explicit interest in mystical religions. A recent alternative technology exhibition in Britain featured Transcendental Meditation, the Divine Light Mission and a talk about the astrological significance of geodesic domes alongside practical and workmanlike demonstrations of windmills, solar energy devices, pottery and blacksmithing.

There is similarity between the 17th-century and 1970s alternative movements not only in this mystical tendency but also in their information gathering and disseminating activities; in their Utopian vision; in their apocalyptic sense that time is very short and that current patterns of civilisation are ending; and in their stress on using knowledge and practical skill to meet the real needs of people. Both movements are motivated by what this book refers to as 'humanitarian and social objectives', and by a belief that science should be accessible to ordinary people and should be something they can use for their own practical purposes – the term 'people's technology' illustrates this well. In the 17th century, this attitude meant that the craftsman was the equal of the intellectual; in the 1970s it means growing one's own food or building one's own windmill.

Despite these similarities, there is, of course, a world of difference between 17th-century Puritans and today's eco-freaks, organic farmers and windmill builders, and perhaps in only one respect is the analogy between them significant. This is that, in discussing ways of making future technology more sensitive to human aspirations and to environmental needs, we are setting out again on an enterprise which partly failed in the 17th century, and the danger of failure today is in some ways the same – the hard mechanistic discipline of the opposition is being answered by an emotive anti-rationalism or by woolly mysticism and not by effective disciplines which would allow the new direction of progress to be explored fully and fruitfully enough for it to constitute a credible alternative.

During the four years since the text of this book was completed, I have been much occupied with this question of disciplines in alternative technologies, and I have made practical experiment within the particular alternative field which is known as 'intermediate' or 'appropriate' technology. This is concerned with the non-industrialised, developing countries, and reports on it I have been writing deal with agriculture in Swaziland, houses in Botswana, hand-pumps in India and water supplies generally. In each case, I have tried to clarify technological problems by the use of disciplines capable of allowing the design of equipment to be related more effectively than is possible in conventional technology to a broad consideration of people's needs, wishes and capabilities.

Thus I have experimented with a series of *criteria* for the appropriateness or fitness for purpose of specific techniques; I have used descriptive, *historical methods* of thinking and writing to explore the broad context of technical problems; and I have used a non-quantitative form of *systems theory* (as advocated on pp. 319–20, and for which there is precedent in the *Whole Earth Catalog* and in the design methods advocated by Christopher Alexander).

All these approaches confer some benefits, but more fundamental than any of them is a part of the necessary discipline which has to do with defining the objectives for any proposed technological development. For people who hold a one-dimensional view of technical progress, objectives do not need to be thought out in detail, because there is assumed to be only one forward direction, and so for any particular function, only one 'best' way of doing it, given currently available techniques.

But in looking at the work of people who thought like this and who were responsible for selecting hand-pumps for use at village wells in India, I found that they could not agree among themselves about which hand-pump model was 'the best'. On further investigation, it became clear that these people were in fact pursuing different directions of progress with different objectives, though without acknowledging it; and by subdividing the humanitarian and social objectives shared by all of them into a hierarchy of more specific objectives, to do with welfare, social development and self-reliance, it was possible to rationalise their different choices of pump. In addition, of course, the (often unstated) objectives of the villagers themselves were not always compatible with the objectives perceived by the technical staff from government and aid agencies who chose the pumps, and this had to be built into the analysis also.

All these efforts to develop an alternative discipline for

technology have recently been surpassed in vision (though not necessarily superseded in detail) by Robert M. Pirsig's beautiful and penetrating investigation of the subject. He discusses the period of disillusion with technology, which began in the 1960s, and the contemporary retreat from rationalism into a romantic, mystical or hippie mood. He then suggests how the 'classic' hard rationalism of a practical science (in his case, motorcycle maintenance) may be reconciled with the wholeness of a 'romantic' world view. He does this by providing a reasoned philosophical view of the intuitive methods of craftsmen, and for the kind of situation in which a technological problem is solved by one's 'feeling' for a subject rather than by analytical thought.

He might have quoted George Sturt, describing how a 'good wheelwright knew by art but not by reasoning the proportion to keep between spokes and felloes. . . . He felt it, in his bones'. And in this book, I have mentioned how John Smeaton admitted to designing a lighthouse 'as my feelings . . . bear me out' (p. 207). In the 17th century, practical men were trying to talk about the same thing when they spoke of acquiring technical knowledge through a spiritual process, or by 'inspiration' or by 'the light of Nature' (pp. 160–1).

Pirsig sees this non-rational element in the creativity of craftsmen and technologists as the aesthetic recognition of fitness for purpose, rightness, appropriateness or 'quality' – and he compares it with Poincaré's account of the aesthetic feeling which informs the scientist's process of discovery. He suggests that it should be recognised as an essential part of the practice of all technologies and not dismissed as simply belonging to the old-style craftsmen.

It is very striking indeed to turn from this to the work of a leading metallurgist and historian of technology, Cyril Stanley Smith, who asserts that in his experience discovery and invention are essentially aesthetic in nature and motivation. This is particularly true, he feels, of his own specialism, the science of materials, where innovation has often arisen from work in the decorative arts. In words which Pirsig's writing seems to echo, he suggests that the insights of this branch of science might be capable of drawing together the divergent intellectual and practical strands of the other sciences, perhaps in 'a new and more valid alchemy', which may 'rise from the same starting point as the old, namely the desire to place in universal perspective what men working intimately with materials know, feel and understand'.

What is outstanding about Pirsig's writing is that he provides a framework within which this kind of view can be thought about with some clarity and which suggests an orderly and intelligent relationship between the intuitive/aesthetic and the rational elements in technological thinking. This, it seems to me, may be the beginning of the discipline we need – a discipline which retains a rational basis, but combines with it the values, attitudes and modes of creativity which Pirsig and Smith (and some of their 17th-century forebears) speak of.

So far I have written about efforts to inaugurate a new direction for technical progress as if the chief problem is a lack of methods and discipline. But there are other problems too. Technology does not exist apart from the people who create and use it, and its precise forms have a lot to do with the way these people choose to organise their society. One of the problems about the use of intermediate or appropriate technology in the developing countries is that the people there often do not have suitable forms of local organisation to make effective use of the equipment being offered to them. Frequently, it is equipment devised by well-meaning Westerners who have little understanding of the social component of technology or of complex local patterns of social organisation.

In the industrialised countries also, we do not have many social structures with suitable organisation to use alternative technology. And although the necessary changes in society may come partly through unconscious evolution, or through individual efforts to organise self-help groups, village societies or communes, change will be needed at the political and legislative level also. And Dickson sees the great weakness of much alternative technology as its neglect of the 'political dimension' – neglect which implies 'an idealistic concept . . . that does not coincide with the social reality of technology as it has been experienced'.

This is fair criticism in many respects, but it is a mistake to think that the political dimension is the over-riding totality within which all other aspects of technology are worked out – and my book is very largely about some of the other dimensions of technological change. The distinction becomes clear when we consider the symbolic purposes which technology is made to serve, about which Dickson has useful things to say. For example, individuals buy automobiles or household goods, and nations buy armaments, not solely with a view to their utilitarian value but because of what they symbolise. Discussions about more modest lifestyles for an age of zero growth, or about disarmament, rarely acknowledge this, and so become confused as people invent phoney utilitarian or practical purposes for their acquisitions, and nations invent unreal threats to justify their arms.

The *Report from the Iron Mountain* almost a decade ago explained how the armies, structures and industries associated with preparedness for war in fact perform many non-military functions. Many of these functions can be described in terms of the 'symbolic objectives' discussed in this book and have to do with 'ideological clarification' and building national unity.

As a partial substitute for the non-military functions of war, the Iron Mountain report suggested that a massive space programme could fill the place of the armaments industry in the economy and would provide an equally potent, but less dangerous, symbolism to express national goals and national prestige – rather as the building of cathedrals in the 12th century provided an effective substitute for the non-military functions of the Crusades (p. 42).

Dickson's argument is that the symbolism of armaments, or of cathedrals, is largely invented by the ruling groups within society as a means of controlling the mass of the people. Thus Dickson sees the building of the cathedrals as a way in which the Church could extend its influence over craftsmen, artisans, and I would add, merchants.

There is much truth in this, but to present such political aspects of a creative technological movement as the whole of the picture seems wrong. From the viewpoint of the architects and stone masons who built the cathedrals, the work was something that carried conviction because of its symbolic meanings, whether concerning the New Jerusalem, the glory of God or the prestige of their own home town. It was these things which fired the imagination and sparked the immense burst of artistic and technological creativity which the cathedrals represent. We need to understand the reality of the symbolism, and not just its political uses, if we wish to understand the ideals and objectives which give rise to discovery and invention in technology. So I do not agree with Dickson that 'technological development is essentially a political process'. It is partly a political process, but at the point where creativity and invention occur, it is the values and ideals of individuals that matter, and personal appreciations of 'quality' or fitness for purpose. The convictions and sensitivity of the technologist have a validity beyond just the social environment which shapes them, important though that is.

Literature review

This re-assessment and development of ideas contained in *The Maze of Ingenuity* owes a good deal to discussions with Ben van Bronckhorst of Eindhoven Technological University and Charles Webster of Oxford; and to correspondence with Cyril Stanley Smith of M.I.T., author of *A History of Metallography* (Chicago U.P., 1960). Smith's key article on aesthetics in technology is 'Art, technology and science', in *Technology and Culture*, *11* (1970), pp. 493–549, but my quotation here comes from his 'Metallurgy as a human experience', in *Metallurgical Transactions A*, *6A* (1975), pp. 603–23.

Among new books on the history of technology which seek to get away from the one-dimensional view of technical progress are *Television: Technology and Cultural Form*, by Raymond Williams (New York, Schocken, 1975, and London, Fontana/Collins, 1974), and *The Great Instauration*: *Science, Medicine and Reform, 1626–1660*, by Charles Webster (London, Duckworth, 1975).

Though its roots go back to 1970, the term 'alternative technology' was first publicly used in 1972, according to Peter Harper, writing in *Undercurrents*: *the magazine of radical science and people's technology* (no. 5, winter 1973). Other sources I have used for this subject include Peter Harper on 'Soft technology', in *Prospects*, *3* (1973), pp. 183–92; Wil Lepkowski, 'Wanted: a science policy', in *Nature*, *258* (1975), pp. 374–5 (the number for 4 December 1975); and *The Last Whole Earth Catalog* (Menlo Park, California, 1972).

When I mentioned alternative technology in the original text of this book (p. 316), I was able to add a footnote about books then forthcoming by David Dickson and E. F. Schumacher. I have already quoted Dickson's *Alternative Technology and the Politics of Technical Change* (New York, Universe Books, 1975, and London, Fontana/Collins, 1974); it is a very useful, compact summary of issues both historical and modern – it defines (and attacks) the one-dimensional, linear view of history and describes the background of alternative technology in the writings of Ellul

Preface

and Marcuse, and in Roszak's 'counter culture'. E. F. Schumacher's now famous *Small Is Beautiful: a Study of Economics as if People Mattered* (New York, Harper & Row, 1973, 1975, and London, Blond & Briggs, 1973) is a collection of previously published essays, including the one which originally defined intermediate technology in 1965.

Other people who have discussed new directions for technology and for technological society include Ralf Dahrendorf, *The New Liberty: Survival and Justice in a Changing World* (Stanford, Calif., Stanford U.P., 1975, and London, Routledge & Kegan Paul, 1975) and Ivan Illich, *Tools for Conviviality* (New York, Harper & Row and London, Calder & Boyars, 1973). And then there is *Report from the Iron Mountain on the Possibility and Desirability of Peace*, introduced by Leonard C. Lewin (New York, 1967).

On the question of disciplines in technology, I have quoted from George Sturt's classic, *The Wheelwright's Shop* (Cambridge U.P., 1923, reprinted 1963); Christopher Alexander, *Notes on the Synthesis of Form* (Cambridge, Mass., Harvard U.P., 1964) and Robert S. Pirsig, *Zen and the Art of Motorcycle Maintenance* (New York, Bantam, 1975, and London, Bodley Head, 1974), which is certainly likely to become another classic. But the debate about technology is now being so vigorously pursued that these make up only a small proportion of the relevant literature.

Arnold Pacey,
Oxford, 9 June 1976

List of Illustrations

List of Illustrations

Acknowledgements

The thoughts which are expressed in this book have developed slowly over a number of years, and it is difficult to give adequate acknowledgement to all whose ideas, conversation, or companionship in shared experiences, have contributed to the final result. I recall specifically a discussion about George Orwell's *The Road to Wigan Pier*, and I remember long conversations with friends during walks on the Gower Peninsula and the Sussex Downs. A number of the places mentioned in the book awaken other memories, and make me conscious of how much I have gained from teachers and friends, and from my parents, sister and brother.

Where more strictly professional help is concerned, I am especially indebted to J. R. Ravetz of the University of Leeds. He has given me much valuable advice over a period of several years, and without his encouragement the book would never have been finished. The considerable stimulus he has provided will be readily appreciated by readers of his own book, *Scientific Knowledge and its Social Problems*. I also owe a more general debt to Dr Ravetz and several of his colleagues – M. P. Crosland, J. E. McGuire and P. M. Rattansi – for the stimulus provided by their work and teaching. I think particularly of the series of seminars on Newtonian ideas which they jointly gave at Leeds during 1963–4.

As for more specific debts, I am grateful to Richard Hills for much practical detail concerning textile machinery and steam power; to W. N. Slatcher for ideas concerning Thomas Newcomen; and to D. S. L. Cardwell for introducing me to Antoine Parent and Peter Ewart, important figures in chapters four and eight. Charles Webster has provoked much thought about the intellectual history of the 17th century, and Howard Erskine-Hill has discussed 18th-century topics relating to his forthcoming book *Pope's Good Men*. David Farrar has provided

Acknowledgements

many insights into technology in 18th-century Germany and Austria, and I am grateful for permission to quote material from his thesis on the Schemnitz Mining Academy (University of Manchester Institute of Science and Technology, 1971). With regard to the history of technology in Asia, I am grateful to Dick Day for a lead concerning India, and to Kathleen Farrar for an introduction to the history of Japanese science. In the chapters on William Strutt, Peter Ewart, and associated aspects of the industrial revolution, I have been indebted to the late J. D. Chambers and to Maurice Barley of Nottingham University, who first showed me the buildings designed by Strutt; to Michael Egerton for allowing me to use his thesis on Strutt (U.M.I.S.T., 1967); and to Stuart B. Smith and Brian Warburton for un-earthing various details of which I would otherwise have been unaware. In the latter parts of the book, I am indebted to Ron Levy for an introduction to general systems theory; and to George McRobie and A. S. Livingstone for discussions of intermediate technology and related subjects.

I owe a very practical debt to Wilfred Farrar for a lengthy translation from Italian relevant to the section on Galileo. Other valuable help with translation, checking and the preparation of illustrations has been given by Sylvia and David Farrar, and by Gillian and Philip Pacey. For reading various chapters in draft, I have to thank Richard Lorch, J. R. Ravetz, Ron Levy, Howard Erskine-Hill, Barry Barnes and Dick Day. I am especially grateful to Christopher Crosland, who read almost the whole of the book in this way. The faults which remain are not the responsibility of these people, but there would have been many more without their help.

Most of the material in the book was used during 1969–70 in a lecture course I gave to engineering students at Leeds University and to design technology students at Manchester. The book owes a great deal to their response and to individual discussions with other students, some of whom are mentioned above. There is much that I owe to other people in the University of Manchester Institute of Science and Technology (U.M.I.S.T.), particularly for a period of leave of absence during the session 1971–2 which gave me time to finish the book.

Arnold Pacey,
Shaw, near Oldham, 31 December 1972

Part One

INTRODUCTION

Introduction

An approach to the study of ideas and idealism in technology — some concepts and terms defined

This book has two themes which may not, at first sight, seem entirely compatible. Principally, it is about the history of technology – about the changes in ideas and outlook which accompanied the development of technology in Europe between 1100 and about 1870. But another theme, dealt with far more briefly but still with some emphasis, is a discussion of ideals and objectives in the technology of the 1970s.

These are related topics, but the difficulty about discussing them together in the same work is that one may appear to be drawing morals from history – which is usually a mistake – and one's objectivity as a historian may seem to be threatened if the problems of the present are kept too continuously in view. All the same, history books almost invariably reflect the way in which present-day problems are understood, and where historians have little to say on a particular topic it may mean that the importance of that topic in the modern world is inadequately appreciated. Thus it seems that the relative lack of books on intellectual and philosophical themes in the history of technology reflects a failure to recognise certain problems in modern technology – particularly problems about ideals and objectives in technology, and about its discipline and methods. So although the purpose here is to indicate how a gap in writing about the history of technology might be filled, it would be inappropriate to do this without also explaining how the existence of the gap stems from inadequate recognition of certain problems in current technology.

In tackling this two-fold theme, with its rather broad implications, an author would obviously be unable to attempt a definitive work in a single volume. The aim has therefore been to provide an outline of the subject in a form which can be read by anybody with a general interest in technology or the history of technology. The main text is a straightforward, non-technical, historical narrative, with only a few muted references to 20th-century problems. Only in the final chapter are issues in modern technology raised at any length.

Throughout the book, a number of concepts are used which may seem rather unconventional. In the historical chapters, these concepts provide a simple frame of reference for interpreting the nature and direction of technical progress at different periods in the past. The purpose of the final chapter is to indicate very briefly how the same concepts might be used to understand some of the dilemmas of technological development in the 1970s, and to suggest where one might start in working out a 'philosophy of technology' for the modern world.

What lies behind these concepts is the view that technology is partly an expression of the values and aspirations of the people who create and use it. For technological development to occur, the individuals responsible must have specific *objectives*[1] in mind relating to the use of technology and deriving from these aspirations; additionally, they must possess, or must develop, methods, or in general, a *discipline*, for effecting change in their existing technology.

In looking for examples of *objectives* in 20th-century technology, one might begin by considering the economic objectives which have stimulated the development of mass production and more recently automation, and which have led to the introduction of many new kinds of consumer goods; one could also mention military objectives, and the way in which aircraft design and many branches of electronics have evolved to meet military needs; finally, one would probably need to consider the competitive objectives of nations, as instanced by the American effort in the 1960s to reach the moon before the Russians did.

But in addition to these relatively mundane purposes for which technology is used, it would seem that there is often a more idealistic impulse in the minds of those whose creative ability is responsible for innovation and technical change. As Rostow has commented,[2] it is often more important in the history of technical change to consider the 'consequences of non-economic human

1. Words printed in italics in this introduction are used throughout the book with the specific meaning which is indicated here.
2. Rostow, *The Stages of Economic Growth*, p. 2. For full details of books mentioned in these footnotes, see the bibliography.

motives and aspirations'. Thus some technical improvements and inventions have been introduced in conditions where there was no rational economic need for them. The invention of the weight-driven clock around 1300, for example, did not have an economic purpose, and the development of a mathematical basis for engineering was at first solely an intellectual enterprise.

One may explain the position of the engineer or inventor in this context by comparing him to the architect, or to any other artist who depends upon commissions from patrons for the opportunity to work out his ideas. Without such a commission, an architect cannot expect to see any of his designs used in actual buildings. But when he gets a commission, his client or patron will make all kinds of practical demands, and will set a limit on costs. None the less, the architect can usually design a building which reflects his personal artistic ideals and intentions as well as serving the client's needs. Thus the historian of architecture needs to enquire about the practical functions of buildings, and the demands made by clients, but he must also discuss the architect's own artistic intentions. In the same way, the historian of technology should enquire about the personal intentions and ideals of practising technologists, as well as about the practical demands made on their technical skill, and the economic circumstances under which they work. Economic or military needs may give the engineer or inventor his opportunity, but they can rarely provide much stimulus to his imagination. To understand where that comes from, we must ask what it is that really excites him about technology. Is he fascinated by a feeling that technology is a conquest of nature, a strengthening of the weak arm of man? Or is he moved by an ideal of technology in the service of human need? Is he fascinated by machines as artefacts: as works of art, almost; or is he stimulated by the intellectual demands of the discipline of technology? What does he feel about the direction of technical progress – about what it should be progress towards?

In order to discuss questions like these, and to draw a contrast with the economic and military objectives of those who commission and pay for most technical development, it seems helpful to think about the *idealistic objectives* which have influenced the development of technology at various times. There are, indeed, three objectives of this kind which seem relevant to the episodes in the history of technology to be dealt with in this book.

Firstly, there are the objectives of those who have been moved primarily by *humanitarian and social ideals*; one thinks of the way in which many agriculturists, doctors and engineers have directed their efforts towards the needs of people around them, or towards using technology to make people's work less onerous or more rewarding.

Secondly, there are the *intellectual ideals* of those who have been attracted by the rationalism of science or of mathematics, and have tried to make technology more precise in its methods or more logical in its concepts.

Finally, there are the objectives of those who see technology as a kind of exploration to be pursued in much the same spirit as scientific research. But instead of just increasing our knowledge of nature, the objective of exploration in technology is mastery of nature; and the projects undertaken in this spirit are often of a kind where spectacular achievements are possible – achievements which can symbolise man's ever-growing ability to dominate the natural world.

Some of the examples of technical innovation which are described in the earlier parts of this book, such as the invention of the weight-driven clock, are cases where the objectives of technicians and craftsmen were expressed in terms of a quite explicit symbolism. Our language is today much less poetic, but who can doubt that the first landing of a man on the moon was 'a small step for mankind', mainly because of the way it symbolised a new conquest of nature, a triumph for the exploring, adventurous spirit of mankind? It is in this sense, then, that *symbolic objectives* in technology can be discussed. The term is appropriate for describing enterprises in technology which are not of much practical use, but which none the less have the greatest possible significance in some non-utilitarian sense.

Ideals of these three kinds have probably influenced the work done by many practising engineers, chemists, agriculturists and other technologists; we shall consider several historical examples in the following pages. The same ideals also influence widely-held beliefs about the character of technical progress – beliefs which can be discerned as rather shadowy assumptions or half-stated principles in the background of many public discussions of technology. In the late 1960s, for example, when the Concorde project was first undertaken in Britain and France, it was often said that to build a supersonic airliner would represent 'progress' in technology. It was never explained why, nor was it clear what criteria were used to decide that such a thing could be identified with 'progress'. In many arguments of this kind, it seems to be taken for granted that there is only one kind of progress in technology, and that the only choice is whether we accept its implications, and let it carry us forward, or whether we turn away, and let it pass us by. This notion is altogether too simple. Technical progress can take us in any one of several *directions*, and we need to think carefully about ideals and objectives so as to choose the direction in which we want to go.

The title of this book refers to that idea. It is intended to convey an impression of the need to make choices in technology, and of the rather confused sense of direction by which such choices often seem to be guided.

The ideals which have been most important in influencing technological development in the past have changed from one age to another, and there have been consequent changes in the direction of technical progress. When intellectual ideals were most widely pursued, progress tended towards improvement rather than invention – but when men looked to technology for symbols of their virility and power, the emphasis of technical progress was on novelty, invention and spectacular constructional achievement. Examples of technical progress guided by intellectual ideals are to be found in chapters three, four and seven, while contrasting phases of more spectacular development are described in parts of chapters one, two, and six. The kinds of symbol people tried to create in these periods of adventuring inventiveness varied greatly in the course of history. They have included symbols of man's ability to reflect the creative powers of God (chapters two and three); symbols of the level of contemporary civilisation as compared with ancient Rome (chapter six); and, in the less eloquent 20th century, symbols just to mark out new advances in the ever-extending capability of industrial man.

The direction which technical progress might have taken if it had been influenced by humanitarian and social ideals for any length of time is illustrated in several chapters. Ideals about the use of technology in the relief of human need (chapter five) or to promote the public good (chapter six) were often discussed, but with questionable effect. Ideals concerning the proper use of human labour and skill for the benefit of the individual worker and for the benefit of society at large have also attracted much attention in the course of time, but again with only limited effect (chapters one, five and nine).

It will be noted that nearly all these examples have been taken from the period of time between 1100 and 1870. This itself reflects a judgement about when the most significant changes in the direction of technical progress occurred. Ideas about technical change, and about the overall objectives of technological development, have probably not altered greatly since the late 19th century. The formative period in the history of European technology was already over when the first industrial revolution had run its course in Britain. By that time – and before 1870 – the idea of a dynamic, expanding technology allied to a rapidly-growing industry was widely accepted. This idea has persisted with only detailed modification during most of the succeeding century, and only now, in the 1970s, are objectives of this kind being seriously questioned.

One major change in outlook which occurred during the centuries between 1100 and 1870 was closely connected with the intellectual ideals which influenced the development of engineering from the 16th century onwards. This was a time when mathematical methods were sometimes applied to practical problems for entirely idealistic reasons, because people were excited by the rationalism of mathematics, and believed in it as the key to understanding nature. At first, no practical advantage was gained from the mathematical analysis which was used – it was still too elementary – but the long-term outcome could hardly have been greater, because this enthusiasm for using mathematics in a practical context eventually helped to create the basic *discipline* of modern technology.

In order to appreciate the importance of this change, it is useful to compare the discipline of the technologist with the older discipline of the craftsman. In many cases, either discipline can be used for the same purpose. Boat-building, for example, can be carried on by craftsmen or it can be turned into a technology. The chief characteristic of the craftsman's skill is that it is based on long experience of his trade rather than on abstract knowledge. He produces sound designs, but often without being able to explain their logic very fully. He may be able to judge by eye or by feel how big a particular timber must be to carry the load that it will have to support. Long experience of the materials with which he works enables him to do this, even though he may be ignorant of any theory by which the strength of a beam may be calculated. Experience and practical skill also make it possible for a craftsman to design as he builds, with a minimum of drawings on paper. In the most traditional kinds of craftsmanship, no drawings or other paperwork of any kind are required.

One way of judging when, in history, the discipline of technology evolved from the various branches of craftsmanship which preceded it, would be to study the varying extent to which technical drawings were used at different dates. In contrast to the craftsman, the practitioner of a fully-developed technology does all his design work on paper, and uses scientific data to calculate the performance of his constructions before they are built. He may also do some experiments before he completes the design; and like the craftsman, the technologist will have some intuitive insight into his work, derived from experience. But he will usually want to rationalise his insights in scientific language and check them by calculation. The great strength of the technologist's discipline as compared with the craftsman's is that it allows him to design things by drawing and calculation which are outside the range of previous experience; it allows him to explore possibilities which are far beyond the point where the intuition of a practical man can offer any guidance.

Although many craftsmen are mentioned in the following pages, not much is said about their particular discipline. What is of greater interest here is the gradual emergence of the discipline of technology from the stage where simple drawing techniques were being used in 13th-century architecture, to the point where sophisticated mathematical and experimental procedures were being developed in many branches of engineering around 1800.

Dictionaries tend to define technology in terms of 'systematic knowledge' of practical subjects, and clearly such knowledge is essential to the modern discipline of technology. But clearly also, systematic knowledge of this kind did not exist before 1600 or 1650 at the earliest, so technology, defined in this way, did not exist then either. For this reason, terms such as *the practical arts*, or *the mechanical and chemical arts* are used in this book rather than *technology* to refer to the technical skills of earlier historical periods. These terms were often used during the 17th century, and it seems useful to retain them in discussing circumstances in which the craftsman's outlook predominated. If we extend our modern idea of *technology* so that it includes all forms of inventiveness and practical skill, we are in danger of forgetting the historical changes which gave technology its characteristic discipline.

As an extension of this terminology, another term, *the social arts*, is used here to denote the arts of organisation, communication and social welfare. There are circumstances where these subjects need to be discussed as part of the practical arts, because of their relevance to the general process of technical change.

Technology, as something quite distinct in its methods from the older practical arts, was the creation of men who were more interested in its intellectual content than in devising new applications for practical skills. But as it turned out, the new discipline which they pioneered did have an important influence on the purposes for which technology was used, because it was at first far more relevant to engineering than to agriculture, chemistry, or medicine, and led to a greater emphasis on applications involving engineering. This bias is inevitably but regrettably reflected in the following pages, where more stress is given to mechanical technology than to the practical applications of biology and chemistry.

The new discipline of technology influenced the purposes for which technology was used in other ways as well. It proved very successful in dealing with restricted problems in engineering, but it was almost a hindrance to some of the people who wished to use technology for the furtherance of humanitarian or social ideals. As a discipline, it emphasised analytical thinking and used quantitative concepts of limited application; it could not easily accommodate the broad aims and the mixture of human and technical factors which a socially-orientated direction of progress in technology would have required. Thus the efforts made to encourage a more directly social form of technical progress at various times from the 17th century onwards have been relatively ineffective. No suitable discipline existed to support development of this kind; there was no framework of thought adequate to the programme which the advocates of this kind of technology had set themselves.

This is a problem which emerges in the book from historical material; but it raises the question of whether even now, in the 1970s, there is any discipline adequate to the problem of using modern technology for humanitarian or social ends. For the author personally, this was the most compelling question to arise as the book was being written; and it provoked a fairly active investigation of disciplines which seem relevant to creating a socially-orientated technology, including new design methods and the more 'holistic' aspects of general systems theory (see p. 142). The application of these disciplines was also examined, particularly in relation to intermediate technology, ergonomics and agricultural engineering.

Though far removed from the conventional sphere of the historian, these subjects can be approached in much the same way as the historical material in this book – because whether modern engineers or 13th-century craftsmen are being discussed, it is important to understand the *disciplines* used in the application of practical skill, as well as the *ideals* and *objectives* of practical men and their employers. An additional point is that, whether one considers the remote past or the 1970s, one is constantly reminded that ideals, objectives and even disciplines in technology are a reflection of more widely held attitudes. They reflect, in fact, the prevailing values, aspirations, and social or political goals in the community at large. Technology is not value-free; on the contrary, in any community or nation it is an integral part of a wider culture, and is influenced by the same values as those which find expression in art, literature and religion, and in the economic and institutional structures of that community.

This can be illustrated by much recent technical change, both in the industrialised world and in the developing countries. Approaching the matter as a historian, however, the author has found the issue most clearly brought out by such questions as the interaction of early technology in Europe with art, architecture and religion; and by the way in which the contrasting cultures of Europe and China have given rise to markedly different kinds of technology. There are many similar questions which ought to be asked about the cultural roots of technology, and most of them demand a fuller answer than historians in this field have so far given.

Part Two

HISTORY

The cathedral builders: European technical achievement between 1100 and 1280

Introduction: innovations of the 1090s

In the year 1093, foundations were laid for a new cathedral at Durham, on the high, river-bound outcrop where the shrine of St Cuthbert had been established a century earlier. The building was being erected by a French bishop who had lived at Rouen and near Le Mans before being appointed to Durham by William the Conqueror, and its construction combined some of the best technical details of recent French buildings with a number of entirely new and important inventions.

But while this cathedral can be seen as a symbol of the efficiency and skill of the new Norman rulers of England, the Domesday Book, which they had compiled seven years earlier, gave some indication of the technical skills and agricultural resources of the people they now governed. It listed such activities as fishing and the extraction of salt from sea-water; and it recorded the existence of small water-mills at almost 4,000 different places in England. There was more than one mill at many of these sites, so the total number listed was something like 6,000.[1]

Building construction and the use of water-power were two of the practical arts which were developing most rapidly around the year 1100. But despite this, the material civilisation and technical skills of England and France must have been greatly inferior to those that could be found at the same date in some of the Islamic lands around the Mediterranean, especially in Spain, and farther afield, in China. Moreover, it might be said that a thousand years before, the Romans had applied even greater skills to achieve a much higher material standard of life. Thus to begin an account of the origins of modern technology by talking about England

1. Compare Syson, *British Water Mills*, p. 75, and figures for individual regions given by Darby, *Domesday Geography*.

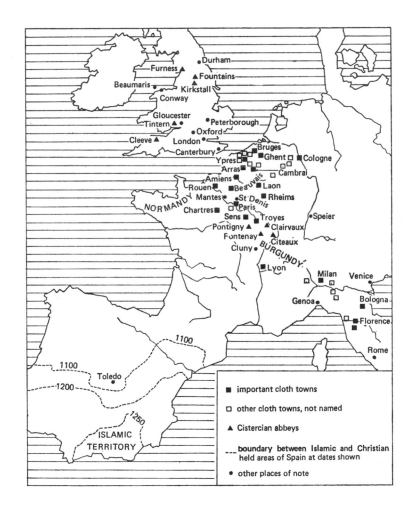

Figure 1

Places mentioned in chapter one, showing the distribution of major cloth towns.

and France in the year A.D. 1100 may seem somewhat perverse.

But although other civilisations had achieved more than Europe, it will be argued here that soon after 1100, Europeans developed their own particular approach to technical matters, which in the long term proved to be uniquely fruitful. So while it may be true that trade routes linked Europe rather indirectly with the East, and that Chinese inventions such as paper were adopted in Europe not long after 1100, it is also true that Chinese attitudes were not imported with them. Paradoxically, indeed, inventions brought into Europe from China and elsewhere were sometimes developed more successfully in Europe than in their country of origin.

Much the same comment can be made about the undoubted debt which Europe owed to the Roman Empire – individual Roman techniques and skills survived in Europe, but a Roman outlook did not. It was from the medieval Arab or Islamic civilisation that Europeans gained much of their understanding of Greek and Roman learning, and it was perhaps from the Arabs that Europe gained most in the technical arts also. From just before 1100, not only did the Arabs pass on to Europe the knowledge they had inherited from the ancient world together with much of their own devising, but they probably also passed on a more adventurous and enquiring attitude to technical matters than the Romans, and perhaps even the Chinese, had possessed. Contact with the Arabs was closer, too, partly because of the crusades, the first of which began in 1098. But of even greater importance was the reconquest of Spain – which can be said to have begun in earnest when the Arabs lost Toledo in 1085, and as a result of which much of the Islamic achievement in learning and technique was taken over and absorbed into European culture.

The years just prior to 1100, then, mark the beginning of a period of about two centuries when Europe was to absorb many important technical ideas from several Chinese and Islamic sources. So both in terms of the influx of ideas from other civilisations, and in terms of the indigenous technical skills exhibited at Durham Cathedral and in the Domesday Book, the 1080s and 90s do seem an appropriate point to begin this history. Even more important for the theme of this book is evidence, presented below, of a change which occurred in people's thinking about technical matters, and a stirring of the imagination which enabled Europeans at about this date to grasp the immense possibilities of technical progress in a way which the Romans had never done, and the Chinese perhaps only momentarily.

Fundamental to all this, however, and making possible the changes of the 12th and 13th centuries, was the underlying prosperity of the Norman period. Much of this was derived from the numerous water-mills noted in the Domesday survey and from such agricultural techniques as the rotation of crops and the use of a heavy-wheeled plough which had been inherited from earlier centuries. And it is perhaps significant that agriculture and the use of water-mills had already by 1100 excelled most Roman practice. But of course, with other practical arts where the Romans had achieved more, Europe had fallen well below their achievement, and much had been lost. Building was the technology which the Romans had developed most fully, with their aqueducts and their enormous vaulted public buildings. The secret of much of their success was the way in which they used concrete in conjunction with masonry construction. This important technique had since been lost, and was not entirely recovered until about 1800. And this brings us back to the cathedral at Durham, for the technical problems faced by the builders there were ones which the Romans could have solved using concrete but for which the Norman builders had to develop entirely different solutions. And we may note that, apart from the lack of any knowledge of Roman concrete, there were great problems about making a satisfactory mortar which continued to trouble builders throughout the Middle Ages.

The problem at Durham was to provide a high wide church with a stone ceiling or vault.[2] This was, indeed, the great technical problem in European architecture at the time and the various attempts to solve it had been made in large church buildings on the continent. To provide a stone vault for a church was desirable partly as a protection against fire, for it isolated the timber roof from the body of the church, but the vault was also designed to provide a ceiling of the same texture and colour as the walls below. To the eye, timber roof-beams left exposed would appear to keep the walls apart as independent units; the stone vault, springing from the walls and curving across between them, gave the whole building a more unified appearance.

2. Pevsner, *County Durham*, pp. 18–22.

Now the problem of building a stone vault over any space as wide as the nave of Durham Cathedral was something which had not been attempted in medieval Europe before about 1075. Then, in France and the Rhineland, a number of churches were given simple vaulted ceilings which offered a variety of tentative solutions to the problem. Almost all these vaults were conceived

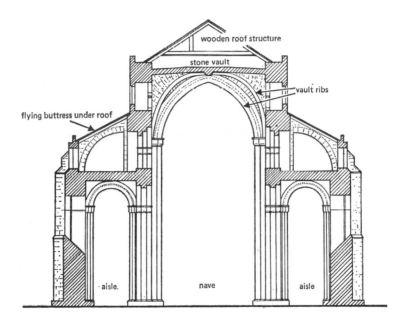

Figure 2
Durham Cathedral: cross-section of the nave.
The cathedral was begun in 1093; the nave was built *c.* 1104–30.

as continuous stone shells forming a smoothly-curved ceiling to the church. The innovation at Durham consisted in subdividing the vault into small areas of 'shell' by means of stone ribs. These ribs were really arches, crossing the church both transversely and diagonally; and in order that they should all reach up to the same height, the transverse arches rose sharply to a point while the diagonal ones were semicircular (see figs. 2–3). This stage in the

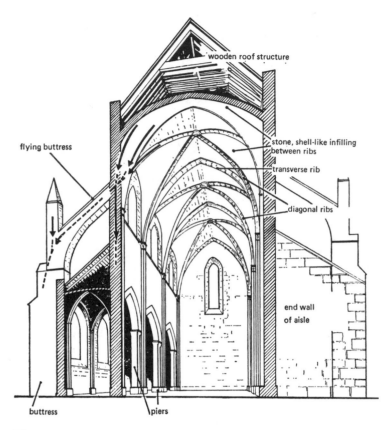

wooden roof structure

stone, shell-like infilling between ribs

transverse rib

diagonal ribs

flying buttress

end wall of aisle

buttress

piers

Figure 3
The principle of the rib vault: arrows and dashed lines show how thrusts (forces) from the ribs are carried partly by the flying buttresses.

development of Durham was not reached until the 1120s. But even then, pointed arches were almost unknown except in a few Cistercian abbey churches, although later in the 12th century they became the most characteristic feature of 'Gothic' architecture.

The ribs in the Durham vaults had both a technical and an aesthetic function. Thus they made possible a stronger structure, which was also lighter in weight, and at the same time, since the ribs were built first and the rest of the vault was filled in later, they made the whole thing easier to construct, involving the use of less centering and scaffolding. The aesthetic improvement obtained by using the rib vault was that its surface, patterned with ribs, could be made to match the piers and walls more closely; stone shafts attached to the piers ran from floor level to the vault, and the ribs were made to continue their vertical line into its curving shape.

The introduction of rib vaults at Durham gave rise to one major structural problem. The forces resulting from the weight of the vaults could not simply be supported by the piers and walls, because they did not act downwards, but rather they exerted an outward thrust, tending to push the walls apart. In addition, these forces were concentrated into a very small area at the convergence of each group of ribs. It was necessary, therefore, to buttress the piers high up, at the level where the walls had to withstand these forces. To do this by building conventional solid buttresses against the piers would involve blocking the aisle of the church, however. So instead, a buttress was built against the aisle wall, and a leaning, bridge-like piece of masonry was made to span across the aisle to the point where the vault thrusts needed to be counteracted; and this device constituted what was probably the earliest flying buttress in western Europe.

The three technical innovations at Durham, then, were the rib vault, the pointed arch and the flying buttress. Their introduction served well to illustrate the medieval craftsman's skill and his capacity for change; it is also instructive to note how the new techniques were worked out with a knowledge of recent continental buildings (e.g. Speier Cathedral on the Rhine), and perhaps even drew on knowledge of the pointed arches used by Islamic builders in Spain. The bishop who began the building work was perhaps also responsible for assembling master craftsmen with this knowledge, for he had just previously spent three years travelling on the continent.

The question arises as to whether other practical arts besides building possessed this capacity for innovation. Building is the one medieval art of which there are extensive remains and good documentation, but it seems likely that if more were known about contemporary machines, particularly water-mills, a parallel development would be noted – that is, one would be able to discern a fairly rapid improvement in design and utilisation from the middle of the 11th century. The Domesday Book gives some evidence of such innovations, although much of it is difficult to interpret. Fulling-mills, for example (used for the finishing process on woollen cloth), may possibly be referred to there; they were certainly used in the 12th century and played a very important part in the textile trade from the 13th century onwards.

The skills necessary for the building of machines developed in parallel with the art of building if only because, to some degree, the same people were responsible for both. The architect of a cathedral would be a master craftsman whose job included not only the design of the building, but also such work in mechanics as the construction of hoists for lifting heavy stones to great heights. Detailed evidence of this is lacking for the builders of Durham, but eighty years later, William of Sens, architect of Canterbury Cathedral, impressed the monks there by making, as they wrote, 'the most ingenious machines for loading and unloading ships, and for drawing the mortar and stones'.[3] Judging by the size of stones used high up in the cathedral walls, it seems that William's hoists had a capacity of about half a ton. Such a machine would be worked by a windlass, but there was another type of hoist used by the builders for lifting the stones of the vault. This was the 'Great Wheel', supported on the roof beams above the vault, and powered by a tread-mill.

Another master mason known for his interest in mechanical subjects was Villard de Honnecourt. He is now famous for the notebook he filled with sketches, which included a water-wheel driving a saw, a screw-jack for lifting heavy weights, and a mechanical eagle which turned its head. Villard's notebook dates from about 1235, but it seems highly probable that master builders of about 1100 would have the same breadth of interests. And since in many places where they worked, such men would be the most expert craftsmen available, they must sometimes have been called on for advice about the construction or repair of a local mill.

Practical arts and the monastic orders

After 1100 the improvement of water-mills was perhaps most actively pursued by the monks and lay brothers belonging to the

3. Quoted by Pevsner, *European Architecture*, chapter 3, pp. 78–9.

abbeys and priories which proliferated at this time. For in these institutions, the arts of building and milling, agriculture and water-supply were carried on side by side. And the organisation which linked together the abbeys of each order proved to be a very effective means of communicating technical ideas and practical skills from one part of Europe to another.

The pattern of life within most of the great abbeys was based on the programme laid down by St Benedict about A.D. 530. But with the passage of time, there was a tendency for the monks to lose the enthusiasm and relax the austerity for which their predecessors had been noted, and this led to a whole series of attempts to reform Benedictine monasticism and restore its observances. Most of these reforms gave rise to new monastic orders, all of which followed versions of the Rule of St Benedict. In the 11th and 12th centuries, the Carthusians, the Grand-montines, the Cistercians and the Premonstratensians were just a few of the new orders founded. An older foundation in the Benedictine tradition was the Cluniac Order, one of whose characteristics was a highly centralised form of government. The thousand monasteries which the Cluniacs eventually had in Europe were all subject to the Abbot of Cluny. But the system was very cumbersome, and when the Cistercian Order began to expand, early in the 1100s, a more flexible arrangement based on mutual visitation and meetings of abbots was adopted. Other orders had their own methods of supervision and communication, but probably the Cistercians were the most efficient at disseminating technical information.

The Cistercian Order originated at Cîteaux in Burgundy, in 1098, where, in an uninhabited, uncultivated area of forest, a group of monks settled with the aim of following the Rule of St Benedict more strictly than was possible in the prosperous monastery from which they had come. From Benedict's instructions they learned that they should live separately from other people, and that they should devote part of their daily routine to manual labour. So they felt that their monastery should not possess lands or wealth outside its own boundaries, but should be self-supporting in its material needs – and that their own labour should be the means of achieving this. Such a programme did not leave time for the elaborate services which the Cluniacs observed, and at Cîteaux a simpler timetable of services was justified by reference to Benedict's authority, for he had wanted monks to work in the fields as well as in the choir, and had ordered things accordingly.

The little abbey at Cîteaux remained an obscure foundation until the year 1112, when a young nobleman and some of his friends decided they had a vocation to become monks there. This man, known to us as St Bernard of Clairvaux, provided the dynamism which, by the time of his death in 1153, had led to the foundation of 340 Cistercian abbeys all over Europe.

Interest in technical matters was perhaps stimulated by the way in which St Bernard re-emphasised the importance of manual work.[4] His teaching on this subject underlined St Benedict's view that labour should play an important part in the life of a monk, alongside intellectual effort and religious devotions. Labour, on the land or at any other necessary task, could be thought of as yielding wealth of a spiritual as well as of a material kind; everybody should do work on each of three levels – manual, intellectual and spiritual. Just as men had an obligation to think and to pray, so also they had an obligation to do manual work. It was perhaps natural in this context that monks should think about the techniques they used in the course of their work, and endeavour to improve them.

In a Cistercian monastery, there were particular times laid down during each day for different activities. The lay brothers were supposed to devote seven or eight hours to manual labour, and the fathers four or five hours; this did not differ much from the Rule of St Benedict, which allocated five and a half hours to manual work.[5] A further period (two or three hours) was to be given over to reading and study; and all the monks were to devote four or five hours each day to their spiritual duties: prayer, meditation and the offices of the Church.

The large amount of time devoted to manual work led to a somewhat paradoxical situation. Intended as part of a spiritual discipline, the work done was supposed only to make each abbey self-sufficient in its material needs. But it was often done so effectively that products like wool and iron were turned out in far greater quantities than were needed by the monks themselves. There was a market demand for these things, and it was permissible to sell, although the monks were warned: 'let not the

4. Bernard's views are summarised by Vignes, *Saint Bernard et son temps*.
5. *Rule of St. Benedict*, caput 48. The programme varied somewhat according to the season, and on Sundays more time was devoted to reading.

sin of avarice creep in; but let the goods always be sold a little cheaper than they are sold by people of the world, that in all things, God may be glorified.'[6] This injunction was perhaps too finely balanced, for the abbeys were soon in receipt of a large money income; in the course of time they became very wealthy, and the monks found themselves acting as estate managers and businessmen rather than labourers.

But that was much later, and what concerns us now is the way in which technical information could be passed from one abbey to another as part of the normal system of communication within the Cistercian Order. Fountains Abbey in Yorkshire may be cited as an example, for when it was founded by a group of Benedictine monks who had decided to adopt the Cistercian rule, they sent messages to St Bernard, asking his advice. As a result, a certain Geoffrey came from Clairvaux to instruct them in the new rule. When money became available for building on a large scale, it seems to have been Geoffrey of Clairvaux who designed the new abbey, instructing the monks about the plans of Cistercian monasteries elsewhere, which were very standardised, owing partly to the strictness of the rule. The rule, for example, forbade the building of towers, though Fountains and Kirkstall Abbeys later acquired them. Churches were not to be of excessive height either, and should not have porches, sculpture or stained glass. But the actual construction of the buildings was a technical matter in which the monks would be free to use the best methods available locally, so long as these did not involve excessive decoration. Thus at Fountains, there is evidence that English masons erected the buildings, using their own methods for most detailed work, while probably only the overall design was by Geoffrey. But his influence serves to illustrate the speed at which technical ideas were transmitted within the Cistercian Order, for some buildings at Fountains completed in 1147 were tunnel-vaulted in the same way as comparable buildings put up at Clairvaux in 1140.

Pointed arches were used by the Cistercians from the 1120s onward, and the pointed tunnel vaults used at Clairvaux and Fountains became very characteristic of Cistercian architecture at this time, although technically these vaults were not so advanced as the rib vaults first conceived at Durham in 1093. Rib vaults were used again at Gloucester about 1120, and in

6. *Rule of St. Benedict*, caput 57.

France they were adopted for the abbey church of St Denis near Paris about 1140 and at Sens Cathedral about the same time. Sens was near to several of the major Cistercian abbeys in Burgundy, and it was mainly from there that Cistercian builders learned the technique of rib vaulting. They used it first at Pontigny Abbey soon after 1150, and from there this method of vaulting spread to many other abbeys of the Cistercian Order.

Building is one technological activity of the Cistercians for which good evidence remains, but they also had an interest in other technologies. Kirkstall Abbey near Leeds was famous for the forge started there about the year 1200, and elsewhere in England the Cistercians played an important part in the development of iron-making. Iron was needed for agricultural implements, and by soldiers for armour and weapons, but it appears that the Norman conquest of England had largely disrupted the activities of existing smiths. The Cistercian monks in England played an important part in re-establishing furnaces for smelting iron ore: they seem to have prospected for ore, and certainly exploited the main iron stones in northern England fairly systematically.[7] The monks at Fountains worked both iron and lead in Nidderdale, and Furness Abbey exploited the haematite ores of the west coast, becoming famous from 1235 for the high quality of the iron produced there. Most Cistercian abbeys had some mineral rights, and in the Forest of Dean, Tintern Abbey is known to have acquired a forge soon after its foundation in 1131.

Methods of smelting iron were of course primitive. The iron ore, charcoal and limestone were heated together; the iron was then taken from the furnaces in the form of a soft, but not molten, mass with a great deal of slag mixed in it. By repeated hammering the slag could be forced out, and the iron was shaped into bars and plates suitable for the blacksmith to use for making tools or weapons. Now in fulling-mills, water-wheels were made to operate hammers by means of a series of cams or trips fitted to the water-wheel axle. The same principle could be used in hammer forges, and such devices were to be found in connection with Cistercian abbeys in both England and France. In case any reader should think that the part played by the Cistercians is being exaggerated, it is worth noting that out of 30 documents

7. Schubert, *A History of the British Iron and Steel Industry* . . . , pp. 101–105.

which mention 12th-century hammer forges in France, 25 were written by Cistercian monks.[8] Of course, monks would often keep better records than other people, but this is still good evidence of their interest.

Agriculture was the one essential form of work with which Cistercian monks had to be concerned, and since they normally established monasteries in remote and wild landscapes, they were responsible for bringing vast amounts of virgin land into cultivation. In England, they were highly important in promoting sheep-farming and the wool trade. Water-supply was another problem with which they dealt, but here they made things relatively easy by siting their abbeys near to rivers. Then by means of a series of conduits and canals, water could be diverted from the river to supply fish-ponds, the abbey kitchens, and the 'lavatorium', where they washed. After passing through these places where fresh water was required, the water from the river would flow beneath the rere-dorters, or latrines, continuously flushing them clean. Usually the water was made to flow from one building to another along stone-lined channels and drains, but lead pipes would sometimes be used, as in the elaborate 12th-century water-system installed in the monastic buildings at Canterbury, and in the water-supply to Westminster Palace.

But in Cistercian abbeys, water would not only be supplied to the kitchens and used for washing away refuse; it would also be used to drive water-wheels. For although the monks believed in manual labour as part of their vocation, they did not believe that this labour should ever become sheer drudgery; they were therefore anxious to mechanise the more menial tasks. Another motive for developing water-wheels was that the abbeys were sometimes short of labour. They were supposed to be self-supporting communities, but could not have succeeded as such without the lay-brothers. These men were members of the abbey who were not in Holy Orders, and who spent a large part of their time working in the fields or on building work. They formed an essential part of the Cistercian community, and in the 12th century probably outnumbered the monks. Later on their numbers dwindled, but it seems doubtful whether there were ever sufficient lay-brothers for all the work that needed to be done in building an abbey, in working its fields and in maintaining supplies of essential materials. So water-mills would play an

8. Forbes, in *A History of Technology*, vol. 2, p. 610.

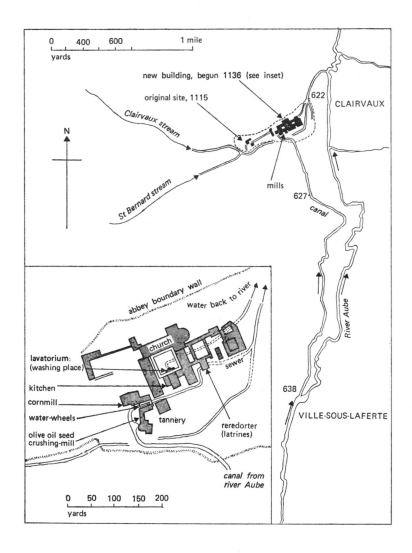

Figure 4
Clairvaux Abbey: the water-supply system at its fullest development.
New buildings, begun 1136, were sited about a quarter-mile from the
original site so that water from the River Aube could be used to supplement
the flow from the two small streams.

essential part in the economy of an abbey wherever they could be used. At Clairvaux, for example, the river drove corn-mills, worked a fulling-mill and a tannery and various crushing-mills, as well as supplying the kitchen and washing-places and flushing clean the latrines. At Fontenay, another French Cistercian abbey, the buildings which housed water-powered workshops still survive, and it is clear that they included a forge. The best remaining example in England is at Fountains Abbey, where a 12th-century stone building measuring about 24 feet by 100 feet originally housed two water-wheels.[9]

The use of water-mills was developed by other sectors of society than just the monasteries, and in the region of France to the north and west of Clairvaux, a total of 200 mills were in use during the 13th century.

There had been 60 a century earlier, and only 14 in the 11th century, so even allowing for gaps in the records of earlier periods, this represents a rapid increase.[10] Of course, many of these would be corn-mills of the simplest kind, but a similar growth in numbers is revealed by a count of fulling-mills mentioned in English documents.[11]

In addition to this extensive use of water-power, the windmill (of the post-mill type) was introduced about 1150 or 1170; and the invention of the horse-collar some 150 years earlier had allowed horses as well as oxen to be used as draught animals. So it is clear that one major characteristic of European technology prior to 1300 was the development of the use of power. Before that date, every possible source of natural power – rivers, tides, winds, animals – had been exploited. The amount of power available to supplement the unaided physical labour of men must therefore have increased by a large factor. This meant that a much higher level of material culture was possible than had been conceivable before, amounting to a change as momentous as the inauguration of the iron age. Other parts of the world, such as China and the Middle East, had gone through this same revolution in the use of power several centuries earlier, but no other civilisation had carried it through so intensively. Thus by 1250 or 1300, foundations had already been laid for the later technological ascendancy of Europe. To build on that foundation, much had

9. Luckhurst, *Monastic Watermills*, p. 9.
10. Forbes, in *A History of Technology*, vol. 2, p. 609.
11. Carus Wilson, in *Economic History Review*, vol. 11, 1941, pp. 48–50.

still to be done to improve the very primitive machines of this period – but no further source of power existed for exploitation until the steam engine was invented.

Commerce and the cathedrals

Work done in the monasteries was part of a spiritual discipline and was not aimed at producing goods for market. The improvements made by the monks in water-supply, building techniques and agriculture might therefore be seen as to some degree the result of an 'idealistic' approach to technology. Though, as mentioned earlier, the monks did in time become businessmen, and sell much of their produce, initially the direct influence of the profit motive on their practical and technical activities was probably very limited.

Not all of 12th-century life was like this, however. There were commercial towns in northern France and Flanders where cloth manufacture was a major industry; and in northern Italy silk and cotton industries flourished, and merchants made fortunes in trade with the East. Ships from Venice and Genoa sailed to the eastern Mediterranean to bring back ginger, mustard, almonds, silk and various metals. And the merchants who promoted these voyages set up joint stock companies and insurance schemes to protect themselves against loss. An example illustrating how joint stock companies began to evolve would be an individual merchant who, instead of putting all his money into one ship, would have, perhaps, a quarter-share in four ships sailing on different routes. From as early as the 1070s, merchants were using this arrangement to ensure that even if one ship was wrecked none of them was ruined, because other vessels would bring home a cargo and yield a profit.

In these circumstances, improvements made in shipbuilding and silk manufactures must have been strongly influenced by economic pressures. Thus innovation would be the product of quite different conditions from those in which monastic craftsmen worked; where commercial motives had probably been minimal in the earlier Cistercian abbeys, they would tend to predominate in the north Italian merchant cities.

The same would be true in the cloth trade of northern Europe. Raw wool bought by merchants from the English was spun and woven at Ypres and Ghent in Flanders, or in French towns such as Cambrai or Amiens. A typical weaver in one of these towns had perhaps a couple of looms in his house or workshop, which would be worked with the aid of one or two other men and an apprentice. In Ghent there were about 4,000 weavers, and since the total population cannot have exceeded 30,000, most of the labour force must have been employed in this trade. Flemish cloth was in demand all over Europe, and local merchants sent it to England or to north-eastern Germany, from where their ships would return with corn, or with new supplies of raw wool. Trade over longer distances was organised mainly by Italian merchants, who bought cloth in Flanders, had it dyed and finished in the textile towns of northern Italy, and sold it in the eastern Mediterranean area.

It would seem, then, that in France and Flanders, as in Italy, there was a large area of life dominated by commercial activities. Any technical innovation, such as the introduction of an improved loom, would thus be influenced by the merchants' desire for larger output and bigger profits, and perhaps resisted by the clothworkers' need to protect their livelihood.

But however much the inhabitants of the cloth towns were preoccupied with the demands of commercial life, they did have idealistic and imaginative impulses which were capable of being mobilised with technological effect. And it was the Church which mobilised them with the most conspicuous success, as the cathedrals of northern France will show. Many of these great churches were built in the cloth towns, and reflect the enthusiasm of merchants and artisans for enormous projects which the Church had set in motion.

Thus, at the risk of over-simplification, we can say that during the 12th and early 13th centuries, there was some technical progress motivated principally by ECONOMIC considerations, and some which principally served IDEALISTIC purposes. Human motives are often very mixed, and to draw too sharp a distinction would be false. But contrasts can be drawn between the predominantly economic objectives of merchants in pursuit of their business, and the predominantly non-economic aims of the cathedral builders, or, in their early years, of Cistercian monks. It is this kind of contrast which provides the main theme of this book, the argument being that idealism can provide a driving force for technical change – idealism embracing social or religious purposes, or even abstract symbols and intellectual schemes.

The cathedral crusade

The circumstances in which huge cathedrals were built in the commercial towns of northern France arose from the growing secular culture of those towns and the way in which the Church reacted to it. No longer were monks and clergy the only educated people to be found. Bankers, lawyers and merchants had all, of necessity, to be both literate and numerate. And the universities founded at Paris (around 1150), Oxford (1190), Bologna (1200) and elsewhere were training men for the secular professions of law and medicine.

In 1096, the Church had effectively mobilised the idealism and the spirit of adventure in a restless and increasingly secular society by means of the first crusade. This military expedition to Palestine fired the imaginations of nobles and knights, to whom it was presented in the language of chivalry and religion, and for a while it absorbed their energies and resources in the service of the Church. The crusading ideal remained alive for two centuries and more, but subsequent crusades in 1147, 1187 and 1204 were less successful than the first, and did not, in any case, appeal to the townsmen so much as to the nobility.

So a new kind of movement was needed in which the townsmen could participate, and such a movement was launched in the middle of the 12th century. It happened about the time when the King of France was absent on the second crusade, and when the Regent ruling in his stead was Suger, Abbot of the great monastery of St Denis near Paris. Suger was fired by the political ideal of a partnership between Church and State. This already existed in the organisation of the crusades, and it was given a rather special expression while he was Regent, and so a leader of both.[12] The ideal was represented also by Suger's abbey church at St Denis, for that was a major religious centre in France, and it was also the church where the Kings of France were crowned. So in this building, the glories of both King and Church were celebrated together.

Suger began to reconstruct the church building at St Denis in the late 1130s, acting to some degree as his own architect. Every part of the structure he planned had some symbolic intention, as his writings show, and every element in its architecture expressed something of his philosophical or political ideals.

12. von Simson, *The Gothic Cathedral*, pp. 62, 75–6, 90.

As building work progressed, Suger was caught up in advance preparations for the second crusade, and the rebuilding of the church came itself to symbolise some of the ideals of a crusade. In the course of time, Suger's enthusiasm for building caught the imagination of other people. Between 1150 and 1280, about eighty cathedrals were built or rebuilt in France, many in the cloth towns in the north of the country. In effect, Suger had inaugurated a new sort of crusade, and one which was enthusiastically pursued by merchants and townsmen in the way in which the military crusades had previously engaged the enthusiasm of knights and nobles. Thus one historian has thought it right to talk about this wave of church building as 'the cathedral crusade'.[13]

Here, then, was an idealistic movement with a constructive, material objective. What were its technical consequences? Briefly, they consisted in the development of techniques for building very high vaults supported by flying buttresses. The period of most active innovation was between 1160 and 1180, although many advances were made both before and after those dates.

To put the matter in a fuller perspective, it must be explained that the structure of the abbey church of St Denis made use of some of the innovations which had first appeared at Durham, particularly the pointed arch and the rib vault. However, the architectural scheme to which these elements contributed was so novel that the rebuilding of St Denis may justly be regarded as the beginning of the new system of architectural design which is now known as the 'Gothic'.

In this respect, though, its novelty was shared to some extent by Sens Cathedral in Burgundy, where a rebuilding scheme was begun in the 1130s. Work was not finished at Sens until 1160, while at St Denis it was virtually complete in 1144. The common features of the two buildings owe much to the personal friendship which existed between Abbot Suger and Bishop Henry of Sens. The two men clearly discussed architectural matters, although in some respects Sens developed along different lines from St Denis. Its design, in fact, had an important formative influence on architectural development. William of Sens came from there to England in 1174 to rebuild Canterbury Cathedral, and English architecture gained much from his example.

13. Gimpel, *The Cathedral Builders*, p. 45.

It is worth comparing the churches at St Denis and Sens with the cathedral at Durham, because the two later buildings contain the first major development of the rib vault since the time, about forty years earlier, when it was introduced at Durham. In both of them, the pointed arches and rib vaults were used to create a structure with a far lighter and less massive appearance than at Durham. Thus, for example, where the main supporting piers at Durham had been made in the form of 11-foot-diameter drums of stone, at Sens the corresponding members consisted of much lighter columns paired together. It was the resulting sense of lightness in structure which was the essence of Gothic. The new style and technique of building was tried out tentatively in a few more French churches, including particularly Noyon Cathedral (begun *c*. 1150), but it began to show its full potential only in the 1160s, most notably in the building of the cathedral of Notre Dame in Paris.

At Notre Dame, one can see two of the most spectacular features of construction which were characteristic of the cathedral crusade – the systematic exploitation of flying buttresses, and the tendency towards enormous size, especially in the height of the vault. Whereas, prior to the 1160s, the vault of a large church might be 70 or 80 feet above the floor as at Sens, at Notre Dame it was increased to 110 feet – and the church was made exceptionally wide as well, with an extra aisle on each side.

Since its introduction at Durham, the flying buttress had not developed very far, because there were very few buildings in which its use was essential. But the extra height of the vault at Notre Dame increased the need for some kind of buttressing that would counteract the outward thrust of the vault, while at the same time the great width of the two aisles, and the desire to refine the solid supporting members within the building, meant that the use of an elaborate system of flying buttresses was now a necessity. Thus after the start of construction at Notre Dame in 1163, and up to about 1180, there must have been a great deal of intensive work done on the design of what was effectively a new system of buttressing. Very soon after the flying buttresses at Notre Dame were begun, they were adopted for the building of the Collegiate Church at Mantes, between Rouen and Paris, which had been begun about 1170. Here, part of the building had been completed without the use of such buttresses, and this had meant that the walls which supported the vault at the level of the aisle roofs were 5 feet thick; but in the later parts of the building, where the architect was able to incorporate flying buttresses, he felt free to reduce this wall thickness from 60 inches to 16 inches. Structural developments of this kind naturally led to there being fewer large masses of masonry visible on the inside of the building, and allowed the development of progressively larger windows.

During the next seventy years, flying buttresses became extremely elaborate and sophisticated structural devices, and the characteristic appearance of a French cathedral when seen from the east was that of a forest of buttresses and their supporting piers which almost entirely obscured the windows and walls of the building itself. There might be flying buttresses at two or even three levels, each aligned to serve a specific function. Thus, at the highest of the levels, the buttress would act as a brace to the roof, taking care of any outward thrusts from the roof truss itself, and, more important, bracing the building against wind pressures. Lower down, the main buttress would be arranged to support the vault; and sometimes there would be a third level, at which another buttress would support the aisle vaults.

All this is characteristic of the most advanced phase of medieval construction, which was reached in the mid-13th century, after the completion of Notre Dame and of the cathedrals at Chartres (begun in 1194), Rouen (1200) and Rheims (1211). These are often considered to be the best examples of the 'High Gothic' style and among the finest of all the medieval cathedrals, but developments in structural techniques which followed their completion led to an even more spectacular kind of architecture. The best way of explaining this is to say that the aim was now to create a church inside which no solid masonry walls could be seen at all, but only slender shafts soaring upwards with immense areas of stained glass in between; and for a ceiling, there would be an array of stone ribs echoing the shafts which rose up to support them from below. Only outside such a building would one be aware of the immensity and complication of the buttresses needed to support it. Apart from the use of flying buttresses this architecture was made possible by the invention of window tracery, a part-technical, part-aesthetic innovation which allowed really big windows to be made.

The strong vertical emphasis of such an interior could be strengthened by adjusting its proportions so that it would appear high in relation to its width; but the actual height of interiors of

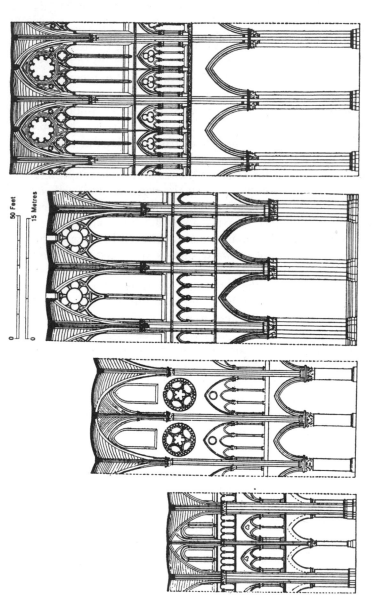

Figure 5
Bays from four French cathedrals, drawn to the same scale, and showing the increasing height of vaults.
From left to right, Noyon Cathedral, designed *c.* 1150; Notre Dame, Paris, as designed *c.* 1170; Rheims Cathedral, *c.* 1211; and Amiens Cathedral, begun 1220.
(Source: figs. 32, 34, 38 and 39 from the 5th edition of Nikolaus Pevsner, *An Outline of European Architecture*, Pelican Books, 1957)

50 Feet
15 Metres

cathedrals was progressively increased, and height itself seems to have become a matter for competition between one architect and another, and between one town and another. Thus, while Chartres Cathedral was of about the same height internally as Notre Dame (110 feet), the vaults at Rouen and Rheims were about 125 feet above the floor in both cases, while Amiens Cathedral, begun in 1220, had a vault soaring up to 140 feet above the floor. There was rivalry between the citizens of Amiens and the men of Beauvais, two of the bigger commercial towns in northern France, so when the rebuilding of Beauvais Cathedral was begun, in 1247, it was felt to be essential that the dimensions of Amiens Cathedral should be exceeded. The vaults at Beauvais were therefore pushed up to the extraordinary height of 157 feet. The dimensions of Beauvais were equalled by Cologne Cathedral, which, despite its distance from northern France, is a closely related design. Like Westminster Abbey (rebuilding scheme begun 1245), Cologne Cathedral (1248) was partly the result of French architects working on foreign soil; but while Westminster Abbey is a modest, anglicised version of Rheims, at Cologne the interest in enormously high vaults, vast expanses of glass, and soaring vertical shafts had its most sensational result.

The same interest in building to great heights was expressed on the exterior of the buildings by towers surmounted by spires. The cathedral at Chartres, for example, now impressive enough with its two spires, was originally intended to have eight of them: likewise Reims was to have six spires, while at Laon, five towers were completed. This 'vehement verticalism' of the exteriors, 'the supreme expression of the heavenward urge',[14] was in most cases still to be realised when the cathedral crusade exhausted itself in the 1250s and 60s.

After this time, there were no developments in cathedral architecture with any wide technological significance. The structural sophistication of Amiens, Beauvais and Cologne Cathedrals was the culmination of a long series of experiments in which many different structural techniques were tried out. Those which were successful were used again and again, and improved each time, while those which were associated with the subsidence or collapse of part of a building were abandoned. Improvement must have been largely a trial and error process, but what is noteworthy is the continuing willingness to experiment. A similar

14. Pevsner, *European Architecture*, chapter 3, pp. 91-2.

courage and openmindedness, and a similar spirit of enquiry, must have pervaded other technical arts at this time, and must account for the improvements and inventions made in them, but only in cathedral building can it be so clearly observed.

All this raises questions about the extent of a 13th-century mason's understanding of the engineering problems he faced. Obviously he lacked the kind of knowledge a modern engineer would have, yet it is clear that the masons usually knew very precisely where buttresses ought to be and at what height their counter-pressures were needed. To this extent, then, their experiments were guided by knowledge. Their trial and error was not just groping in the dark, for they had a considerable insight into what shape a building should be: insight which was aided by geometrical rules of design which will be mentioned in chapter two. And as it turns out, the successful design of masonry structures depended more on getting the shape, that is the geometry, right than on calculating the magnitude of forces in the modern way.

Now of course, cathedral building is not technology in any normal modern sense; it is an art form, expressing religious truths through symbolism, and religious emotion through mass and space and soaring height. It expresses other things as well – civic pride and mercantile prosperity – but also a mood of restlessness, of never being content with what has been achieved, whether in the moral, or the aesthetic or the material, spheres. It gives evidence too of an enthusiasm for experiment in both aesthetic and structural matters, as if the builders, always unsatisfied by their handiwork, were continually lured on by higher ambition. There was almost a moral imperative about it, rather of the sort expressed by St Bernard in the 12th century when he said that 'a man who sets before himself a greater good and then does a lesser, sins'.[15] The cathedral builders had set before themselves a very great good, but never accepting that they had attained it, they were continually driven on to explore and experiment, and to attempt the untried.

They were spurred on too by the competitive spirit which arose among the independent commercial cities, and since the citizens of these towns clearly made comparisons between their own and neighbouring cathedrals the progress made in terms of size or aesthetic effect must have been quickly appreciated. Thus

15. Williams, *Saint Bernard*, p. 54.

although it cannot be claimed that the townsmen were conscious of technical progress as distinct from changes in architectural style and aesthetics, we can say that they were deliberately and successfully promoting change in an art which had a strong component of engineering and mechanical skill. Thus, possibly for the first time in history, a society was consciously committed to systematic and deliberate change in a wide range of practical arts. In this restricted sense, the 'cathedral crusade' can be taken as the beginning of the modern phase in the history of technology – the phase in which the development of techniques moved from the evolutionary to the revolutionary stage: that is, from a state in which craftsmen make occasional small changes in their art, and from one generation to another gradually improve their skill and the stock of inherited experience, to a stage where changes are deliberately made in order to approach some un-realised ideal which is always one step beyond what current techniques make possible. The continually questing mood of the cathedral builders, at any rate, is characteristic of the spirit that brought modern technology to birth.

The cost of the cathedrals

The enthusiasm of medieval society for their cathedrals can be assessed to some degree by the money spent on building them. Some of the best information for this it to be found in the accounts of the Office of the King's Works in England. But in studying these accounts it is as well to remember that 13th-century prices have to be multiplied by something more than a hundred before comparisons with modern values can be made. Westminster Abbey, for example, where a rebuilding scheme was begun in 1245, had cost about £41,250 by 1272; this would be equivalent to several millions at 20th-century prices, but only about two-thirds of the building had been completed for that sum. Had it been completed in the 13th century, its total cost would perhaps have been £70,000. This figure can be put into some sort of perspective by comparison with the series of great castles begun in north Wales in 1283. Of these, the one at Beaumaris had by 1300 cost £11,400 and needed a further £3,000 for its completion, while Conway Castle and town walls had been completed before this date for about £15,000.[16]

16. Brown and others, *The History of the King's Works*, vol. 1, especially p. 156.

It would seem from this that at the end of the 13th century, £15,000 in English currency would build a large castle while four or five times as much was needed for a church of cathedral size. Much of the difference would be accounted for by the sculpture and stained glass and perhaps the shrine of a saint. None the less, much of the great cost of a cathedral was due to the refinement and sophistication of the structure; stones used in the construction of arches, buttresses and vaults needed to be very accurately cut, and so were more expensive than the much larger quantities of stone used to build a castle. Thus the cost of building a cathedral was in part a reflection of the great concentration of specialised skills involved.

Westminster Abbey is larger and more elaborate than many other English cathedrals, and this must be accounted for largely by the generous contributions made by Henry III, who took a close interest in the construction. The official history of the Office of Works states that 'Henry's expenditure on the Abbey was well over £40,000, a sum which to him represented the best part of two years' income, and whose modern equivalent could hardly be less than £4,000,000'.[17] According to the same arithmetic, the modern equivalent of its total cost would be £7,000,000. And since the Abbey, both in its size and method of construction, followed French precedents more closely than English ones, this figure must be about right for the larger French cathedrals as well.

The question arises as to how this money was raised during the cathedral crusade. For although the French King made gifts to some cathedrals, such as Chartres, contributions on the scale of Henry's could not be looked for. Thus it was within the towns where the cathedrals were built that much of the money was raised. Local merchants would probably be the biggest contributors, and they would usually be granted indulgences in exchange for their benefactions. In addition, the guilds or trade corporations in a town would each donate a window or some other specific item for the cathedral. But it was by the exhibition of saints' relics that the great mass of the population was reached, and this brought in money from even the poorest people, as well as from pilgrims who travelled great distances to see such things. Sometimes, too, a cleric from the cathedral travelled through the country showing relics and preaching as a means of raising

17. *The History of the King's Works*, p. 156.

money. In 1124, when Abbot Suger began raising funds for the rebuilding of his abbey, St Denis, near Paris, he estimated that three-quarters of the money would be contributed by pilgrims, while the ordinary revenues of the abbey would make up the rest.

The immensity of the task of fund-raising can be assessed if one recalls that the towns which built the big cathedrals would typically have a population of about 20,000 people, many of whom would be craftsmen with an income of something like two shillings a week.[18] Thus raising £70,000, even over a period of twenty years, was only possible because of the enthusiasm of the people for their cathedrals. One has only to think what the problem would be if a modern town of 20,000 people had to raise £7,000,000 for a civic project. But there was inevitably a minority of people who questioned the spending of money on this scale for such unnecessarily large constructions. These critics of extravagant building schemes included Ailred of Rievaulx who was a Cistercian monk, Alexander Neckam and Petrus Cantor. The latter was one of the clergy at Notre Dame in Paris, and is known for his preaching against usury; in 1180, when his own cathedral was being rebuilt on a large scale, he complained that 'monastic or ecclesiastical edifices are raised from the usury and breed of barren metal among covetous men, and from the lying deceits and deceitful lies of hireling preachers'.[19]

Half a century earlier, St Bernard, abbot of the Cistercian monastery of Clairvaux, had criticised monks of other orders for 'the vast height of your churches, their immoderate length, their superfluous breadth, the costly polishings, the curious carvings and paintings which attract worshipper's gaze...'. Bernard went on to criticise the way in which the money for all this was raised by the exhibition of relics. People's eyes, he said, 'are feasted with relics cased in gold, and their purse strings are loosed. They are shown a most comely image of some saint, whom they think all the more saintly that he is the more gaudily painted... The church is resplendent in her walls, beggarly in her poor; she clothes her stones with gold, and leaves her sons naked.'[20]

18. Gimpel, *The Cathedral Builders*, p. 73; Brown and others, *The History of the King's Works*, pp. 139 and 374.

19. Quoted by Gimpel, *The Cathedral Builders*, pp. 45–6; see also Nelson, *The Idea of Usury*, p. 10.

20. Quoted by Coulton, *Art and the Reformation*, appendix 26.

St Bernard wrote a great deal in this vein, and did his best to ensure that Cistercian abbeys had plain, undecorated buildings, limited in size to what was strictly necessary. There was, indeed, a strong streak of puritanism in Bernard's attitude, reflected also in his more strictly religious writings. And the similarities of Bernard's view with those of the later Puritans who were products of the Reformation is so striking that one historian has used the phrase 'the high ancestry of puritanism'[21] to describe the Cistercians. One reason given for the similarities is that both Cistercian monks and later Puritans were reformers of the kind who wished to revive the customs of the early Christians. For the monks, a first step was to go back to the earliest and simplest form of the Rule of St Benedict. But beyond that they wished to return to the forms which had been observed in the first century of the Christian era, and which, they thought, would bring them 'closer to the historic Christ'. These sentiments were no doubt in St Bernard's mind when he asked, despairingly, 'who will give me to see before I die, the Church of God as in the days of old, when the apostles spread their nets to take not gold or silver but the souls of men?'[22]

From this desire to revive the spirit of the early Church, then, sprang the injunctions about plain and simple buildings, and an austere way of life; connected with it was also the idea that work – manual labour – had a moral value and was part of one's vocation. In all this, the comparisons which can be drawn between the ideals of 12th-century monks and 17th-century Puritans are worth mentioning because of the link between a high valuation of work and a progressive outlook on technical improvement which can be observed among both groups. Of course, there were important differences as well, but the similarities are sufficiently close to give pause to those historians and sociologists who identify the work ethic solely with the later Puritans, and who refer to it as a 'protestant ethic'. If this latter term is to be used, it must be understood that Protestantism was a continuing part of the Christian tradition, and not something that originated with the Reformation.

These considerations also have some relevance for the 20th century; and it will be argued in the final chapter that a reconsideration of work and its place in social and technological

21. Coulton, 'The high ancestry of Puritanism', in *Ten Medieval Studies*.
22. Williams, *Saint Bernard*, p. 142.

development is one of the urgent needs of the 1970s. Other echoes of the 12th and 13th centuries will be found later in this book. The restless, vigorous, innovating attitude of the cathedral builders, for example, has its parallel in more recent times, as the critics of the cathedral builders also have.

But the most important point is the way in which economic pressure on technical progress was relatively limited in extent during the 12th century, so that some kinds of innovation came about largely as a result of ideological influence. There were two particular groups of people for whom this was most notably true – Cistercian monks and the cathedral builders – and there were two prominent men who were outstanding for their exposition of the ideals of the two groups – St Bernard among the Cistercians and Abbot Suger at the outset of the cathedral crusade. The two men knew each other personally and discussed their differing ideals. In their attitudes to the crusades and in politics generally, they had much in common, but Bernard was obviously critical of Suger's lavish building schemes.

Beyond the world of cathedrals and abbeys, there was, of course, the life of commerce – the merchant ships in the Mediterranean and the North Sea, the clothworkers of Flanders and the silk-throwers of Italy. There was significant technical innovation in these areas of life: some of it will be discussed in the next chapter. However, it does not seem necessary to go into much detail about innovation in this sphere, as it has already been quite fully discussed by economic historians.

What seems most significant is the contrast between economic objectives in technical progress and the influence of ideas and idealism. The different kinds of objective – economic or idealistic – represent different directions which technical progress could take. 'Progress' indeed is a misleading word to use about technology, because it implies steady advance towards a single, universally accepted goal. In fact, the direction of technical progress has varied in the past. The choice of direction is always open, not least in the middle 20th century, and it is important to appreciate the full range of choice which is available.

The different directions which technical progress took during the 12th and 13th centuries may be illustrated, somewhat crudely, by means of a diagram (fig. 6). Progress in some of these directions led to innovation which was 'useful' in economic terms. Sometimes, as in the monasteries, the 'usefulness' of an invention

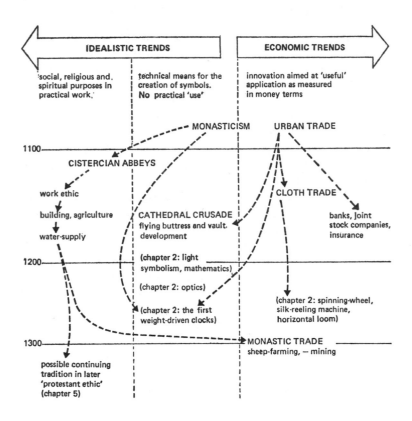

Figure 6
Schematic representation of different directions of technical progress during the 12th and 13th centuries.

was, in theory, a matter of spiritual criteria, while among the cathedral builders, technical progress took a direction which had no practical purpose at all, and was of no 'use' to anyone. The technical effort that went into the cathedral none the less had immense symbolic importance.

In this chapter, a rather general view has been taken of these different kinds of progress. But it is also necessary to study them in a more personal and individual way, and to ask, what was it that stirred in the imagination of people at this time? That is unanswerable; but it is a question worth considering, because invention depends on the exercise of imagination, and idealism is important in the history of technology partly because ideals are often a more effective trigger to the imagination than are economic incentives. It seems important, then, to say something about this in relation to individual craftsmen and their patrons. The subject will be tackled in the next chapter in the belief that it can provide a clue as to what it was that kindled the restless, creative genius out of which modern technology was eventually brought to birth.

2

A century of invention: 1250–1350

Attitudes to technical progress

To believe in and welcome technical progress would have been something anomalous in the 13th century. Such a belief had scarcely ever appeared in any earlier period or civilisation, and was not strictly compatible with the ideology of medieval Europe. Much earlier, among the Greeks and Romans, the most common attitude was symbolised by the story of Prometheus. It was he who gave men fire stolen from Olympus, taught them many of the arts, and was punished by being chained to a rock. So indeed might men be punished if they tried nature too far. When sailing-ships were introduced, more mariners were drowned than before sails were invented. Invention was a dangerous occupation, and an unnecessary one, for all the arts needed by men had been supplied by Prometheus and other remote heroes.

In the 12th and 13th centuries, the cathedral builders were continually inventing new techniques and trying them to the limit. Where they failed, buildings collapsed or towers fell, as happened at Lincoln Cathedral around 1237. But these craftsmen and their patrons continued to experiment, and in a context where the possibility of technical progress was not fully recognised, they effected, paradoxically, a considerable and impressive progress. So one is bound to ask, what was their attitude to the improvements they were making?

There is not much evidence bearing directly on this question, but one factor in the thought of the 12th and 13th centuries does seem relevant: the very close attention which was paid to the last book in the Bible and its portrayal of the end of the world. What kind of progress was possible if this was the destiny of man? It was understood that the present order of things in the world would come to an end in the near future. The Bible described in some detail what would happen. First there would be a series of unprecedented disasters: plague, wars, fire and the appearance of the Antichrist. Then the forces of evil would finally be defeated, a thousand years of peace would ensue, there would be a Last Judgement of sinful mankind, and then the New Jerusalem – a new order of things – would be established on earth.

The Franciscan friar Roger Bacon was one 13th-century writer who believed that the Antichrist would appear in the very near future, but who also had a special interest in technical matters. In many of his writings, Bacon gives a strong impression of advocating technical progress. But in common with most of his contemporaries, he took a pessimistic view of humanity, among whom, he thought, corruption and evil would increase until all was swept away at the end of the world. The forces of evil, including the Antichrist himself, would use all manner of natural and artificial devices to confound mankind, and it was necessary for men to improve the practical arts in order that this threat could be overcome. Similarly, the extension of knowledge was necessary as a means 'of preparing Christendom to resist more successfully' the corruption which was coming,[1] and which would precede the end of the world. The technical progress and the search for knowledge which Roger Bacon advocated had a special purpose, and was strictly limited in time by the forthcoming apocalypse. So although he expressed an enthusiastic interest in the technical achievements of his age, he could not state any belief in a sustained technical progress.

The idea of progress was 'glaringly incongruous' with Bacon's understanding of the world. 'When he looked forward into the future, the vision which confronted him was a scene of corruption, tyranny and struggle under the reign of a barbarous enemy of Christendom; and after that the end of the world. It is from this point of view that we must appreciate the observations which he made on the advancement of knowledge.'[2]

The same attitudes were expressed by the cathedral builders in the sculpture which formed part of their work. Very frequently, and on prominent parts of a building, such as the main doorway, they depicted the end of the world, and the Last Judgement. It seems reasonable to suggest that their views were in some ways

1. Bury, *The Idea of Progress*, p. 27; Bacon, *Opus majus*, trans. Burke, p. 633; also, on the date of the Antichrist, p. 289.
2. Bury, *The Idea of Progress*, p. 28.

similar to Roger Bacon's, and that their efforts to improve technical skills were not conceived as a means of improving the condition of man within the present order of things; but rather, they were reaching forward to meet an eternal order, a New Jerusalem, which the cathedral itself symbolised. The conviction was that by 'reaching out to the immaterial through the material, man may have fleeting visions of God'.[3] This, perhaps, was the meaning of the technical progress which Roger Bacon advocated, and which evoked the enthusiasm of the men who built – and paid for – the cathedrals.

How cosmic speculations and theological dogmas could affect the mundane activities of the artisan will be discussed in more detail towards the end of this chapter. For the moment it is sufficient to draw a contrast between the views of Roger Bacon and the attitudes current in the 16th century. By that time, technical progress was appreciated in a humanistic sense; but the evidence which was quoted to show that real progress had been made in western Europe most frequently took the form of lists of inventions, including, ironically, a large number of 13th- or early 14th-century date – the mariner's compass, gunpowder and firearms, clocks and the Italian silk-twisting machines. Of the other inventions commonly mentioned, only printing and such specialised items as the Toledo waterworks belonged to the period when technical progress was coming to be recognised. Thus even if the men of the 13th or early 14th century did not believe in technical progress, that belief as it was first formulated in the 16th century was based very largely on their achievements.

Firearms and textiles: some inventions of c. 1250–1350

The enthusiasm of the cathedral builders seems to have flagged soon after 1250; fewer large churches were built and the pace of innovation slowed down. None the less, the period between 1250 and 1350 was one of prolific invention in some of the other technical arts. Here the historian faces a difficulty, however, in that none of these inventions can be documented as precisely as, for example, the earlier series of minor innovations which marked the development of the flying buttress. All that can be done in some cases is to say that most of the crucial stages in their development took place in the century between 1250 and 1350.

3. Mâle, *The Gothic Image*, p. 20.

Thus, for example, it is not known when the first weight-driven clock was successfully made, but it is clear that by 1350 several large astronomical clocks had been built.

Some of the innovations of the period have been attributed to Chinese influences, and it is certainly true that around 1250, Europeans had better opportunity than either earlier or later to make the difficult journey to China. Those who went included Joannes de Plano Carpini (1246), William of Rubruck (1253) and Marco Polo (1260). Through these or other contacts, Europeans may have learned something about the incendiary chemical mixtures used by the Chinese, and from this knowledge, gunpowder was perhaps developed. The details of this are very obscure, but what is not in dispute is that before 1350, Europeans had developed gunpowder and its applications far beyond anything that had been conceived in the East. For where the Chinese had used gunpowder mixtures mainly as incendiaries or in firecrackers, the Europeans were soon concentrating their efforts on developing cannon. By 1350, firearms had been in use for perhaps three decades, and at about this time, Petrarch was able to reflect ironically on technical progress of a kind. He said that the 'instruments which discharge balls of metal with most tremendous noise and flashes of fire . . . were a few years ago very rare . . . but now they are become as common and familiar as any other kind of arms. So quick and ingenious are the minds of men in learning the most pernicious arts.'[4]

It is probable, however, that firearms did not change the nature of warfare in any decisive way until much later, and if attention is confined to the period 1250–1350, it was perhaps new devices for spinning and weaving which made the biggest material difference to European life. Here, the Ypres 'book of trades' dating from around 1310 provides some of the most interesting evidence, for it includes illustrations of most of the processes involved in making cloth. From it, one can see that one of the most important innovations in the weaving trade was the horizontal loom, which may, like many other things, have come from the Islamic civilisation, perhaps via Spain. But in 1310 it was still a fairly recent invention, and offered several advantages over earlier looms in which the cloth was woven in a vertical position. With the

4. Quoted by Cipolla, *European Culture*, pp. 35–6; this is also the source for comments about possible Chinese influence in the development of gunpowder.

Figure 7
An Italian silk-reeling machine drawn by Vittoria Zonca *c.* 1600.
The spindles are made to rotate by a large wheel or drum which revolves inside the circular framework, which in turn may be driven by a waterwheel. This machine is probably quite similar to the ones used *c.* 1300 from which it developed.
(See A. G. Keller, *A Theatre of Machines*, Chapman & Hall, 1964, p. 8)

horizontal loom, some operations were controlled by means of pedals, leaving the weaver's hands free to pass the shuttle backwards and forwards.

It is worth recalling that the cloth trade at Ypres and throughout the Low Countries was based on wool, but that in Italy there were also silk and cotton manufactures. One major innovation in the silk industry was a machine for twisting and reeling silk thread which originated at Lucca, perhaps in the 13th century. Detailed references exist to a machine being used there about 1330, as well as at Bologna, where some silk-workers from Lucca had settled, but the only illustration earlier than the one reproduced here is a rough sketch made in 1487. With these machines, thread was wound on to horizontal reels from rows of vertical spindles below, being twisted in the process by the rotation of the s-shaped flyers. How closely the machine of 1330 resembled this is uncertain, but it is clear that on some early examples (see table below), one worker could operate 200 or more spindles simultaneously.

Table 1. Early Silk-Twisting Mills
Data on some early recorded examples.

Date	Number of Spindles	Number of Reels
c. 1330	240	2 rows
1385	—	4 rows
14th century	480	5 rows of 16 reels
14th century	240	2 rows of 12 reels

It seems probable that the introduction of the silk-twisting machine was related to the invention of the spinning-wheel, which occurred at about the same time. Here it must be explained that silk did not have to be spun in the usual sense. Individual fibres are very long, and to make a silken thread it is only necessary to twist several fibres together. In contrast, wool and cotton have relatively short fibres, and to make a thread or yarn from wool means not only twisting the fibres together, but also drawing out the yarn while it is being twisted, in order to lock the short fibres together. From a very early date, this operation had been performed by means of a spindle and whorl, which really meant that it was all done by hand with the aid of only very simple tools and a spindle on which the yarn could be wound.

The earliest spinning-wheel, introduced in the 13th century, consisted simply of a frame to support the spindle, and a wheel and pulley to make it revolve. The twisting and drawing operations in the spinning process were still a matter of the manual skill and judgement of the worker. This type of spinning-wheel was known as the 'Great' Wheel to distinguish it from a second type, the 'Saxony' Wheel, in which the simple spindle was replaced by a bobbin and flyer device. By this means, the twisting part of the process was mechanically controlled, and it became possible for the thread to be wound continuously on to the bobbin as it was spun.

Now the earliest reference to a Great Wheel dates from 1298, when these machines were in use for spinning the weft, but not the warp threads of cloth made at Speier on the Rhine. On the other hand, the bobbin and flyer was not illustrated anywhere earlier than a German work of around 1480 and a little later in Leonardo's notebooks. Most authors take this to mean that the Saxony Wheel, with its bobbin and flyer, was introduced about 200 years later than the Great Wheel. The matter is open to doubt, however, because Italian silk-twisting machines of the 13th century almost certainly employed some form of bobbin and flyer, and as Patterson[5] points out, '13th century Bolognese twisting mills are closely analogous to spinning devices'; these mills were probably in use as early as 1272. Similarity in working principle between machines used for wool and for silk has therefore led Patterson to wonder whether the spinning-wheel, and particularly the Saxony Wheel, may have been introduced considerably earlier than the sparse documentary evidence suggests. He has also pointed out that the earliest pictures of bobbin and flyer devices show a fully-developed mechanism, so there must have been simpler and more experimental versions of the same thing long before these sketches were made in the late 15th century. For these reasons it seems fair to suggest that the Saxony Wheel should be grouped with the Great Wheel and the Italian silk-throwing machine as one of the inventions of the period between 1250 and 1350.

5. Patterson, in *A History of Technology*, 2, p. 205.

The weight-driven clock

Of all that was achieved in the practical arts during the period under review, the invention of the weight-driven clock has attracted most attention from historians. Part of the reason is that although documentary evidence is small in quantity and difficult to interpret, there is very much more known about the clock than about almost any other contemporary invention. But another reason for emphasising it is the way in which this invention is supposed to have led to new concepts of time, making possible the whole pattern of modern life, in which so much is regulated by the clock. On another score, there is sometimes excited comment about the way in which the clock has on occasion been taken as a paradigm of all machinery, so that it is seen as a sort of parent to the whole of our mechanically-minded civilisation.[6] On a more technical level, it is rightly pointed out that the clocks were the first machines to be made entirely of metal; all other medieval machinery was made mainly of wood, whereas early clocks not only had metal gear-wheels rather than wooden ones, but their mechanism was supported in an iron framework.

Those who argue that the weight-driven clock gave rise to new concepts of time and more precisely-regulated habits of life usually point out that in the 13th century it was monks who most often needed to know the time. This was because of the offices which were said in church at regular intervals. The Rule of St Benedict, compiled in the 6th century, gave instructions about the times of these offices, and referred to them by names which indicate the method of counting the hours which was then in use. The interval between sunrise and sunset was divided into twelve hours, so that each hour during daylight was longer in summer than in winter. The office said in church at sunrise was called Prime, and other services were Terce (at the third hour of daylight), Sext (at the end of the sixth hour: that is, at noon) and None (at the ninth hour of daylight). There were also two services at about sunset, the times of which could easily be determined by watching the sky. Thus the problem of measuring time was most acute for the services said during the day, and also for one that was said in the eighth hour of the night. The usual time-measuring instruments in the 12th century were

6. All these points are made by Mumford, *Technics and Civilization*, pp. 12–18.

sun-dials, hour-glasses and water-clocks, and the monks developed water-clocks to particularly good effect. The flow of water through a small hole provided the measure of time, and such devices, equipped with alarm mechanisms, were often used to wake the monks for the night office. There is a story that in 1198, at the abbey of Bury St Edmunds, the clock woke the monks during the night just in time for them to put out a fire which had started in their buildings. What is more, the clock contained sufficient water for it to be of considerable help in extinguishing the flames.[7]

This story suggests that a water-clock could be fairly large, or at least could include a fairly large vessel of water. The alarm mechanism would be set in motion when the water in this vessel reached a particular level; then a weight would be released, whose fall would in turn ring a bell. In a machine of this kind, one of which is described in an 11th-century manuscript, the weight was attached to a cord, and as it fell, unwinding the cord, it made a drum rotate. This probably worked a mechanism by which an iron bar was made to strike the bell repeatedly. It has been suggested that the origin of the weight-driven clock is to be found in a modification of this mechanism, where the bar which struck the bell evolved into the 'foliot' bar of an escapement. Here it must be explained that the earliest weight-driven clocks were made to keep time, rather approximately, by a mechanism known as the 'verge and foliot'. This was a rather curious affair, in which a heavy bar (the foliot), pivoted near its centre, was pushed first one way and then the other by the action of a toothed wheel, which was only free to move through the space of one tooth for each vibration of the bar; the wheel was driven through simple gearing by a weight suspended from a drum (see fig. 8). Whether such a clock ran fast or slow depended largely on the size of the weight; other weights could be added at the ends of the foliot, and the size and position of these would give a further 'fine' adjustment. The earliest *surviving* clocks in which the foliot mechanism was used are those belonging to the cathedrals at Salisbury (1386), Rouen (1389) and Wells (1392). The famous Dover Castle clock is probably rather later.

This, very briefly, is the way in which the invention of the weight-driven clock can be explained if only utilitarian needs for

7. Edwards, *Weight-driven Chamber Clocks*, pp. 9–10. These alarm clocks were known as '*horologia excitatoria*'.

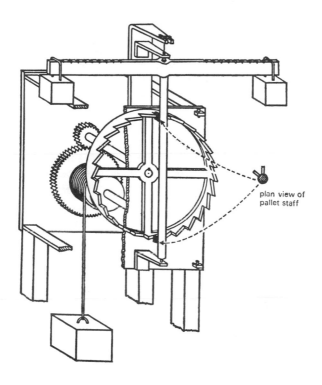

plan view of
pallet staff

Figure 8

Principle of the 'verge and foliot' mechanism.

The horizontal iron bar with weights at either end is the foliot. Fixed to its centre point, immediately below the thread suspension, is a vertical spindle, referred to on the diagram as the pallet staff. This is the verge. It carries two projecting pieces of metal, the pallets, which engage with the teeth of the crown-wheel in such a way that only one tooth may pass the pallet during one complete swing of the foliot.

(Source: Aubrey F. Burstall, *A History of Mechanical Engineering*, Faber & Faber, 1963, fig. 72, p. 130)

a timepiece are considered. But it seems doubtful whether questions of utility can really account for this invention, because in practice early weight-driven clocks were neither reliable nor accurate, and water-clocks were probably more satisfactory for time-keeping. The first weight-driven clocks were, indeed, more probably made for reasons of the intellect or imagination independently of any utilitarian or economic incentive. There was an interest in mechanical things for their own sake, which was already strongly developed in Europe by 1300, but more than that, the first clocks provide an excellent example of how *ideas* may influence the direction of technical progress.

Some clue as to the kinds of idea which influenced the invention of the clock is provided by the earliest examples of which there is a detailed description. For while the earliest *surviving* clocks are the relatively simple ones already mentioned which date from around 1390, the earliest clocks of which full details are available were far more complex, and were built by Richard of Wallingford at St Albans around 1330, and by Giovanni de' Dondi at Padua in 1364. The main purpose of the two latter machines was to indicate the position in the zodiac of the sun, moon and planets. The Padua clock did this by means of seven dials, one corresponding to each known planet, one for the sun and one for the moon. Now, devices which represented the positions of the planets had existed in many forms for a long time before the invention of the clock. Sometimes they were intended only to illustrate the principles upon which the planetary motions were understood; but often they were designed as computing-machines which could be used to predict the positions of various heavenly bodies. The simplest form of computing device was the astrolabe, which was as easy to work as a modern slide-rule, but which yielded information about only the fixed stars. By adding gears and additional dials, Arab astronomers devised astrolabes which also showed the motions of the sun and moon. This seems to have been done by about the year A.D. 1000, but the earliest geared astrolabe of this type to *survive* is dated 1221, and was made in Persia. It had eight gear-wheels, with teeth shaped like equilateral triangles, and the mechanism was turned by hand. The technical significance of this kind of instrument was that trains of gears had to be designed for it in which the relative speed of rotation of various wheels needed to be precisely specified.

During the 11th century, Islamic astronomers also invented the equatorium, an even more complicated device used to calculate the positions of the planets. This was being used in Spain by about 1025; and when the expanding Christian civilisation of Europe began to take over the Islamic territories in Spain during the late 11th and 12th centuries, knowledge of the equatorium passed into Europe along with much other astronomical information.

'No Islamic examples of the equatorium have survived, but from this period onward, there appears to have been a long and active tradition of them . . . they were the basis for the mechanized astronomical models of Richard of Wallingford (and Giovanni de'Dondi).'[8] They were the basis, in other words, for the clocks designed by these men. The faces of these clocks were not marked with the hours or used for telling the time but were the dials familiar to users of the astrolabe and, more particularly, the equatorium. The only difference was that these dials were turned continuously by the fall of a weight. They represented the fulfilment of an ambition to make powered astronomical models keep pace with the moving planets. There was no utilitarian reason for doing this; it was just that the idea of a man-made machine synchronised with the heavens had immense symbolic value. Such a machine was really itself an artificial universe.

The argument, then, is that the clock evolved through the gradual development of astronomical machines of this kind, which were effectively models of the planetary system. The point has been summarised by saying that 'the mechanical clock was less a new way of telling the time, than a simplification of those complex artificial universes which had been popular for many centuries'.[9]

A wheel to move with the rotation of the heavens

This is an interpretation with which not everybody will agree. But even those who prefer a simple account of the invention of the weight-driven clock, to the effect that it was the result of improvements to monastic alarm mechanisms,[10] must at some point discuss clocks in terms of astronomy. In the absence of a clock, people tell the time by watching the passage of the sun and stars across the sky, and the purpose of a clock is simply to provide a convenient indication of where the sun is at any moment. In some ways, then, every clock is a working model of the sky.

8. de Solla Price, *On the Origin of Clockwork*, p. 100.
9. Keller, in *British Journal for the History of Science*, 4, pp. 176–8.
10. As does Edwards, *Weight-driven Chamber Clocks*, p. 19.

The special significance which this idea had around 1300 can be understood only if one knows something about the picture of the universe which was then current. It was a view which had been inherited from the Greek civilisation of the distant past, and was based on the idea of a spherical earth, fixed and motionless, at the centre of the universe. Around the earth in circular orbits moved the moon, the sun and the planets. Finally, just beyond the orbit of Saturn, the most distant planet then known, there was the sphere to which all the stars were fixed; this was the outer shell of the universe, so far as men could see, and it too revolved about an axis which was marked, very nearly, by the pole star. Thus while the stars could be seen to move together across the night sky, the pole star alone was almost stationary.

The luminosity of the heavenly bodies, and their untiring motions, seemed to show that they were of a different nature from anything known on earth. For on the earth there is no fire that burns continuously like the sun without being consumed, and there is no motion that does not run down and stop: none, that is, except the tides, and they were rightly thought to be influenced by the moon. And for a clock to be a true working model of this wonderful planetary system which gave men their sense of time, it would have to work rather as the tides, being somehow driven by the continuous motions of the heavens, and keeping in step with them. The clock, if it worked perfectly, would have to run with a perpetual motion.

How widespread such ideas were among the inventors of the clock is very much open to question; but it cannot be denied that they played some part. This can be illustrated by the writings of a group of people who were active in the 1260s and perhaps earlier, among whom Pierre de Maricourt, author of an essay on the magnetic compass, provides the clearest evidence. Written in 1269, Pierre's essay was sent as a letter from Italy, where he had gone with the army of Charles of Anjou. It was addressed to a soldier friend living near Pierre's home in northern France, and while it is possible that Pierre was himself a soldier, it is usually assumed that his job in the army was that of a craftsman – an armourer or a builder of siege engines.

Maricourt and Foucaucourt (Fontancourt), the villages from which Pierre and his friend had come, were only a short distance from the home of Villard de Honnecourt, the stonemason or architect (see map, fig. 9). Pierre and Villard had some interests

in common, so it would seem quite likely that they were ac-
.quainted with each other. Pierre's circle of friends probably
included Roger Bacon (*c.* 1215 to *c.* 1292), and perhaps also a
certain Robert, author of a treatise on the astrolabe. Both these
Englishmen spent many years in France.

Between them, this group of scholars and craftsmen provides a

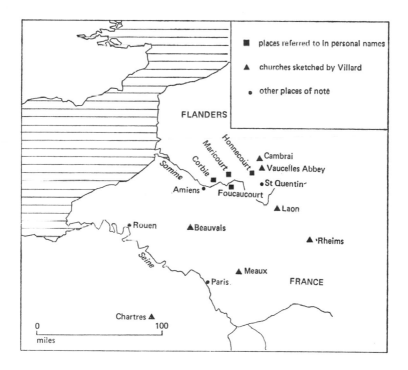

Figure 9
Places associated with Villard de Honnecourt and Pierre de Maricourt.

valuable indication of the thinking of men with a practical turn
of mind. In particular, all four of them were interested in water-
clocks and similar mechanisms, and also in perpetual motion.

Pierre's comments on these devices form part of his letter on
the magnet, in which he argued very cogently for the idea that the
magnetic compass was linked to the heavens by some hidden
force or 'virtue'. The magnet in a compass pointed always to the

pole star, or almost so, and therefore must be linked with the axis of rotation of the heavens. The magnet had poles of its own, as Pierre showed, and ought therefore to have its own axis, about which it could turn with a perpetual motion.

To demonstrate this it was necessary to cut a magnetic loadstone into a spherical shape, pivot it at its poles, and align it with the axis of the heavens. 'If now the stone be moved according to the motion of the heavens, you will be delighted in having discovered such a wonderful secret; but if not, ascribe the failure to your own lack of skill rather than to a defect in nature ... With such an instrument you will need no timepiece, for by it you can know the ascendant at any hour you please, as well as all other dispositions of the heavens which are sought for by astrologers.'[11]

This device, then, was supposed to function as a clock, and it illustrates the connection between clocks, astronomy and perpetual motion in Pierre's thought. His ideas on the subject were elaborated in the second part of the 'Letter on the magnet', where he described another method of achieving perpetual motion 'by means of the virtue or power of this stone'. The device involved in this shows certain similarities with a mechanism described in 1271 by Robert the Englishman, who was mentioned above. Robert seems to have shared Pierre's interest in making a wheel to revolve in time with the heavens. But Robert's machine did not involve a magnet, and historians have suggested that he was describing an early but unsuccessful attempt to make a weight-driven clock. It certainly included a wheel that would rotate once every twenty-four hours: 'Clockmakers are trying to make a wheel which will make one complete revolution for every one of the equinoctial circle, but they cannot quite perfect their work. But if they could, it would be a really accurate clock, and worth more than an astrolabe or other astronomical instrument for reckoning the hours ... The method of making such a clock would be that a man make a disc of uniform weight in every part so far as could possibly be done. Then a lead weight should be hung from the axis of that wheel so that it would complete one revolution from sunrise to sunrise.'[12]

Pierre de Maricourt was the first European author to discuss magnetism in any detail, but the first reference to the magnetic

11. Pierre de Maricourt, 'Letter on the magnet' (*Epistola*), I, 10.
12. Quoted by Thorndike, *The Sphere of Sacrobosco*, p. 230.

compass in Europe is to be found in a work written by Alexander Neckam about seventy years earlier (*c.* 1200). But although the compass had been in use for some time before Pierre wrote, it seems likely that he made significant improvements to the two versions of the instrument which he discussed. His wide practical interests were known to Roger Bacon, as Bacon mentioned in a work called *De secretis*, a few years before the 'Letter on the magnet' was written; and further references occur in three *Opera* by Roger Bacon which were written around 1266–7.

In the first of these works, after describing the armillary sphere, Bacon commented that a 'faithful and magnificent experimenter' (presumably Pierre) was trying hard to make such a sphere 'out of such material and by such a device that it will revolve naturally with the daily rotation of the heavens'.[13] He supported the idea that this was possible by saying that after all, the tides move perpetually in time with the motions of the moon and sun. These comments again call to mind the wording which Robert the Englishman used to discuss wheels which would rotate once every day, keeping in step with the stars.

Clocks and cathedrals: 1140–1280

It is impossible to say whether the views of Roger Bacon and his colleagues were shared by the men who made the first weight-driven clocks around 1300. But it is clear that Roger, Pierre and Robert all thought about clocks in terms of a celestial prototype: the motion of the sun and stars was the only perfect clock, and any man-made timepiece ought to imitate the heavens not only in precision of movement but also in an untiring and continuous motion.

Men with practical experience would without doubt recognise that this was an unattainable ideal. But even ideals which are known to be unattainable are capable of influencing the action of men. This one certainly was, and its influence perhaps accounts for the restless inventiveness of the time. There was a desire to test nature, and to see how near to the celestial prototype human devices could come.

The inventiveness of the people who devised the clocks and textile machines of the period 1250–1350 recalls the prolific inventiveness of the cathedral builders in the previous hundred

13. Quoted by Crombie, *Robert Grosseteste*, pp. 204–8, 210.

years, and recalls too their attitude of never being content even
with the stupendous achievement of a Chartres or an Amiens.
If the clockmakers inherited their outlook, it does not seem
surprising. The 13th-century craftsmen shared to some degree
in the Roman view that 'architecture is divided into three parts:
building, clocks and machines'.[14] This is shown by the sketch-
book of Villard de Honnecourt, which was compiled over a
period of perhaps thirty years from *c.* 1235, and which Pierre de
Maricourt could, just possibly, have seen. Apart from the many
drawings related to architecture and sculpture, Villard sketched a
perpetual-motion machine, some gadgetry probably connected
with the mechanism of a water-clock, and the large masonry
case in which such a clock would be housed. The latter is labelled
unmistakably: 'this is the housing for a clock'.[15]

With this community of interest between clockmakers and
cathedral builders, one may well enquire in the same terms about
the reasons for the inventiveness of both groups. If some clock-
makers saw the sun and stars as a kind of celestial prototype for
their machines, did the cathedral builders have the stimulus
of any similar imaginative ideal? In the previous chapter it was
said that there was some stimulus from mutual competition
between one building project and another. But were there also
more noble, perhaps religious, ideas which would work within the
imagination of the builders rather as the idea of a celestial clock
played on the thoughts of Pierre de Maricourt?

Reasonably clear answers can be given to these questions
because statements about the significance of church buildings can
be found in the liturgy for the consecration of a new church, in
the writings of Abbot Suger in the 1140s, and also in the sculpture
which adorned the buildings themselves. And this evidence
makes it plain that every church was understood partly as a
symbol of the New Jerusalem which St John the Divine had seen
in a vision descending from heaven. This vision was described in
the book of the Bible which in the 12th century was called
'Apocalypse', but which in many modern Bibles is entitled 'The
Revelation of St John'. It symbolised a new order of things
which would come about after the end of the world as we now
know it, and after the Last Judgement. To help portray this

14. Vitruvius, book I, 3.
15. 'c'est li masons d'on orologe'; *Album de Villard de Honnecourt*, ed.
Lassus, p. 11.

idea in the French cathedrals of the 12th and 13th centuries, a sculpture depicting the Last Judgement was often given pride of place above the main western entrance, so that a visitor to the cathedral would have to see this event represented before he symbolically entered the heavenly Jerusalem.

The idea of a church as the New Jerusalem had other layers of meaning. It could, for example, be related to the historic Jerusalem and to the great temple which Solomon had built there.[16] In the liturgy for the consecration of a new church, it could be used to mean that the New Jerusalem was a place where God would dwell among men (Revelation xxi, 3)[17] and the symbolism was underlined at this ceremony by marking the new building with twelve crosses, corresponding to the twelve foundation-stones of the heavenly city (Rev. xxi, 14).

St John the Divine had described the New Jerusalem in some detail, and his account suggested several images which church architects could use. They could not, of course, attempt a literal interpretation, but they did seize on certain aspects of it – its great height, and the several references to its being made 'of pure gold, transparent as glass' (Rev. xxi, 11, 18, 21) and glittering 'like some precious jewel or cut diamond'. Such an effect could be created in a cathedral by the glowing reds and golds of translucent stained glass. And as building techniques developed which allowed stained glass windows to be made increasingly large, men could recall that the New Jerusalem needed neither sun nor moon because 'it was lit by the radiant glory of God' (Rev. xxi, 23).

This symbolism worked in a rather different way from the idea that a clock represented the motion of the heavens, but the difference was not so great as it may seem. The sun and the planets and the stars were thought to be quite different in kind from earthly, material bodies; they were literally 'heavenly bodies' in much the same sense as the New Jerusalem was a heavenly city. Abbot Suger in 1140 said that his church was built 'in likeness of things Divine', and Pierre de Maricourt could have said the same in 1269 about the magnetic clock he

16. Panofsky, *Abbot Suger on the Abbey Church of St. Denis*, p. 105.
17. The gospel read at this ceremony was Luke xix, 2–11, while Revelation (Apocalypse) xxi, 2–5 was used in place of the Epistle; see Andrieu, *Le pontifical romain*, pp. 176–95.

proposed. Thus there was a sense in which the cathedral builders, like the clock-makers, had a celestial prototype.

There was here an echo of the teachings of Plato, who had said that all material objects were merely corrupt and distorted representations of 'eternal ideas' which were to be found only in heaven. Any triangle drawn by a man could only aspire to be a rough sketch of the idea of a triangle; any motion on the earth could only approximate to the uniform circular motion which the heavenly bodies exhibit; and it would follow that the earthly Jerusalem which the crusaders had tried to save – and the great churches of France – were all of them imperfect models of the heavenly City of Jerusalem which the Bible had described.

Light, geometry and architecture: 1140–1280

Plato's thought was very influential in the 12th and 13th centuries,[18] particularly in the highly imaginative interpretations which had been given to it by such later writers as Plotinus (*c*. A.D. 250), Dionysius (*c*. A.D. 500) and St Augustine (A.D. 354–430). The 'neo-Platonic' philosophies developed by these men influenced the development of the technical arts in at least two ways: firstly, through the stress which Plato had laid on mathematics, and secondly, because the relationship between terrestrial and heavenly bodies, which neo-Platonists envisaged, could be used to support a theory of astrology and magic.

The latter point can be explained by recalling that the stars belonged literally to 'the heavens' and had quasi-spiritual quantities,[19] but terrestrial matter was intrinsically corrupt, dead and without 'form'. It was indeed only through power which came from a higher order that life and motion was possible on earth at all. The tides in the sea were driven by the action of the moon; compass needles were drawn to the pole star; and all life depended on the light of the sun. Indeed, light was the most powerful of all the forces that came from the heavenly bodies.

The most important exponent of this point of view was Robert Grosseteste, a teacher at Oxford early in the 13th century and Bishop of Lincoln from 1235 to 1253. Grosseteste studied mirrors, lenses and light in a thorough and almost scientific

18. The first part of Plato's *Timaeus* was well known, and had received special emphasis at the school of Chartres in the 12th century.
19. *Timaeus*, 41, trans. Lee, p. 56.

manner. He was not alone in this, and not long after his death in 1253, spectacles with convex lenses came into use in Italy. But Grosseteste's study of light was inspired by a near-astrological view of its powers. For he believed in a 'light-power or virtue' which was directed on to the earth from the heavens. This special radiation 'was the basis of all bodily magnitude and of all natural operations, of which the manifestations of visible light was only one . . . The concentration of light-power or virtue from the heavens on to the earth . . . caused the differences in climate observed in different parts of the globe, the growth of plants and animals, the transformation of one of the four elements into another, the astrological influences varying with the configurations of the planets, and the rising and falling of the tides.'[20]

Pierre de Maricourt was also interested in light, and in particular its reflection by concave mirrors. What is more, he spoke of a 'virtue' which was directed on to the earth from the sky. This 'virtue' was not light – not in the ordinary sense – but the power which caused a suspended lodestone or compass needle to point always to the north. So Pierre remarked that the 'poles of the lodestone derive their virtue from the poles of the heavens. As regards the other parts of the stone, the right conclusion is, that they obtain their virtue from the other parts of the heavens.'[21] But the magnetic virtue was discussed in very much the same terms as those which Robert Grosseteste used to describe light, and Pierre, who must have known of Grosseteste's work,[22] evidently thought about light and virtue as similar kinds of phenomenon. So Pierre said that one experiment on 'the virtue of lodestone, I will explain in my book on the action of mirrors'[23] – presumably because the two things were for him related subjects.

Other metals and minerals besides lodestone were supposed to receive different virtues from various heavenly bodies, and there was a close link between the idea of celestial forces influencing magnets and the tides and the ideas of alchemy and astrology. The sun was associated with gold, the moon with silver and the five known planets with five other metals. It was through these

20. Crombie, *Robert Grosseteste*, pp. 109, 112.
21. Pierre de Maricourt, *Epistola*, I, 10.
22. Crombie, *Robert Grosseteste*, p. 207.
23. Pierre de Maricourt, *Epistola*, II, 2; the book on mirrors has not survived.

and many other connections as well as through light and the magnetic virtue that all kinds of remarkable things, including perpetual motion, might be effected by man.

However, what was of greater importance for the development of the practical arts in the 12th and 13th centuries was the interest then shown in mathematics. This was again encouraged by what people had read of Plato's *Timaeus*, especially at the school of Chartres, where Platonism was a direct stimulus to mathematical learning. For Plato had emphasised that the universe was mathematical in its structure (*Timaeus*, 31, 32, 36), and it followed that mathematics was needed if one was to understand nature. This attitude was interpreted by St Augustine in such a way that the simple numerical relationships in which Plato had been interested took on a theological significance. Three was the number of the Trinity and so of God; four stood for matter; seven, the sum of three and four, signified mankind; and twelve, the product of three and four, was the number of the apostles and so of the Church. Number was impressed upon everything and was a sign of the Divine wisdom.

It was often Augustine's version of Platonism which had the strongest influence in the 12th century; St Bernard of Clairvaux studied Augustine's number theory, and suggested its use to regulate the proportions of Cistercian churches. If the lengths of two walls could be arranged in the ratio of 3 to 4, or if the sanctuary of a church could have 12 columns (as Suger's did), this was of great symbolic value.

Mathematics, of course, must always play an important part in the art of building, because it is necessary for surveying and for setting out the plan of a building on the site. But Abbot Suger's abbey church of St Denis, near Paris, and the contemporary cathedral at Sens were pioneers of the intensely geometrical 'Gothic' style of architecture. The artistic effect of the Gothic style was always to stress line rather than bulk, and such architects' drawings as survive from the Gothic period always stress the linear characteristics of designs. One writer of 1140–50 said that the work of a building craftsman consisted of 'practical geometry . . . the forming of lines, surfaces, squares, circles and so on in natural bodies'.[24]

Now it is interesting to note that this new Gothic architecture

24. Dominicus Gundissalinus, quoted by von Simson, *The Gothic Cathedral*, p. 33.

was being developed in France at just about the time when the first Latin translation of Euclid's great work on geometry arrived there. These translations had been made from Arab versions of Euclid, and before this, medieval Europe had been largely ignorant of the mathematical achievements of the ancient Greeks.

At the cathedral school at Chartres the rediscovered theorems of Euclid were carefully studied, and it was there that they were first taught. Chartres, in fact, became for a time the most important school of mathematics in the West. This was at least partly because it was already a place where Platonic thought received close attention, including the first part of the *Timaeus* and Augustine's ideas about numbers. For Plato's emphasis on mathematics greatly stimulated interest in geometry.

Master masons and architects who were working in the region would naturally share this enthusiasm, not only because of the practical value of geometry in their work, but also because some of them were probably taught by masters from Chartres. The cathedral schools, which were the predecessors of the universities soon to be founded at Paris and elsewhere, often enrolled pupils who intended to become skilled craftsmen.[25] Such were the architects of the cathedrals – literate men who knew Latin and who were quite capable of keeping in touch with academic geometry; they were men who could write about mensuration and surveying: one anonymous French author of the 13th century described methods used by masons for finding the areas of triangles, octagons and circles.[26]

The sketch-book of Villard de Honnecourt contained similar instruction in geometry; he wrote about what 'the art of geometry commands and teaches' with a philosophic conviction suggestive of Platonism. But it was on a severely practical level that Villard was most concerned to discuss geometry, for the craftsman constantly needed to use it in order to ensure that the objects he made were precise in shape and dimensions.

The method can be illustrated by reference to the screw-jack which Villard drew in his sketch-book. It is so rough a drawing that one wonders whether he could have made such a machine

25. Frankl, *The Gothic*, pp. 35–9, 133; von Simson, *The Gothic Cathedral*, pp. 55–6.
26. MS. in the Bibliothèque Sainte-Geneviève, Paris, quoted by Gimpel, *The Cathedral Builders*, p. 122.

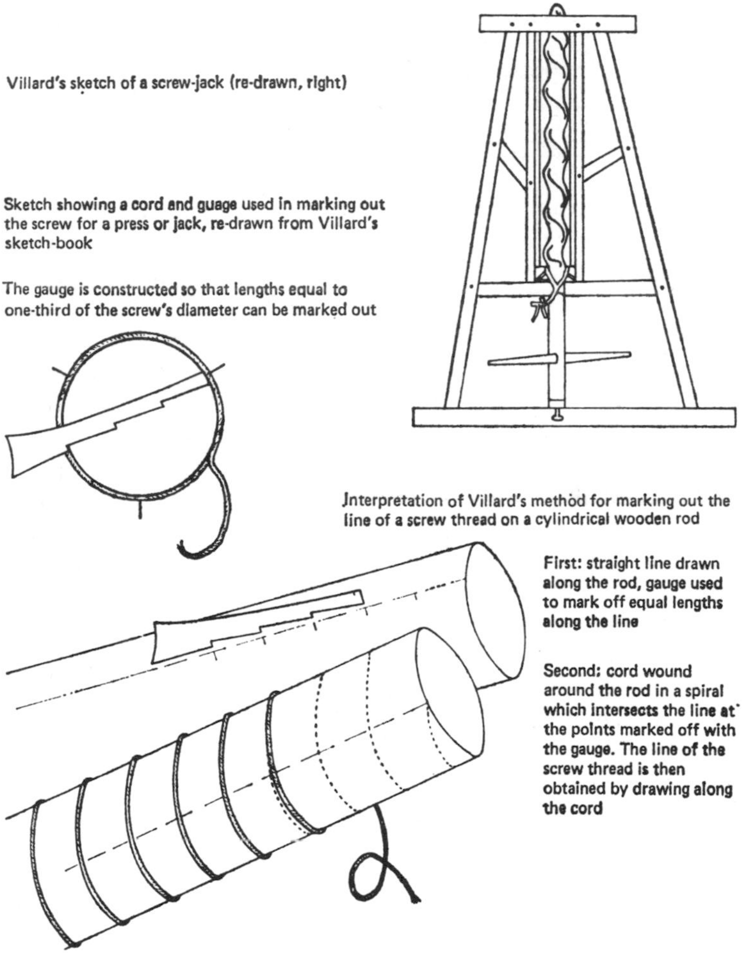

Villard's sketch of a screw-jack (re-drawn, right)

Sketch showing a cord and guage used in marking out
the screw for a press or jack, re-drawn from Villard's
sketch-book

The gauge is constructed so that lengths equal to
one-third of the screw's diameter can be marked out

Interpretation of Villard's method for marking out the
line of a screw thread on a cylindrical wooden rod

First: straight line drawn
along the rod, gauge used
to mark off equal lengths
along the line

Second: cord wound
around the rod in a spiral
which intersects the line at
the points marked off with
the gauge. The line of the
screw thread is then
obtained by drawing along
the cord

Figure 10
Diagram after Villard de Honnecourt's sketch of a screw-jack.
(Specially drawn for the author by D. M. Farrar)

with any reliability. However, instructions about cutting screws which were added to the book a little later show that this sort of job could be done carefully and accurately.

In the example given, the screw was to be made from a cylindrical wooden rod and its pitch was to be one-third of the diameter of the rod; a sketch showed how intervals of this length were to be marked off. There were no calipers or even rulers by which one could ascertain that the diameter of the rod was, say, $4\frac{1}{2}$ inches; neither could a ruler be used to mark off the

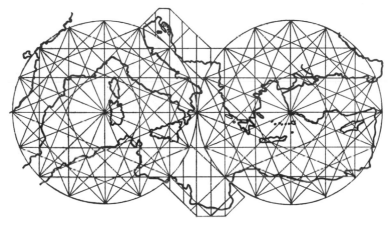

Figure 11
Geometrical method for drawing a sea-chart; after the *Carta Pisana* of *c.* 1275, the earliest map based on direct measurements.

required $1\frac{1}{2}$-inch intervals along its length. So the technique was to mark the diameter of the rod as a length of another piece of wood, then use the standard geometrical construction to divide a line into three equal parts. With these three equal lengths clearly marked on the piece of wood it became a purpose-made gauge. Then to complete the job, a straight line was drawn along the length of the rod, and the gauge was used to mark off the required intervals. Finally, a length of cord was wound in a spiral which intersected these points. So by drawing along the line of the cord, one obtained the line of the screw-thread directly.

Another practical application of geometry was in the drawing of sea-charts. The merchant seamen whose ships plied from Venice and Genoa set course by means of the magnetic compass and roughly estimated the distance they travelled on each bearing. Sailing-directions for all ports, islands and headlands

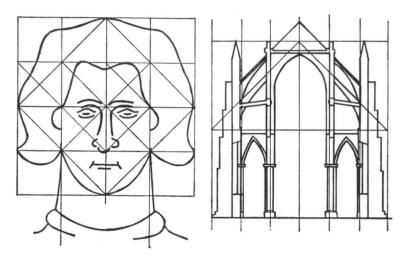

Figure 12
'*Ad quadratum*' design.
(a) Construction-lines for drawing a man's face, as suggested by Villard de Honnecourt, *c.* 1235.
(b) Construction-lines used in designing the section of Westminster Abbey, *c.* 1245, as conjectured by R. A. Brown, H. M. Colvin and A. J. Taylor, *The History of the King's Works*, H.M.S.O., Vol. I, 1963, p. 153.

were compiled, specifying the direction to steer from, say, Genoa, and how far to sail on that course. In the 13th century, not long after Euclid's geometry had come to be taught in Italy, it was seen that these sailing-directions could be represented geometrically. With two circles, each marked with sixteen points of the compass, sailing-directions for the whole Mediterranean could be illustrated on a single chart. Such charts were the first maps to be made on the basis of direct (if approximate) measurements, and the earliest that survives dates from around 1275.

In the design of buildings, geometrical procedures comparable with the two preceding examples were used. The best-known technique was the system of construction-lines based on the geometry of the square, by which the height of a cathedral vault and other dimensions were worked out. This method of 'ad quadratum design' was probably used in building most of the major 13th-century churches. Evidence for its application at Amiens, Beauvais, Cologne and Westminster is fairly clear, and an accompanying figure shows how the ad quadratum construction-lines may have been set out in the latter case.

A comparable approach to a different problem is provided by the square and its diagonals which Villard de Honnecourt suggested as an aid for drawing a man's face in correct proportion. This too is an ad quadratum method. But other aspects of the geometry used in 12th- and 13th-century architecture have come to light from studies of the drawing-instruments used at this time. These differ somewhat from the instruments used by a modern draughtsman, because, as we have seen, rulers for making precise measurements were not available, and measuring-tapes were not used on building-sites. Moreover, architects did not draw their plans to scale, and dimensions were not usually marked on them. Instead, a long measuring-rod or 'Great Measure' provided a base-length from which other dimensions were constructed geometrically. The most important instruments were a set-square and compasses. A length of cord attached tautly to a fixed point was used on the building- site to mark out arcs of large radius. The set-square was L-shaped, with the arms tapered in such a way that the outer and inner edges of the square could represent two right-angled triangles with slightly different proportions; these triangles then formed the basis for a series of geometrical constructions which were used in the design of church buildings. B. G. Morgan, who has recently discussed the use of this square in great detail,[27] believes that its earliest application in England was at Bristol Cathedral in 1298; it had probably been invented in France in the 12th century, and was illustrated by Villard de Honnecourt in a part of his book compiled about 1250. Its introduction at Bristol may be connected with a man significantly called William the Geometer who was buried there soon after 1300.

For the cathedral builders, then, mathematics was a basic discipline; but of course other aspects of 13th-century thought

27. Morgan, *Canonic Design.*

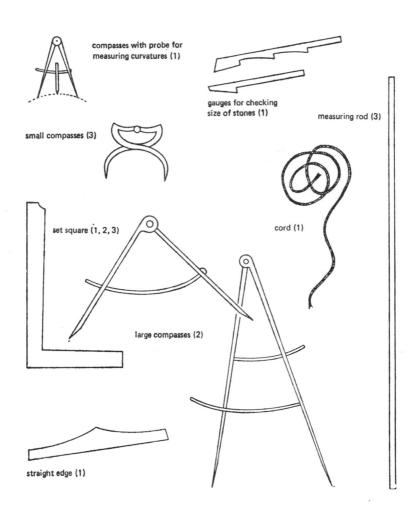

compasses with probe for
measuring curvatures (1)

gauges for checking
size of stones (1)

measuring rod (3)

small compasses (3)

set square (1, 2, 3)

cord (1)

large compasses (2)

straight edge (1)

Figure 13

13th-century masons' drawing-instruments.
(Sources from which these are known: 1. notebook of Villard de Honnecourt;
2. life of St Offar, 13th century; 3. tombstone of Hugh Libergier, mason, 1263
(Diagram specially drawn for the author by D. M. Farrar)

could influence them as well. In particular, this was a period when the works of Aristotle were receiving close attention, having not long before been reintroduced into Europe from Arab sources. This interest in Aristotle coincided with, and reinforced, a growing emphasis on the orderly classification of knowledge, and in the middle years of the 13th century such authors as Albertus Magnus and Vincent of Beauvais embarked on ambitious encyclopedic works which discussed the whole of contemporary knowledge according to carefully-thought-out systems of classification. The culmination of these studies was the work of St Thomas Aquinas, a pupil of Albertus Magnus. Aquinas, who died in 1274, provided a masterly synthesis of Christian doctrine and Aristotelian thought: St Thomas, who saw his vocation as the ordering of human thought, once re-marked that an 'architect' was a man who knew how things should be ordered and arranged, and that the word could be more appropriately applied to a philosopher than to a builder.[28]

In practice master masons rarely called themselves architects at this time, but in some respects their work did reflect the ordering of knowledge which the Aristotelian philosophers had effected.[29] For example, the numerous sculptured figures in 13th-century cathedrals were often arranged to illustrate the classification of knowledge put forward by encyclopedists such as Vincent of Beauvais. Vincent described the practical arts in terms of a number of limited categories such as alchemy, metal-working and building. In the north porch of Chartres Cathedral there are carved figures representing these same three practical arts – metal-working is represented by a man with an anvil; building by a man holding a set-square and compasses; and alchemy by the figure of a *magus* who holds a scroll marked with the signs of the planets and metals, and who has a dragon at his feet. Other figures represent medicine and painting, and a man with a plough stands for agriculture.

Imagination and technical change

While the world of learning came to be dominated by Aristotelian thought, with its fondness for classification and the rational

28. Frankl, *The Gothic*, p. 135.
29. See Panofsky, *Gothic Architecture and Scholasticism.*

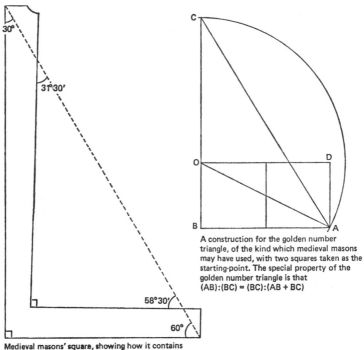

30°

31°30'

58°30'

60°

C

O

D

B

A

A construction for the golden number
triangle, of the kind which medieval masons
may have used, with two squares taken as the
starting-point. The special property of the
golden number triangle is that
(AB):(BC) = (BC):(AB + BC)

Medieval masons' square, showing how it contains
both a 30° –60°-90° triangle and a golden number
triangle

Re-drawn from B. G. Morgan *Canonic Design in
English Medieval Architecture*

Figure 14

The type of set-square used by masons in the 13th century for marking out
pieces of stone before they were cut to shape, and for setting out the plans
of buildings. The square could be used to draw either of the two kinds of
triangle shown, and the ratio (AB) : (BC) was frequently reflected in the
proportions of the finished building.

(Based on information from B. G. Morgan's *Canonic Design* and drawn by
D. M. Farrar.)

ordering of knowledge, artisans and craftsmen continued to operate with ideas which owed more to neo-Platonism than to Aristotle. They continued to discuss astrological influences, light, magnetic virtue, and heavenly prototypes for clocks and cathedrals, none of which could easily fit into an Aristotelian frame of thought. Perhaps most stimulating of all was the notion that both clocks and cathedrals were imperfect images of heavenly things, which one should seek to bring as near to perfection as possible. In the period prior to 1250, this had spurred the cathedral builders to raise vaults higher and make windows larger with every job performed. And in the years after that date, the same attitude, applied to the celestial clock of the planetary system, inspired men to experiment with magnets, levers and wheels until they had made a weight-driven clock which came near to imitating its celestial ideal.

All this is important for an understanding of the origins of modern technology, because although the 'work ethic' discussed in chapter one explains some aspects of the industrious nature of Western man, and indicates a reason for his interest in technology, it does not explain his success as an inventor. For such an explanation, one necessarily has to talk about the ability to visualise a distant objective, the impulse to imagine something that is as yet unrealised, and the inclination to search for some practical way of translating vision into reality.

Even today, in the most technical of contexts, innovation is an imaginative act. One reason why 13th-century Europeans proved to be so good at it was simply that they were very imaginative people. There was plenty to stimulate the imagination – in the symbolism which has been described here, in the religious mysticism of the time, or earlier, in the secular mysticism of 12th-century love poetry. (Mysticism of either sort can be seen as the exercise of imagination for a special purpose.) Add to this the flux of ideas deriving from Greek thought, Christian theology and the technical knowledge of Islam and the East, and one can see that the mind of 12th- and 13th-century man had much to feed on.

All this helps to explain the 'high technology' of the time, if that phrase may be used to describe the cathedrals and clocks. But there was also the more mundane and practical work which found its biggest achievements in the new textile machines of the 13th and 14th centuries. These provide some corrective to any overemphasis on the symbolism of the cathedrals. Medieval artisans were obviously capable of working within a severely practical frame of reference for much of the time, and we should not suppose that they were always entranced by a highly-coloured symbolism. But the machines developed for use in this more practical sphere of activity were far simpler and less technically ambitious than anything involved in clock-making. The silk-twisting machine was, indeed, the only really complex industrial mechanism.

So this was a period when much of the most advanced technology was stimulated by imaginative and not material motives. The historian does well to remember that 'to discover economic causes is to some degree a craze with us, and sometimes leads us to forget a much simpler psychological explanation of the facts'.[30] With 13th-century technology, the psychological explanation is a matter of symbolism and of ideas about celestial objects which seem remote and strange to 20th-century thinkers. But these ideals provoked an enormous thrust forward in the practical arts, and helped to create the state of mind in which people could envisage technical improvement, and work to achieve it.

30. Huizinga, *The Waning of the Middle Ages*, p. 22.

3

Mathematics and the arts: 1450–1600

The age of the printing press

In works of a kind once popular which portrayed the history of technology as a series of great inventions, the discussion of the weight-driven clock in the last chapter would be followed here by an account of the invention of printing. The first books to be printed in Europe were probably produced about 1448 at Mainz on the Rhine. The printing-office responsible had been set up by a certain Johann Gutenberg, a goldsmith, and he is conventionally regarded as 'the inventor' of printing by moveable type.

So simple a view of the matter is not really acceptable. None the less, the introduction of printing by type in the mid-15th century is a topic which serves well to begin this chapter on Renaissance books and scholarship.

Printing had been in widespread use for a considerable time before Gutenberg, first in China and then in the West. But only pictures and playing-cards had previously been produced in Europe, and these were printed from blocks, without the use of type. What was invented some time before 1448 was metal type, the pieces of which could be assembled to represent the page of a book. When sufficient copies had been printed, the type could be used again, rearranged to represent quite different words and sentences. They system depended on having large numbers of pieces of type, strictly standardised in size and shape. This requirement was met by making the type from a tin-lead alloy similar to pewter, and casting it in a copper mould such as pewterers used. Probably several people had experimented with this technique before Gutenberg produced the first printed book.

The idea that Gutenberg was the sole inventor of printing grew up at the end of the 15th century, at a time when people had come to think of the work of any great artist, or poet, or inventor, as the product of special creative genius which the majority of ordinary men did not possess. The idea that men could be truly creative was a new and exciting idea at this time. Creation had previously been thought of as the prerogative of God; now it was seen to be an activity in which mankind could share. But it was not just anybody who could partake of this god-like attribute – only rare individuals such as 'the divine Michelangelo'.[1]

When ideas such as this were applied to thinking about technical change, they immediately led to the idea of invention as a unique act of creation, rather than as an evolutionary process to which many minds might contribute. Stress on the individual as creator was very characteristic of Renaissance art, and it affected technology also, because at this time, artist, architect and engineer were often one and the same man. An example is Filippo Brunelleschi (1377–1446), one of the pioneers of Renaissance architecture. He invented hoists for lifting stone, and boats for carrying it, as well as special techniques used in constructing the dome of Florence Cathedral. His inventions were rewarded by prizes, and in one case he was granted a patent of monopoly for a three-year period.[2] This was in 1421, and is the earliest known instance of a patented invention. The practice of issuing such patents eventually gained wide acceptance – it was formally adopted in Venice in 1474, and in England in 1623 – and this gave even more emphasis to the role of the individual inventor.

As individual invention had been recognised in this way during Brunelleschi's time, it should come as no surprise that when printing came into general use a little later, people began looking back to its origin in the hope of identifying an individual of genius who invented it. Gutenberg's name became well known; and his early success with printing by moveable type seemed to be an outstanding instance of an invention which could be credited to a named individual.

The idea of invention soon came into such prominence that it was taken to represent the essence of technical progress. Writers made lists of inventions, and very often special attention was given to firearms, printing and the magnetic compass as the

1. Panofsky, in *The Renaissance: Six Essays*, pp. 173–4.
2. Praeger, 'Brunelleschi's inventions', in *Osiris*, 9, p. 474.

greatest of recent inventions. A certain Polydore Vergil produced a book of inventions in 1499; another was written by Jean Taisnier in 1562. Jean Fernel in 1548, and Francis Bacon after 1600, also used great inventions as indicators of technical advance.

Today, most historians of technology would reject this attitude, although it has influenced many popular works on the subject. As one historian has remarked, it is misleading to present invention 'as the achievement of individual genius, and not as a social process'.[3]

The social process which led to the 'invention' of printing consisted partly in the development of earlier forms of printing; partly in the numerous experiments with type which several people seem to have made in the 1440s; and partly in a widening literacy and a growing demand for books. All these developments were most marked in Italy, although they could also be observed in the Low Countries, in Paris, and in a few German cities, like Cologne, Augsburg and Mainz. That the ground was already well prepared before Gutenberg's time is shown by the rapidity with which printing by type came into use. Within thirty years of the establishment of Gutenberg's press at Mainz, there were 236 printing presses in Italy, 78 in Germany and 68 elsewhere; by 1500, 532 presses had been established in Italy, 214 in Germany and 304 elsewhere. Venice was the most important centre; in 1500 there were nearly as many presses in Venice as in the whole of Germany.[4]

The demand for books was one result of the complex cultural change for which the term 'Renaissance' has already been used. Beginning in Italy around 1400, the Renaissance brought a great revival of scholarship and learning. The printing-press grew up in the service of Renaissance scholarship, and the art of printing was a Renaissance technology. Thus much of its early development took place in Italy. The demand for printed books and the early development of block printing began in Italy, and it was there that printing by type proliferated most rapidly. This is a point to be emphasised, despite the undoubted success of Gutenberg of Mainz as the pioneer of 'book-production as an organised industry'.[5]

3. Ashton, *The Industrial Revolution*, p. 11.
4. Parsons, *Engineers . . . in the Renaissance*, p. 106.
5. Michael Clapham, 'Printing', in *A History of Technology*, vol. 3, 1957, p. 377.

Scholarship and engineering during the Renaissance

In a brief survey of the history of technology such as this there is inevitably the appearance of a long gap between the very fruitful 13th century and the introduction of printing by moveable type. It is, of course, a gap in appearance only, because ideas and techniques continued to develop. But the hundred years between about 1350 and the 1440s saw relatively few technical developments of major importance. The pace of technical change was certainly slower than it had been before 1350, and slower too than it was to be after 1450. More generally, one author[6] has seen this as perhaps the lowest point in European history, and has listed a wide range of evidence for declining vitality, not simply in the practical arts, but throughout society. There are other points of view, especially for somebody studying the history of mathematics or literature, but for the historian of European technology, this is certainly a bleak period.

In accounting for this, it is conventional to mention the Black Death epidemic, which began in 1348 and spread over most of Europe, and the widespread consequences of the Hundred Years War between England and France (1337–1453). Whether these events can entirely explain the slow pace of technical progress after 1350 is a matter for argument, but what seems clear is that by about 1450 Europe was making a very vigorous recovery from its period of decline, and that this recovery was most marked in Italy.

Italy had suffered less than other parts of Europe during the century after 1350, and it emerged with a marked pre-eminence in trade and commerce. The cloth trade of Flanders and the wool exports of England were now largely controlled by Italian merchants and bankers. The growing wealth of the north Italian cities where these merchants had their headquarters, especially Florence, gave a powerful stimulus for the development of the fine arts and also engineering. Numerous civic improvements were begun, including canals, drains, harbours, and fortifications, as well as a great deal of ordinary building. In this environment, mathematics and academic studies of architecture flourished.

Before discussing more strictly technical matters, we need to

6. Trevor-Roper, *The Rise of Christian Europe*, pp. 161–2, 180.

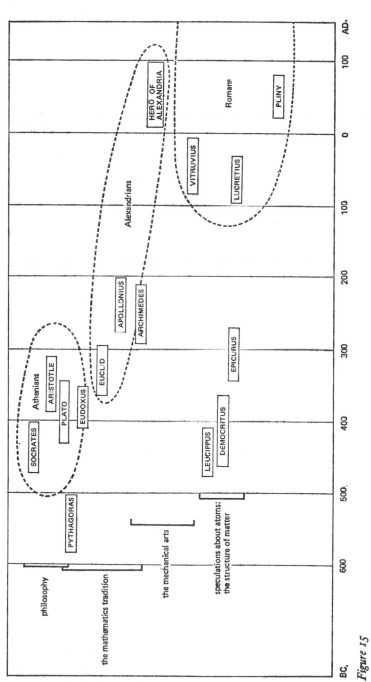

Figure 15
Time-chart of Greek authors mentioned in chapters three and four.

say something about the academic, scholarly side of this movement. Much effort was directed towards understanding the
ancient civilisations of the Greeks and Romans. Books written
by Greek and Roman authors were edited or translated, and
printed on the newly-invented press, so that they became more
widely available than before. This was important for engineering
and the practical arts because the Greeks and Romans had left a
considerable technical literature. For example, Pythagoras in the
6th century B.C., and Plato around 400 B.C., had stressed the
importance of mathematics. Euclid, about a century after Plato,
had codified and summarised existing mathematical knowledge
in his great work on geometry. Living at Alexandria in Egypt,
Euclid was one of the first members of a great school and library
there which produced many of the most important technical
writers of the next three or four centuries. Near the end of this
period, Hero of Alexandria wrote about pneumatics and described
many mechanical gadgets and novelties; his work attracted a
lot of attention during the latter part of the Renaissance period.
The greatest author to write on mechanics was Archimedes, a
Greek living in Sicily who was killed in 212 B.C. by an invading
Roman army. His work was quite closely related to that being
done at Alexandria at the time, but he seems to have been a
practical engineer as well as a brilliant mathematician.

The Romans were much less active in science, although
Pliny (A.D. 23–79) had written much that was of interest. But one
Roman book which greatly attracted Renaissance scholars was
written about 30 B.C. by the architect Vitruvius. This book not
only discussed architecture, but described machines and the
various engineering techniques which architects needed to use.
During the Renaissance, architects and scholars studied the
remains of Roman buildings, many of which survived in Italy,
and the writings of Vitruvius and others were interpreted in the
light of what they saw. Because a great deal of engineering
came into these scholarly, almost academic studies of Roman
architecture, some branches of engineering came to be included
among the 'liberal arts': that is, they became accepted alongside
more conventional literary and mathematical subjects as being
worthy of study by a man of learning. The close connection
between architecture and engineering also meant that many of the
people who actually planned and supervised engineering works
were artists or architects of one sort or another. For this reason,

the Renaissance has sometimes been characterised as a period of 'artist-engineers'.[7]

Alberti as engineer and scholar

One scholar and man of learning who could also be thought of as an architect-engineer was Leone Battista Alberti (1404–72). He was the author of the first major book on architecture to be printed on the newly-introduced press. Published in Florence in 1485, this book had actually been written about 1450.

Alberti was an architect of a new kind. For while the designers of buildings had traditionally been practising craftsmen who had gained their skill while working as stonemasons or carpenters, Alberti came of a patrician Florentine family; he was an athlete as well as a scholar, and spent the first part of his career working in the papal civil service in Rome. During his stay there, he made a close study of the ruins of ancient Roman buildings, comparing what he saw with what Vitruvius had written about architecture.

Alberti's own book on architecture covered a wide variety of subjects, and many branches of engineering came within the scope of his scholarly interest. Thus after describing the problems of planning a city, Alberti discussed drains and sewers (book IV, chapter 7);[8] bridges of wood and stone, with piled foundations for the latter (IV, 6) and the construction of fortifications (V, 4). He wrote about harbours (IV, 8) and the use of rivers for navigation. Then he discussed shipbuilding, a subject on which he had enlarged in another book, now lost. Here he could refer again to Roman precedent, for in 1446 he had been responsible for raising some parts of a Roman ship from Lake Nemi (V, 12).

As with all architects, Alberti had to design hoists and lifting-gear for raising large stones on building-sites, and he included three chapters on this subject (VI, 6–8). His account was enriched by many classical references, particularly to the exploits of Archimedes. But Alberti could offer little advance on the methods used by Vitruvius, his chief virtue being a careful

7. Or 'artist-technicians', the first term being Olschki's; see Klemm, *A History of Western Technology*, p. 123, and Gille, *The Renaissance Engineers*, p. 80.

8. Subsequent references are simply to chapters in the book, which was published in English in 1726 with the title *Ten Books on Architecture*, and has recently been reprinted in facsimile.

attention to such details as that the axle of a pulley should be made of iron with a diameter of between one-sixth and one-quarter of the radius of the pulley.

The most interesting of Alberti's chapters on engineering were those concerned with water supply (x, 2–12), for which the requirements varied according to whether the water was to be used for drinking, for driving water-mills, or for industries like tanning. He gave instructions for digging wells, mentioned the Roman aqueducts, and discussed the relative merits of carrying water through pipes or through open canals. He explained surveying methods which could be used to ensure that such canals, when built, would have a continuous gentle slope, and he briefly mentioned navigable canals, in which boats could negotiate a change in levels by means of pound-locks (x, 12).

The greater part of Alberti's book was taken up with architecture proper – the design of houses, churches and other buildings – and the sections dealing with engineering were all concerned with public works of one kind or another. Public works would come fairly naturally into an architect's range of interests, but their status at this time was also enhanced by the fact that the Romans had excelled at this kind of technology.

Although Alberti's scholarship was literary rather than mathematical, there were three kinds of mathematics which he mentioned – mechanics, surveying and proportion. What Alberti said about the first two of these was very limited, and he commented: 'My Design is to speak of these things not like a Mathematician, but like a Workman' (vi, 7). But it is clear that the mathematics of architectural proportion was of considerable importance to him. He thought that one principle here should be 'the Imitation of Nature, as the greatest Artist at all Manner of Compositions' (ix, 5), and in particular, something might be learned by studying the symmetry and proportion of the human figure. Another principle was based on a supposed analogy between the beauty of a fine building and harmony in music. It seemed that the mathematics of musical harmony could be applied to buildings, because 'the same Numbers, by which the agreement of Sounds affects our Ears with Delight, are the very same which please our Eyes and our Mind' (ix, 5).

The origins of these ideas lay in the writings of earlier neo-Platonist authors, and the way in which they had used the mathematical speculations of Pythagoras and Plato. It seems likely that the Pythagorean philosophers of the ancient world had made experiments on the strings of musical instruments, moving a bridge, like the bridge on a violin, along the length of a string, and noticing the pitch of the notes produced when the string was plucked. The notes, of course, varied with the position of the bridge, but what particularly interested the Pythagoreans was that musical harmonies seemed to correspond to simple ratios in the length of the string. Thus, if the length of the string was halved (1/2) by a bridge, it produced a note exactly one octave higher than it had done to start with. If only two-thirds (2/3) of the string could sound, the note would be higher by the interval of a fifth; and if three-quarters (3/4) of the original length could vibrate, the note would be higher than the original one by the interval of a fourth.

So the Pythagoreans found that the basic notes in their musical scale, which can be represented as C, F, G and 'top' C, corresponded to different ratios involving the first four numbers (1, 2, 3, 4). They regarded this discovery not just as applying to numbers, but as giving a clue to the harmony of the whole universe. The squares and cubes of these numbers gave other indications of the mathematics of the cosmos, so the complete sequence was: 1, 2, 3, 4, 8, 9, 16, 27.

Because Alberti thought that the arts should reflect the structure of the universe, nature being the 'greatest Artist' (IX, 5), he believed that these numbers were applicable in architecture. Good architecture should reflect the mathematical order of things, just as music did, and should make use of the same simple ratios. This might mean, he suggested, that the rooms in a house should have sides whose measurements were in the ratio of 3 to 2, with the height equalling the width. Or alternatively, a room might have the measurements of a double cube: that is, it would be two units long, one unit high, and one unit wide. Applied to a church, the same principle might mean that the nave would be twice as high as it was wide.

Interest in proportion developed in a somewhat different way among some of Alberti's contemporaries. He had already mentioned that the human body offered an example of good proportion; now the painter Piero della Francesca, a close friend, set out to measure human bodies, in order to try to discover simple ratios in their proportions. A little later, Leonardo da Vinci and Albrecht Dürer were engaged in similar projects

Dürer, a German from Nuremberg, had visited Italy several times, and had come to share some of the enthusiasms of the Italian artists. Thus in 1500 he wrote that a certain Jacopo (or Jacobus) de' Barbari who had written 'on the measurement of the human body . . . [was] a Venetian by birth, and a delightful painter. He showed me a man and a woman which he had drawn according to certain measurements. At that time it would have meant more to me to learn his theories than to have discovered a new continent. But the said Jacobus would not expound his system to me.'[9]

Renaissance neo-Platonism

The search for simple ratios in the proportions of the human body, and these related theories about proportion in architecture, were stimulated during the 15th century by a growing interest in the ideas of Plato. In Florence, from the 1460s onwards, a group of scholars informally constituted themselves into an academy modelled on Plato's academy in ancient Athens. Their outlook was literary rather than mathematical, but they were well aware that written above the door of Plato's academy had been a notice forbidding the entry of anyone ignorant of geometry; and Plato's support for the Pythagorean theories of numbers and ratios was well known. It was entirely appropriate, then, that Alberti should have become one of the first members of the Platonic academy in Florence.

The central figure in the academy, however, was Marsilio Ficino (1433–99), the son of a physician who lived near Florence. Ficino himself had studied medicine, but never practised it; he was deeply religious, and after much hesitation, was ordained priest at the age of forty. Between about 1460 and 1477, he translated all of Plato's works. Previously, the many people interested in Plato's ideas had been able to read only fragments of his writings. Ficino was the first man for many centuries to study Plato as a whole. And Plato's sweeping view of God, of man and of the whole universe so impressed Ficino that he set about constructing a philosophy of his own which brought together the principles of Platonism and Christianity. It was a joyful creed, which stressed human love and the beauty of the world.

Plato himself had been less ready to recognise the beauty of

9. Quoted by Descargues, *Dürer*, p. xiv.

earthly things. He had defined beauty in terms of mathematics, and had felt that ordinary matter was a debased and corrupting thing, distorting the abstract mathematical beauty which had been present in the original idea of the world.

'Happily, the practical-minded Florentines ignored Plato's teaching on this point, while adopting as a working hypothesis his interpretation of the universe in terms of simple, regular, mathematical beauty.'[10] Thus one can talk about a mathematical study of natural beauty in Italy at this time, which affected all the arts and sciences. Besides Alberti's work on beauty and proportion in architecture, and besides the studies of proportions in the human figure, there were also mathematical researches in astronomy and geography.

In all these studies, measurement came to be used as an empirical tool in a way that had never happened before. One result of this was that new techniques of making drawings were evolved in which measurements could be unambiguously recorded – which, of course, meant drawing to scale. Brunelleschi is said to have 'invented' scale drawings of buildings just before 1420. This approach to architectural drawing may be contrasted with the methods used by builders of cathedrals in the 12th and 13th centuries (chapter two). They had used geometrical construction rather than measurement to derive the proportions and shapes of their buildings. The elaborate drawings which they made did not have to be to scale; what had to be shown in them was the geometrical relationships between the parts of a structure. Sea-charts were sometimes drawn to scale in the later 13th century, but scale maps were not often produced until much later.

The work of Piero della Francesca and Albrecht Dürer on the proportions of the human body led them naturally to record their measurements of men's bodies in scale drawings. And this was closely connected with another technique of which these two artists were pioneers: that is, perspective. In one set of drawings of the human head, made carefully to scale by Piero della Francesca, part of the artist's purpose was to construct an accurate perspective of the head. Scale drawings are a necessary preliminary to making any geometrically accurate perspective representation, so scale drawing and perspective were logically related inventions.

10. Cronin, *The Florentine Renaissance*, pp. 140–42.

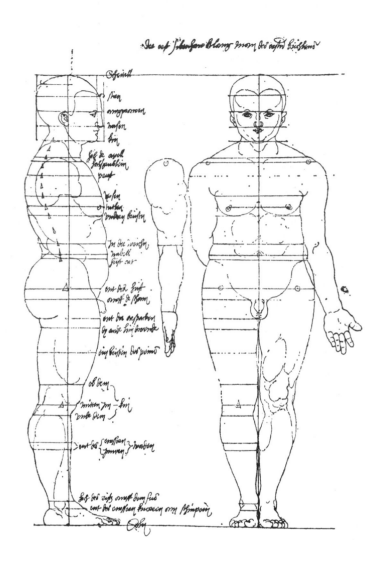

Figure 16
Albrecht Dürer, *Proportion Figure in Profile and Full Face, c.* 1523.
(Courtesy of the Fogg Art Museum, Harvard University, Bequest—Charles A. Loeser.)

Although it was a long time before engineers began to use these drawing techniques, scale drawings and projections related to perspective were ultimately of crucial importance in engineering. So these innovations, which resulted largely from the Renaissance interest in proportion and measurement, must be regarded as among the most important technical developments of the period.

One of the first men to study 'scientific' problems in the spirit of the new Platonism of the 15th century was Paolo Toscanelli (1397–1482), one of Alberti's colleagues among the learned men of Florence. As an astronomer, Toscanelli studied comets and made some extremely accurate observations of the altitude of the sun at different seasons of the year. These observations showed up errors in existing astronomical theory, and since this theory did not have the simplicity and mathematical elegance which a Platonist looked for, Toscanelli was only too ready to criticise it. So too was Nicolaus Copernicus, a young man from Poland who came to Italy to study in 1496. He was influenced by Italian neo-Platonism, and may perhaps have known of Toscanelli's astronomical studies. At any rate it was Copernicus who, much later, provided a new theory of the universe in which the sun, not the earth, was the centre around which the planets in their orbits were supposed to travel.

Measurement, as we have seen, was a key idea among some neo-Platonist students of nature. Toscanelli's interest in measurement was applied not only to astronomy but also to the problem of deciding how large the continents of the earth ought to be when represented on a map. He was rightly convinced that Asia was much larger than people had previously imagined, and he questioned travellers about journey times and distances in order to try to form an estimate of its size.

His ideas on this subject reached the ears of a young Italian seaman, Christopher Columbus (1451–1506), who had sailed to Ireland, and perhaps even as far as Iceland. In those countries, there was rumour of land even farther to the west – in fact, Greenland. In 1478, Columbus wrote to Toscanelli about the prospects of reaching Asia by sailing westward into the Atlantic. The reply was encouraging, and with his letter Toscanelli sent a chart showing the islands of Japan and the East Indies in relation to the coasts of Europe. From surviving fragments of the correspondence, it is known that Toscanelli thought the distance between Europe and the East Indies to be about 130° of longitude. Assuming a figure for the earth's circumference which as it turned out was too small, Columbus deduced that Japan should be about 3,000 miles to the west of Spain – that is, about the distance which America proved to be. When he finally reached America in the 1490s, he persisted in thinking that the coasts and islands he was exploring were part of Asia.

The renewed Platonism of Florence thus played its part in fostering studies of the natural world which, with their measurements, maps and scale drawings, were almost of a 'scientific' character. In encouraging such work, neo-Platonism would seem to have been promoting a rational view of nature and of the arts.

But there were other tendencies in neo-Platonism as well. Plato's view of the world had been a poetic, and even a religious, one. Numbers and geometrical shapes could be given a mystical significance. Discovery and invention could seem to be the product of inspiration, not of deduction and experiment. Marsilio Ficino, himself a religious man, in some ways threw into prominence these aspects of the Platonic tradition.

Thus, astrology was given intellectual justification by the neo-Platonic world view, because the stars and planets radiated light and 'virtue', which was a vital influence on terrestrial life.[11] Toscanelli, as the leading astronomer in Florence at this time, was also the leading astrologer, and Alberti was not beyond consulting an astrologer as to the best time for laying the foundation stone of a building.

The opinion that knowledge was derived from inspiration rather than the exercise of reason was closely connected with these views about secret astrological forces which affected the pattern of human life. Just as it was only an isolated individual genius who could make an invention, so only a few specially-endowed men could have access to any deep knowledge of the natural world. Hidden to the normal processes of investigation, this knowledge was regarded as 'occult'; its main branches were astrology and alchemy, and its practical applications constituted magic.

That such ideas could accompany the more rational and empirical studies which have been described here may seem paradoxical. It is, none the less, a fact that Renaissance neo-Platonism stimulated a revival of magical practices, and that in

11. Compare similar opinions in the 13th century; chapter two above.

the following century, enthusiasm for astrology and magic reached a peak. As Renaissance ideas spread beyond Italy, so too did interest in alchemy and astrology; in chapter five, below, it will be necessary to discuss some of the consequences. For the moment, however, it is sufficient to concentrate on those aspects of neo-Platonism which supported a mathematical view of the world and gave a sense of burning conviction to work dealing with measurement and proportion, or scale drawing and perspective.

These subjects were perhaps being most actively pursued in Florence during Alberti's later years, but the tradition continued for a long time after this, and the somewhat later contributions of Dürer and Leonardo da Vinci have already been mentioned. Leonardo, of course, is famous for other reasons as well, particularly for his notebooks with their numerous drawings of machines. He would appear to have been an engineer and inventor of rare originality. But to give him too much attention is misleading. He was not typical of his contemporaries, and he probably had little influence on engineering practice; his notes and sketches of machines were not available to many people in the 16th century, and almost nobody learned anything from them. As one historian has said, if Leonardo 'had not existed, the history of European technology would have been the same'.[12]

Agriculture and architecture in the Venetian Republic

A century after Alberti, an architect with similar ideals about the application of mathematics to building was Andrea Palladio (1518–80). He was a native of Vicenza, a prosperous little town in north-eastern Italy which was then within the boundaries of the Venetian Republic. Much of his career in architecture was spent in building houses for gentlemen from Venice, whose wealth had its origin in the merchant ships which were based there.

Over the years, Venice had grown prosperous by its ships, which sailed into the eastern Mediterranean, providing a vital trading-link between countries of the East and Europe. But in Palladio's time its commercial pre-eminence was threatened. Venice had some of the largest ships afloat, but other countries

12. Cipolla, *European Culture*, p. 19; see also the very perceptive assessment by Gille, in *The Renaissance Engineers*.

now had much faster ones, which were cheaper to operate. By the 1530s, too, the new sea-routes opened up by voyages of exploration around the coast of Africa were beginning to divert trade away from the Mediterranean. Portuguese, Spanish and Dutch ships sailed the Indian and Atlantic Oceans, and carried cargoes that had once been the Venetians' staple trade. The Venetians

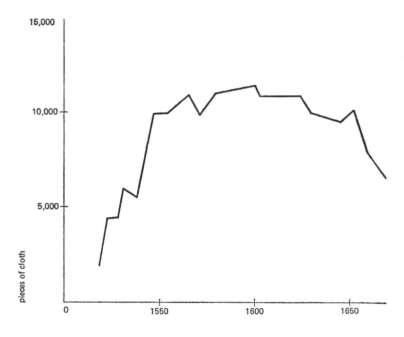

Figure 17
Trends in the production of cloth within the Venetian Republic.
(For more detail, see *Cambridge Economic History of Europe*, ed. E. E. Rich and C. H. Wilson, vol. 4, p. 484)

realised that to maintain their prosperity they would have to rely less on trade and pay more attention to the development of their own internal resources. Thus the 16th century saw the growth of cloth manufacture (see graph, fig. 17) and of glass-making in and around Venice, and there were already many thriving printing-shops. But most significant of all, the Venetians embarked on a vigorous policy of agricultural development in their hinterland. Between the 1530s and about 1610, there was a series of land-drainage schemes and projects for the control of flooding from rivers. Waste land was enclosed, improved cereals were introduced from Turkey, and wheat was grown in vastly increased quantities.

In 1556, the Venetian senate created a Board of Uncultivated Properties which administered state subsidies for land reclamation, and co-ordinated the efforts of individual landowners. Marshes were drained and brought into cultivation; canals and embankments were constructed to prevent the overflow of rivers. Merchants from Venice, tired of the risks of maritime trade, sought more secure investments by buying estates and becoming gentlemen-farmers.

This agricultural revolution, as it can appropriately be called, involved a considerable amount of engineering and building work, not only in connection with the drainage of land, but also involving the construction of farm buildings. Much of this development was being undertaken by men from Venice who had moved out of the city to live on their estates, and it was very often Palladio whom they commissioned as architect of the villas in which they lived, and the farm buildings which surrounded them. Palladio's success lay in his 'functional and utilitarian' designs, which at the same time were based on 'the classical heritage, so as to lend an air of cultivated grandeur to the country estates of gentlemen who still thought like city dwellers'.[13]

A map showing the distribution of Palladio's villas (fig. 18) also indicates some of the areas where agricultural improvement was being most actively pursued in the mid-16th century. The villa at Bagnolo, for example, stood on the banks of a river whose flooding had recently been brought under control, thus allowing nearby land to be more efficiently farmed. The villas at Mazer, Fanzolo and Fratta Polesine were all examples of a design which Palladio had evolved in which the farm buildings were built directly on to the house as a pair of long, projecting wings.

Palladio probably gained some of his ideas about the design of farm buildings from reading Alberti's book. There it was explained that a farm should have stables for draught oxen and horses, with suitable drains, a shed for carts, ploughs, harrows,

13. Ackerman, *Palladio*, p. 53.

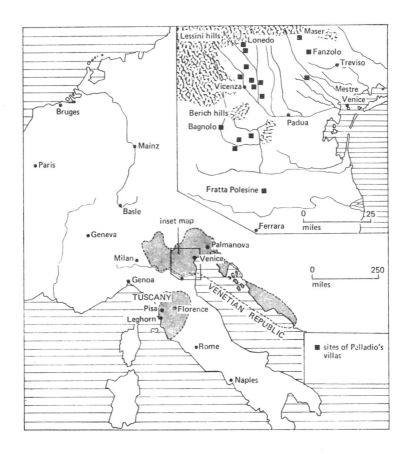

Figure 18

The Renaissance: Italy and neighbouring areas in the time of Palladio and Galileo. Shaded areas represent the Venetian Republic and Tuscany (the Republic of Florence). The inset map shows the location of villas designed by Palladio in association with land-reclamation and other agricultural schemes

yokes and hay baskets, a place for wine and oil presses, and a threshing-floor in the open.[14] Where Palladio made his most distinctive contribution was in providing for such needs by means of a scholarly, classical architecture in which, we may note, number theories of proportion played a big part.

14. Alberti, *Ten Books on Architecture*, v, 15 and 16.

One of the gentlemen-farmers for whom Palladio built a villa was Daniel Barbaro. A scholar as well as a farmer, Barbaro wrote books on mathematics and studied Aristotle and Vitruvius. His house at Maser was notable for the water works which supplied fountains in the garden and water for the kitchen. Any overflow or waste from these works was then used to irrigate the gardens. Palladio designed this water-system in collaboration with Barbaro, and one is reminded of Alberti's interest in water-supply problems. Water supply was, indeed, one of the branches of engineering most closely connected with architecture.

Another architect with an interest in the subject was Giovanni Battista Aleotti, a contemporary of Palladio who had a reputation as a designer of theatres. He was the architect of several churches and public buildings in Ferrara, a city to the south of Venice and just beyond its borders. As official surveyor there, Aleotti designed fortifications, planned various drainage-schemes, and suggested a water-supply system for fountains in the city. But Aleotti's importance rests on his studies of Hero of Alexandria, and on the edition of Hero's book on pneumatics which he published in 1589. Besides a translation of Hero's text, this contained four appendices dealing with practical devices. One of them showed a four-cylinder force pump driven through a crank-shaft by a water-wheel.

Palladio himself wrote a book, which was published in 1570; it dealt with the design of villas and country houses, and was not a work on the theory of architecture. However, the proportions for buildings which Palladio recommended show very clearly that he was using a version of the theory of harmonic proportion. In this connection, it is significant that he was one of the founder members of a society for the cultivation of the arts and sciences in his home town, Vicenza. One of his friends in this society was Sylvio Belli, a man with mathematical interests who in 1573 published a book on proportion which was a conventional treatment of the Pythagorean number theory.

By this date, such a book may have seemed a little old-fashioned. Simple number theories of proportion were no longer so readily accepted as they had been in Alberti's time. Palladio perpetuated the use of such proportions in architecture, but he did not think it appropriate to discuss their theoretical background. At the same time, a new generation of music theorists was becoming sceptical of the Pythagorean number theory of harmony. Among these was Vicenzo Galilei (1533–91), one of several Florentine scholars who were attempting to reconstruct a Greek style of musical drama and whose work was of importance for the origins of opera. As a practising musician, Galilei had found that number theories were inadequate to explain the complex harmonies used by contemporary composers: and he did experiments with vibrating strings to try to arrive at a better understanding of their behaviour.[15]

Galilei's work on this subject was taken further by his more famous son, Galileo Galilei (1564–1642), who wrote extensively on many aspects of mechanics and the practical arts. The style and effect of his writings is, in fact, well illustrated by his comments on the theory of music. Continuing with his father's argument, Galileo pointed out that whether somebody listening to music was conscious of harmony or discord depended on the kind of vibration transmitted through the air to the listener's ear. If several notes heard together produced a regular pattern of vibrations, the eardrum could easily respond, and the listener experienced a pleasant sensation which he called harmony. But if the pattern of vibrations was very irregular, the eardrum would have difficulty in following the motion; the listener would feel discomfort and say he had heard a discord.

The old theory, in which simple ratios were associated with harmonious combinations of notes was a misleading half-truth, Galileo implied. One could not develop a theory of music by tinkering with numbers and ratios, but one should try to understand the mechanics of the vibrating string and the mechanics of the eardrum.

Galileo's work marks the end of a long period in which people believed strongly in the value and importance of mathematics in all the arts, but without being able to connect their ideas about mathematics to what we would today regard as 'real' problems. Galileo had identified some real problems in the theory of music, and had shown how mechanics provided the sought-after connection between music and mathematics. But in the process he put a crudely materialistic theory of harmony in place of vague but lofty notions about numbers being related to cosmic harmony. Enjoyment of music was no longer imagined to be some kind of response to the harmony of the universe; it

15. Drake, in *Journal of the History of Ideas, 31*, 1970, p. 496.

was now just a matter of experiencing 'a tickling of the eardrum'.[16]
There was a great gain in clarity if one adopted this point of
view – but at the expense of trivialising what many people
feel when they are moved or exalted by a noble piece of music.

Galileo in the Venetian Republic

Galileo was a Florentine by birth and education, but he spent
his most fruitful years at the University of Padua in the Venetian
Republic. He was a teacher there from 1592 until 1610, and so
was able to witness the last of the big land-reclamation schemes in
the hinterland of Venice. His interest in this work is shown by his
writings on machines, and by the patent he was granted for an
unspecified 'device for raising water and for most easily watering
the land, at small expense and with great utility'.[17] This was a
pump of some kind, driven by the power of a horse, and it
apparently worked well when it was tested.

   Later in life, when he had moved back to Florence, Galileo
became involved in other drainage schemes there. He was
appointed 'superintendent of the waters', and in 1630 drew up a
report on the River Bisenzio with the assistance of two practising
engineers.

   While he was still living in Padua, however, Galileo became
involved in other practical projects. The hinterland of Venice
was not only being developed for agriculture but was being
made more secure from a military point of view. The Venetians
were anxious to preserve their independence, at a time when
Austria, just to the north, was growing in importance as part of the
Habsburg Empire. In 1593 they began to construct the fortified
town of Palmanova. Designed by Buonaiuto Lorini, a Florentine
like Galileo, its walls enclosed a regular nine-sided polygon with
bastions at the corners.

   Galileo had to teach some of his students about the design of
fortifications of this kind. On one occasion he was asked for
advice about what mathematical knowledge should be required
'of a perfect cavalier or soldier' in an academy or military school
which was being set up to train the sons of Paduan gentlemen.
Galileo's list of the subjects to be taught encompassed several of
the branches of engineering which had been included in Alberti's

16. Galileo, *Dialogues* [*Discorsi*], p. 107.
17. Quoted by Bulferetti, *Galileo Galilei*, pp. 19–22.

book on architecture: mechanics, navigation, drawing and military architecture, and also instruction concerning the calculation of the range of a gun. Galileo later wrote about the latter subject at some length, and to aid this and other calculations he devised a 'military compass' – a sort of ready reckoner with scales like those of a quadrant.

The military projects and land reclamation schemes in the Venetian Republic were paralleled by similar developments elsewhere, and stimulated the writing of many books concerning things mechanical. Some of these were mere pamphlets, extolling a particular invention, but others were elaborate volumes with excellent illustrations of pumps, cranes and hoists. These books again show that the technologies associated with architecture and fortification were the ones which had gained all the prestige. Industrial arts like textiles, pottery, metal smelting and shipbuilding were, in contrast, very largely neglected.

Hydraulic machinery was given a particular emphasis in a book by Agostino Ramelli, published in 1588 – out of nearly two hundred illustrations of machines, more than half showed pumps. Many of these drawings have a certain science-fiction quality about them; the machines Ramelli drew were often speculative inventions, the product of a lively imagination which had been fired by the excitement of mechanical invention, and he was led by this into absurd elaborations of every conceivable kind of pump. Some had curved cylinders and piston rods, while others anticipated the rotary pumps which were to become practicable only in the 19th century.

A much more important book was the '*Theatre*' *of machines*, compiled by Vittoria Zonca of Padua and published in 1607, four years after its author's death. Of all the contemporary works on this subject, Zonca's was 'closest to the actual mechanical practice of the time'. Thus, where Ramelli showed elaborate combinations of gears and pulleys in which the effects of friction would more than cancel any mechanical advantage, Zonca usually showed the simplest arrangement of gears that would do the job. And while Ramelli largely neglected the industrial arts, Zonca treated them much more fully, giving especially valuable pictures of the silk-throwing mills used in northern Italy (p. 60) and other textile machinery. But even Zonca's enthusiasm for technology could run away with him at times: 'his sober character was touched by the same dreams as his pre-

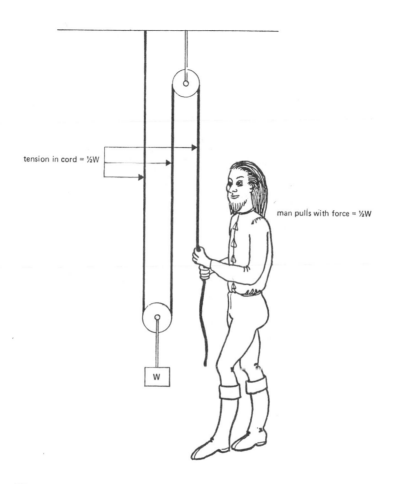

tension in cord = ½W

man pulls with force = ½W

W

Figure 19
A simple pulley-system.

decessors, for the book ended with a perpetual motion machine as
fantastic as any.'[18]

In most of the books about machines which were written
at this time, one question badly needed clarification. There was
an obvious advantage in using machines, but how, precisely,

18. Keller, *A Theatre of Machines*, p. 8.

could that advantage be defined? One of Galileo's acquaintances said that machines could help craftsmen, builders and others, 'sometimes even in opposition to the laws of nature'.[19]

This idea had its source in an ancient Greek book of 'mechanical problems' which was often attributed to Aristotle. It led to some strange and complicated schemes for combining levers, gears and pulleys in lifting-gear and in the transmission systems of cranes and hoists. The claim of the pseudo-Aristotelian author that such devices allowed men to do things that were 'contrary to nature' seems to have produced the belief that as the complexity of a system of gears increased, so was nature increasingly confounded.

The complexity of some of the machines illustrated by Ramelli is a reflection of such a belief, and it appears that similar ideas were current among the artisans and craftsmen who sought employment in the big engineering programmes of the Venetian Republic. At any rate, Galileo attacked this idea more than once, and very effectively unravelled the confused thinking which lay behind it. Machines did not give one something for nothing, Galileo said; the pulley system did not create force (see fig. 19), even though it allowed one to lift a weight 'w' by pulling with a force of only half that. The point was that to lift the weight at any particular speed, the hand pulling on the rope with a force of $\frac{1}{2}$w had to move twice as fast.

Thus when Galileo listed three advantages to be obtained by the use of machines,[20] the first he mentioned was that of being able to choose a speed of working to suit the force available – a large weight could be moved slowly by a small force, provided that the small force produced a rapid motion.

Galileo's second point was that some machines were able to work in positions inaccessible by ordinary methods. For example, a pump could be made to work in conditions where the water to be moved was too shallow for a bucket to be dipped in.

That point applied only in a few cases, but the third advantage which Galileo looked for in machines had wider and more significant applications. It was that machines allowed one to

19. Guido Baldi, quoted by Klemm, *A History of Western Technology*, p. 160.

20. These points occur in a book on machines written by Galileo about 1600 and recently edited by Drake and Drabkin as *Galileo . . . on Motion and on Mechanics*.

harness cheaper sources of power than would otherwise be available; 'the fall of a river costs little or nothing . . . the maintenance of a horse . . . is far less expensive than it would be to sustain eight or more men.'[21] And in the absence of the horse, these eight men would be needed to do the same work.

Galileo ranked this as 'the greatest advantage' of machines; and it is noteworthy that his account of it implied the possibility of evaluating the costs of running water-wheels and horse-gins as well as the cost of labour. Galileo lived in close contact with the merchant communities of Florence and Venice; he would know something of the manufacturing enterprises which they promoted, and the methods they used to control costs and so to safeguard their profits.[22] In the patent previously mentioned, Galileo himself showed a degree of cost-consciousness. He claimed that his new pump would work 'at small expense and with great utility'. It is a matter of some significance that this kind of cost-argument came to the fore in Galileo's formal writings on machines – a subject which could otherwise be treated entirely in terms of academic mechanics. The role of cost-saving considerations in the development of other branches of technology will be mentioned again briefly in later chapters.

Before Galileo left the Venetian Republic in 1610, he tackled another problem which had been confusing local artisans and machine-builders. Some of these people had made great claims for machines they had invented, and had demonstrated their ideas by constructing models. But there were often disappointments, for it was found that full-sized machines made on the same pattern as the models were often not strong enough to perform their function, or failed in other ways.

More experienced craftsmen, and men like Lorini, the architect of Palmanova, knew that there was a fundamental difference between models and fully scaled-up versions of the same design, but could not entirely explain the reason for it. It seemed paradoxical, because the theories of proportion used by architects encouraged people to think only about ratios of lengths and geometrical properties, and these would be the same both for a full-sized object and a scale model. The architects' theories, concerned with the aesthetics and not the strengths of buildings,

21. *Galileo . . . on Motion and on Mechanics*, p. 150.
22. de Roover, 'A Florentine firm of cloth manufacturers', in *Speculum*, *16*, pp. 1–33.

were none the less supposed to be founded on laws of nature, and had sufficient authority to discourage serious thought about the effects of the size of a structure as opposed to just its shape.

Lorini mentioned inventors who, 'not being acquainted with the fundamental principles, rely on the ease with which little models work'.[23] And Lorini also stated that the factor which the traditional mathematical approach neglected was the weight of the materials used in construction; proportion and geometry was all that was normally considered.

It was this point which Galileo seized upon and developed. He showed how the proportions of a building, a machine or any other structure should be related to its size and the weights of its parts. And although his theory was not concerned with the aesthetics of architecture, as Alberti's and Palladio's had been, his work did represent an indirect criticism of theirs, since it showed that the proportions required for a building to be structurally sound would often be inconsistent with the proportions which the harmonic theory called for.

Galileo was evidently working on this problem in 1609, when he wrote to a friend: 'lately I have discovered . . . all the conclusions with their demonstrations pertinent to the strength and resistance of timbers of different lengths, thicknesses and shapes . . . which knowledge is very essential in constructing machines and all kinds of building.'[24] The theorems mentioned were not published until 1638, but it is clear from the way he introduced them that they were the product of Galileo's stay in Venice. In the shipyard of the Venice Arsenal, he said, large ships needed the support of a lot of scaffolding while small ones being constructed under similar conditions did not. Large ships were weaker in proportion to their size than small ones, and Galileo recognised that the same problem occurred here as with the model machines which did not work on a large scale. Again, the crux of the problem was the weight of the timbers from which the ship was made. For if a large ship was ten times as long as a small boat, and if all other dimensions were ten times as great then the volume of timber used in the large ship would be greater than that for the small boat by a factor of ten cubed (10^3). Thus the ship would be a thousand times as heavy as the boat,

23. Quoted by Klemm, *A History of Western Technology*, p. 163.
24. *Opere di Galileo*, x, p. 229.

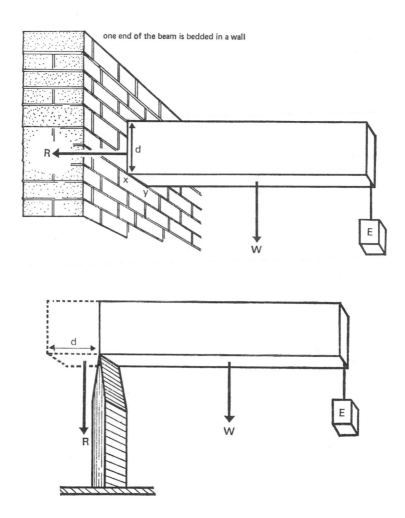

one end of the beam is bedded in a wall

Figure 20

A simplified version of Galileo's theory of beams. The force 'R' in the upper diagram represents the resistance of the beam. It exactly balances the weights 'W' and 'E', just as the extended beam in the lower diagram can be balanced on a knife edge if a weight 'R' is suspended from it.

and Galileo saw that much of its strength would be taken up in merely supporting its own weight.

When Galileo turned to a mathematical analysis of this subject, he considered not ships or machines, but a much simpler kind of structure – a wooden beam projecting horizontally from a wall in which one end was firmly embedded. Following the traditional approach which emphasised proportion and geometry, one might simply consider the shape of the beam – the ratio of its breadth to its length, for example. But Galileo also discussed its weight (marked 'w' on the diagram) and a load ('E') supported at the end of the beam.

What was novel in his approach was that he saw how the beam could be treated as a lever by which a force, 'R', representing the longitudinal strength of the beam, supported the two weights 'w' and 'E'. Then considering a series of progressively larger beams of the same shape, Galileo showed that the weight of the beam increased more than the force 'R', so that eventually there was a limiting size, where a beam could only just support its own weight and could carry no load at all. That is, the lever could be balanced only when the weight 'E' was reduced to nothing.

Once he had pictured a beam sticking out of a wall in this way, it was perhaps quite obvious that the beam could be thought of as one arm of a lever, so that to complete the analysis it was necessary only to imagine the other arm, which represented the beam's resistance to breaking. What is of special interest about this approach is the way in which Galileo was widening the scope of the theory of mechanics as it applied to levers. He could see that levers or pulleys lifting weights, and loaded beams in equilibrium, were both particular cases which could be understood in terms of the same general theory. Thus in principle the theory could be extended to cover the working of every type of machine – water-wheels, horse-gins, cranes and so on – and the equilibrium of every type of structure – ships, buildings, animals' skeletons or the framing of machines. Mechanics was the theory of raising and supporting weights, and for Galileo, it had the same kind of significance as harmony and proportion had for Alberti; it was the one branch of mathematics which provided real clues to the mathematical structure of nature.

In making this point, Galileo had, in a sense, overturned the Renaissance tradition of which Alberti had been the earliest and most important spokesman. He had made Alberti's attitude to harmonic proportion seem misconceived: even the theory of music was for Galileo a matter of mechanics – the flexing of eardrums, and the weights and tensions of strings on musical instruments.

It might also be argued that Galileo was not destroying the Renaissance conviction that mathematics should be applicable to all the arts, but merely showing how it might be made to work. He had reviewed in turn all the subjects with which this tradition had been concerned, ranging from pumps and machines to music and the proportions of the human body, and in most cases he had shown that the ideas which had traditionally been accepted were either misleading or too loosely thought out. But in most cases also he was able to draw together existing knowledge and experience within the framework of a theory based on mechanics – mechanics of the kind that had been studied from the time of Leonardo by a steadily growing number of Italian mathematicians. Galileo was heir to their work and to much else that had been done in the science of mechanics during the 16th century; but above all, he was indebted to the ancient author Archimedes, whose work on mechanics had been translated several times in Italy in the preceding decades. It seems, indeed, that Galileo liked to think of himself as a modern successor to Archimedes – yet if this conceit were allowed him, it would have to be with the qualification that he was also very much the product of the cultural and economic life of Florence and Venice. Thus, much as his mechanics resembled that of Archimedes, it was coloured by the cost-consciousness of these trading communities; it was applied to problems raised by their public-works projects and their architecture; and it was related to their traditional interest in mathematics. Galileo's achievement was to use something from all these traditions in a mechanics that was truly scientific, and in so doing, to lay the foundations for the development of engineering theory.

4

The practical arts and the scientific revolution

Galileo was a major figure in what has become known as 'the scientific revolution' – the reassessment of traditional ideas about the natural world which took place in the 16th and 17th centuries, and the establishment of something recognisably like modern science during the 17th century. It was a revolution which most notably changed accepted views about the shape of the universe, with Copernicus in 1543 suggesting that the earth was not fixed in space but moving in an orbit about the sun; with Galileo in 1610 using his telescope to prove that the planet Venus, at least, had such an orbit, and that the moon was a world of mountains and craters; and with Newton in 1687 formulating laws of motion which explained the earth's orbit.

The new science of this time was not only concerned with the motion of the planets, though; it was also concerned with how this motion was related to such things as the trajectories of cannon balls. It dealt with the earth's atmosphere as well as the earth's motion in space; and it encompassed Galileo's theories about machines and the strengths of beams. What technological application was found for all this?

Around 1600, there were already some examples of the practical application of what might be called 'science', most notably among the groups of artisans which included opticians, clock-makers, and the makers of instruments for use in navigation. Galileo pioneered the use of the telescope in astronomy after its invention by craftsmen of this sort, and he also had ideas about the improvement of clocks. If the motion of a clock was regulated by a pendulum, he thought, instead of by the traditional verge-and-foliot mechanism, the clock would keep time much more precisely. But although Galileo devoted a great deal of effort to the theory of pendulums, he did not persevere with its practical application. So it was not until the 1650s that the first successful pendulum-clocks were designed and built, by two men working in Holland – Christian Huygens, a mathematician, and Samuel Coster, a clock-maker. A similar collaboration of 'scientist' and clock-maker was that between Robert Hooke and Thomas Tompion in England. Hooke was especially interested in the idea of a balance-wheel moving against a spiral spring as an alternative to the pendulum.

Apart from this kind of interaction between 'science' and the practical arts, which was of considerable importance at this time, there were other kinds of academic learning which influenced 'technology', including the Renaissance interest in Greek and Roman technical literature. To a remarkable degree, indeed, the new sciences of the scientific revolution were built on foundations laid by the ancient Greeks. The critical reappraisal of what was found in Greek writings, and the use of what seemed most valuable, was an enormous stimulus. Galileo's debt to Archimedes is a good example.

The practical arts also benefited from these studies, and the series of discoveries and innovations which led eventually to the invention of the atmospheric steam engine began with a typical late-Renaissance interest in the works of Hero of Alexandria, who described a number of pneumatic gadgets and machines in the first century A.D. The steam engine, which was first success-fully operated in 1712, is rated by some as the greatest of the technological fruits of the scientific revolution, but the earliest work relevant to its invention derived from Hero, and seems almost trivial. This work was done by three architect-engineers in the Renaissance tradition who became interested in Hero's writings. They were G. B. Aleotti, surveyor at Ferrara in the 1580s (chapter three above); the architect Giovanni Branca (1571–1640), and Salomon de Caus (1576–1626), a French landscape-gardener and deviser of fountains.

Hero's gadgets had a strong appeal for these men, as also for more speculative thinkers such as G. B. della Porta (1535–1615), the author of a book on 'natural magic'. Porta later wrote 'three books on pneumatics' in which there were several ideas for devices modelled on Hero's. Some of these could draw liquids through pipes, or use steam to lift water (see fig. 21). Influenced both by this work and by Hero of Alexandria, Giovanni Branca,

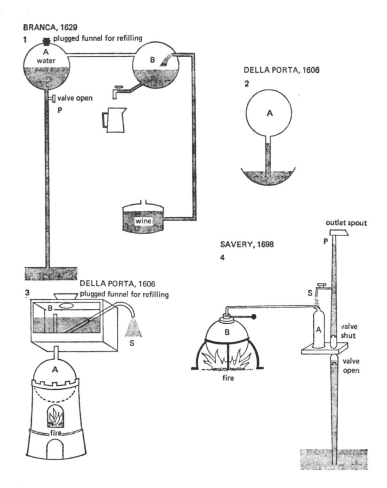

Figure 21

Pneumatic and steam devices owing their origin to late-Renaissance interest in the work of Hero of Alexandria.

1. Design by Branca, 1629. Opening valve P releases water from A. If the plug is air-tight, the air-pressure in A and B is reduced, and wine is drawn into B.

2. Della Porta, 1606. Flask A, with its neck upwards, contains a little water which is brought to the boil. When A is full of steam, it is inverted as shown. As it cools down, steam is condensed and water is drawn up.

3. Della Porta, 1606. Steam-pressure in flask A and space B forces water up through S. The filler funnel is kept sealed.

4. Savery, 1698. Condensation of steam in A by means of spray S draws up water. Then the spray is turned off, and fresh steam from B is used to force water up pipe P.

in 1629, described devices for using steam as a source of power, and elaborated on a wine-lifting gadget invented by Porta.[1]

Salomon de Caus also wrote a book which described pneumatic and steam-powered gadgets, but of greater interest is that in 1609 or 1610 he visited England. There he built pumps and fountains at Hatfield House, at Greenwich Palace and at a house belonging to the Prince of Wales at Richmond. He spent only a short time in England, leaving in 1613, but he seems to have communicated his interest in steam-driven toys to a certain David Ramsay, a member of the Prince's household. Ramsay, like de Caus, was something of a speculative inventor, and took out several patents when this became possible in England after 1624; one of them, dated 1631, was 'To Raise Water from Lowe Pitts by Fire'.[2]

No details are available to show how Ramsay's machine would have worked, but he does seem to have made the transition from thinking about toys and steam-powered gadgets to considering the application of steam to an urgent practical problem, the drainage of mines. So interest in making a steam engine was aroused in Britain by de Caus, and other inventions followed Ramsay's in 1663, 1682, and 1698. The last date refers to Thomas Savery's patent for a device which first sucked water into a closed container by the condensation of steam and then forced it upwards through another pipe by steam pressure. There was 'unceasing effort throughout the seventeenth century to build a practical engine utilising della Porta's concepts directly',[3] and Savery's engine can be accounted for simply in these terms.

The discovery of atmospheric pressure

Hero's pneumatic devices were mostly conceived as table-top models, but the early 17th-century investigators at first thought that they could be made to any size one liked. It was soon found,

1. Keller, in *British Journal for the History of Science*, 3, 1966–7, pp. 338–47; Dendy Marshall, in *Newcomen Society Transactions*, 16, 1937, pp. 1–26.

2. Quoted by Rolt, *Thomas Newcomen*, pp. 23–5.

3. Kerker, 'Science and the steam engine', in *Technology and Culture*, 2, 1961, p. 383.

however, that siphons, suction pumps and gadgets like the wine-lifter would not work through heights greater than about 30 feet. This suggested to Gasparo Berti (*c*. 1600–1642), a mathematician living in Rome, that one should investigate what happened above the 30-foot limit. He therefore arranged a vertical lead tube about 36 feet long so that it could be filled with water from the top and then sealed. A valve at the bottom was closed while this was going on, and the foot of the tube was immersed in a vessel of water. If, after the top was sealed, the valve at the bottom was opened, some water would be seen to run out; the water in the tube settled with its surface at about the 30-foot level, and a space was left above it. Keller[4] comments that this apparatus 'may well be compared with some of Porta's devices. It is indeed almost identical . . .'.

Berti did this experiment in 1641 or 42, and his ideas were developed in the next few years first by Galileo's friend Torricelli, and then by the Frenchman Blaise Pascal. Between them, these two experimenters established the idea that since air has weight, the atmosphere must exert a pressure. The height of the atmosphere was itself limited; the air extended only a few dozen miles above the earth. There was a corresponding limit to the height of water in a vertical pipe which the atmosphere's pressure could support, or to the height of a mercury column in one of Torricelli's newly-invented barometers. It seemed, in fact, that the weight of air in a hypothetical tube long enough to extend vertically to the top of the atmosphere was equal to the weight of water in a tube of the same diameter but only 30 feet long, or to the weight of mercury in a 28-inch tube.

This work, which is described in all standard histories of science,[5] was paralleled in Germany by experiments performed by Otto von Guericke around 1650. Surprisingly, Guericke seems at first to have had no knowledge of what had been done by Berti, Torricelli or Pascal, but worked quite independently, probably on the basis of what he had read of della Porta and similar authors. His approach was therefore rather different from that of the Italians. For example, in an attempt to determine whether a vacuum could be created artificially, he successfully

4. Keller, in *British Journal for the History of Science*, *3*, p. 342.
5. See, for example, the works by Forbes and Dijksterhuis, by Hall and by Wolf cited for this chapter in the bibliography at the end of the book.

pumped water out of an air-tight copper vessel. Improving his apparatus, he soon recognised that air itself was a fluid and, like water, could be pumped out of the vessel. It was then a small step to re-design a conventional pump for this purpose, and in this way von Guericke invented the air pump.

A man of practical bent and wide education, he had helped in the defence of Magdeburg when it was besieged by armies of the Catholic League during the Thirty Years War, and had worked as a military engineer at Erfurt. Although Magdeburg fell disastrously in 1631, von Guericke was held in high esteem there, and was later made burgomaster. It was after the war that he began his work on pneumatics, and this quickly attracted attention. In 1654, when the rulers of the various German states were meeting for the Imperial Diet at Ratisbon (Regensburg), von Guericke gave a public demonstration there of some of his experiments. In one of them, which became famous throughout Europe, teams of horses failed to separate two close-fitting brass hemispheres inside which a vacuum had been produced.

The demonstration particularly interested the Elector John Philip, Archbishop of Mainz and patron of the university at Würzburg; he ordered that Caspar Schott, one of the Würzburg professors, should write an account of the experiments. Schott probably knew of Berti's earlier investigations of the same subject through his former teacher Athanasius Kircher, who had actually been present at Berti's experiments in Rome. Indeed, it is possible that von Guericke first learned of the Italian work through Schott. Both Schott and Kircher were Jesuits, and we may comment in passing that they were just two of many 17th-century Jesuits who had an interest in science – several in Italy during Galileo's time were expert astronomers. And though these men were often out of sympathy with the new ideas of the time, they contributed greatly to the scientific revolution through their researches, and by helping to spread essential information.

Caspar Schott's first account of Guericke's 'hydraulico-pneumatic' experiments was published in 1657, and attracted wide attention throughout Europe. In England, Robert Boyle read the book and immediately arranged for Hooke to build him an air pump like von Guericke's. Meanwhile, Guericke's work was continuing, and in 1661 he did what was perhaps his most important experiment. A cylinder such as might be used as part of a large pump was placed in a vertical position with its open

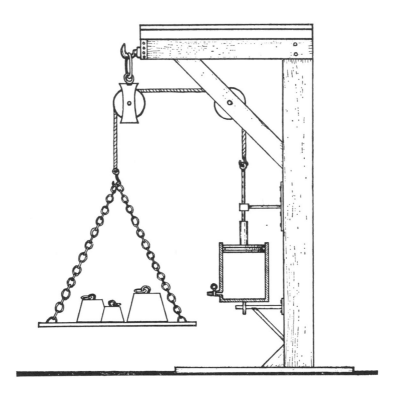

Figure 22

The experiment done by Otto von Guericke in 1661. The air has been pumped out of the cylinder on the right. The pressure of the atmosphere on the piston supports, and may lift, the weights at left.

end upward. A close-fitting piston was held against stops at the top of the cylinder by a cord passing over two pulleys. At the end of the cord, several large weights were suspended (see fig. 22). Air was then pumped out of the cylinder through a valve at the bottom, and when a vacuum had been produced, the pressure due to the atmosphere was sufficient to push the piston downwards into the cylinder, so lifting the weights. The importance of this experiment was that it suggested ways in which the new discoveries about the atmosphere could be given a practical application. It was described in 1664 in Schott's book *Technica Curiosa*, and again in 1672 when von Guericke himself wrote a book.

Galileo's science in France

The cylinder-and-weights experiment of von Guericke had its most fruitful influence in Paris, where an academy of sciences was founded in 1666. Two of the leading members were the Abbé Edmé Mariotte and the Dutch mathematician Christian Huygens. Besides taking an interest in the kind of work von Guericke was doing, Mariotte and Huygens took up many of the problems which Galileo and his friends had raised.

Their action was fortunate, because mechanics and practical sciences were not flourishing in Italy, and the inauguration of the Paris academy of sciences almost coincided with the closure, in 1667, of a similar academy in Florence. This largely marked the end of the 'Galileo tradition' in Galileo's own former home town, and while its closure after only ten years of existence may have owed something to the disapproval with which the Church regarded him, even after his death, it was probably also related to the economic decline being experienced by many of the small Italian states. Even in 1610, when he left the Venetian Republic, he was probably aware that having lost its merchant fleets, Venice was now losing its cloth trade.[6] Other states were affected by similar economic problems, and by epidemics which brought a high mortality. There was little to attract engineers and inventors, or to provide the technological stimulus which Galileo had enjoyed during his time at Padua.

Things were different in Paris, where Huygens and Mariotte in the 1670s found themselves in an environment in which public works and architectural projects were being put in hand on a large scale. And while Huygens's relationship with the science of Galileo may be demonstrated mainly by his work on the theory of pendulums, Mariotte's had more to do with engineering projects of the kind which had been so prominent in Italy during Galileo's time and earlier. Mariotte had a long-standing interest in hydraulics, which found application in work which Louis XIV had begun at the Palace of Versailles. There was a poor water supply at the site of the palace, but the architects had called for numerous fountains in the gardens, and a quite extraordinary pumping-station was constructed to supply them. It was known as the

6. Bulferetti, *Galileo Galilei*; also see above, p. 102, fig. 17.

Marly Machine, and consisted of fourteen water-wheels which pumped water from the River Seine through a total height of about 530 feet.

Mariotte's connection with this undertaking began when he was asked to calculate the best dimensions for the cast-iron pipes which were to be used. This meant calculating the strengths of pipes of various dimensions, and in doing it, Mariotte discovered and partly corrected a defect in Galileo's theory of the strengths of beams.

When he died in 1684, Mariotte left an unfinished book on subjects related to this work. It was edited, and in 1686 published by Philipe de la Hire, a teacher of architecture who had helped with the surveying and levelling of the Versailles water-supply. Besides the work on the strengths of beams and pipes, and on hydrostatic pressure, Mariotte's book contained a theoretical discussion of undershot water-wheels of the type used at Marly. He adapted ideas previously put forward by Torricelli to prove that the force of water on a stationary water-wheel must be as the square of the speed of the current. This calculation was by itself of little value; but in 1704 Antoine Parent, one-time pupil of la Hire, incorporated it in a more complete theory about the working of water-wheels.

Parent's theory was a remarkable achievement, involving what was probably the first application of the differential calculus to an engineering problem, and resulting in perhaps the earliest statement of the mechanical efficiency of a machine. He said that if an undershot water-wheel driving pumps (like those at Marly) was made to pump water back upstream into the source of its own supply, it would pump back only four twenty-sevenths (15 per cent) of the water needed to drive it: in modern parlance, its efficiency would be 15 per cent – although in fact this figure was too low, because of a fault in the reasoning that Parent took over from Mariotte.

Parent himself was not an engineer but a teacher of mathematics in Paris. The young men who came to him for lessons mostly wanted to learn about the theory of fortification and the military arts, and Parent made it his business to gain some practical experience, by attaching himself to an army unit which was at that time – the early 1690s – operating mainly against the Dutch and on the borders of Germany. His scientific interests therefore grew out of a very similar background to Galileo's, and included military problems, architecture and hydraulics. So it seems appropriate that it was Parent who later provided the first fully satisfactory solution to the problem about the strengths of beams which Galileo had raised.

While Parent was working on these problems,[7] Denis Papin, a Huguenot exile from France, was pursuing other scientific ideas of technological significance. Before he left Paris, Papin had worked as Huygens's assistant, and in the 1670s had helped to carry out an experiment which owed a good deal to von Guericke. It will be recalled that von Guericke had arranged a vertical cylinder so that when air was pumped out of it a piston was pushed downwards by atmospheric pressure. This pulled on a rope passing over two pulleys, thereby lifting a weight.

Huygens and Papin constructed a similar apparatus in 1673 and arranged for a small charge of gunpowder to be exploded inside it. The idea was that this would force most of the air out of the cylinder through a non-return valve – a much quicker and easier process than pumping the air out; then, after the gases left inside the cylinder had cooled down, their pressure would be very low, the piston would be pushed downwards, and a large weight would be lifted by a suitable arrangement of ropes and pulleys.

The experiment was successful. A very small charge of gunpowder was exploded in a 1-foot-diameter cylinder and lifted 1,600 lbs. through a height of 5 feet. Here was the basis for a useful engine – but the idea was not developed further. Instead, Papin thought that a more efficient method of creating a vacuum inside the cylinder might be by the condensation of steam. Accordingly he put a small quantity of water in the bottom of the cylinder and applied a flame to make it boil. As the steam pressure inside the cylinder increased, the piston was forced upwards until it reached the top. Then the flame was removed and the cylinder was allowed to cool. A vacuum formed as the steam condensed, and the piston was pushed downwards by the pressure of the atmosphere. Using a $2\frac{1}{2}$-inch-diameter cylinder, Papin was able to make his apparatus raise and lower a 60-lb. weight by successively applying and then removing the source of heat from under the cylinder.

7. For the background of Parent and Papin in the Galileo tradition, see Talbot and Pacey, in *Centaurus*, *16*, 1971, pp. 23–7.

The English steam engine

In 1704, the year in which Parent published his study of the water-wheel, Papin was settled at Cassel in Germany, from where he wrote to Leibniz about the comparative merits of water-wheels and his steam engines as means of driving pumps.[8] By that time he had tried out other types of steam engine, but although many of his devices worked under experimental conditions, he seems never to have perfected any of them as usable machines. This was left to two Englishmen working in Dartmouth – Thomas Newcomen, an ironmonger and blacksmith, with his partner and assistant, John Cawley (or Calley), a plumber. They took the idea of the cylinder and piston which von Guericke, Huygens and Papin had tried out; they adopted the idea of creating a vacuum by the condensation of steam, which della Porta, Savery and Papin had all tried; but to these they added a mechanism of great ingenuity for turning valves on and off in the right sequence, and this automatically controlled the supply of steam and water to their machine. In this way a steam engine utilising the pressure of the atmosphere became a practical proposition.

The Newcomen engine had a cylinder and piston positioned vertically, as in von Guericke's machine. Steam was supplied from a separate boiler, and could be condensed inside the cylinder by turning on a supply of cold water, which sprayed up in a jet from the bottom of the cylinder. When this was done, a vacuum was created, and the piston began to descend as a result of the pressure of the atmosphere, pulling on the end of a pivoted beam above it. Newcomen's engine was designed to pump water from mines such as the ones in Devon and Cornwall near his home, and the purpose of the large pivoted beam was to transform the downward motion of the piston in the cylinder into an upward motion of long vertical rods in the mine shaft which worked pumps at the bottom. When the condensation of steam had finished and the piston had reached the bottom of the cylinder, the pumps had completed one stroke and lifted a certain amount of water from the mine. To start a new stroke, a

8. This letter and other documents relating to Papin and Huygens are printed by Klemm, *A History of Western Technology*, p. 224 ff.

fresh supply of steam was let into the cylinder. It was not high-pressure steam, and could not of itself lift the piston, but once it began to enter the cylinder, the vacuum under the piston was destroyed, and the weight of the pump rods was then sufficient to swing the great beam over and pull the piston back to the top of the cylinder. Then the steam supply was shut off, the condensing water was turned on, and the piston began its descent once again.[9]

The first engine of this kind about which anything is known was installed in 1712 at a coal mine near Wolverhampton.[10] It is significant, though, that this was not an experimental engine or prototype, but a perfected machine. It seems probable that trials had been made earlier with a similar engine, perhaps in Cornwall,[11] and that Newcomen and Cawley had been in a position to build a workable engine from as early as 1705. Before that, it is said, ten years were spent in experimentation, the main problem being to find the best way of condensing steam in the cylinder. It seems likely, then, that Newcomen's invention originated about 1695.

The puzzle remains as to how much Newcomen knew about the devices of von Guericke, Huygens and Papin, which seem to anticipate his engine so closely. While Newcomen was still alive, one man who probably knew him wrote that 'the Engine now used was invented by Monsieur Pappein and others, as I find sufficiently described in their writings from which Mr. Newcomen began to make improvements'.[12]

This is slight evidence in itself, but it seems very likely that Newcomen did know of Papin's work, and in particular of the experiment on condensation of steam in a cylinder. An account of this was first published in the Leipzig journal *Acta Eruditorum* in 1690. It was written in Latin, but a French translation appeared in 1695, and was reviewed in the *Philosophical Transactions* of the Royal Society of London in 1697. Some historians

9. For fuller details of the working principle, see, for example, Dickinson, *A Short History of the Steam Engine*.

10. This is the so-called Dudley Castle engine.

11. Evidence for this and for the dating proposed here is to be found principally in Rolt, *Thomas Newcomen*.

12. Quoted by Musson in his introduction to Dickinson, *A Short History of the Steam Engine*.

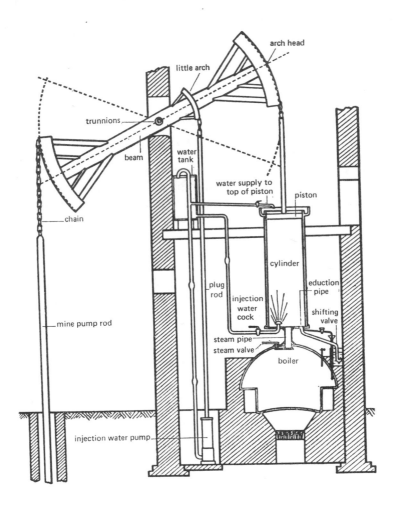

Figure 23

The principle of Newcomen's atmospheric steam engine. The engine is shown at the point where the piston is about to begin its downward stroke. The cylinder is full of steam, but the steam-valve is shut and the jet of injection-water has just been turned on. This will condense the steam in the cylinder, so creating a vacuum, and the piston will be crushed downwards by the pressure of the atmosphere. The condensed steam and injection-water can drain away through the eduction-pipe.

(Source: fig. 7 of H. W. Dickinson, *A Short History of the Steam Engine*, Cambridge University Press, 1939, p. 30)

have felt that these publications were all too obscure for Newcomen, in Dartmouth, to have ready access to them, and there has been much discussion of whether he was in correspondence with members of the Royal Society in London, particularly with Robert Hooke. The evidence is inconclusive, but here it is worth mentioning that Newcomen was a Baptist by religion, that the local Baptist congregation met in a house he leased in 1707, and that Newcomen himself was a preacher.[13] From what is known of nonconformist lay preachers at this date, it seems right to assume that most such men, though often self-educated, were also well acquainted with books and knew where to obtain them.

Another point is that Huguenot refugees – that is, Calvinist Protestants from France – had 'appeared in large numbers in Devon towns following the Revocation of the Edict of Nantes in 1685',[14] and some of them settled in the area where Newcomen lived. In Exeter, the Huguenots who conformed to the Church of England were given the use of St Olave's Church in 1686, while others were helped by the nonconformists. There were still 120 Huguenots of the latter kind in Exeter in 1715, as well as a group in Dartmouth. Papin made several extended visits to England and was himself a Huguenot, so it is possible (though perhaps not likely) that he had contacts in Devon. More to the point is that Newcomen lived in a cosmopolitan community, where it would be easy for him to get translations made of any foreign books which came his way, including Papin's French account of his steam-engine experiments.

Technology and the scientific revolution: a summary

Whatever the precise channels of communication by which Newcomen and Cawley heard of the experiments of von Guericke, Huygens and Papin – and there are several possible ones – Newcomen's 'atmospheric' steam engine was closely related to the apparatus of these experiments in both logic and design. It seems that here is a clear case of an important invention deriving from the scientific revolution. But the lack of definite

13. For details, see Rolt, *Thomas Newcomen*; I am indebted to W. N. Slatcher for pointing out the significance of this fact.
14. Brockett, *Nonconformity in Exeter 1650–1875*.

information about a link between Papin and Newcomen has led some writers to think that any such link would have been extremely tenuous, and that the English steam engine was mainly the product of an untutored empiricism. It is pointed out that Newcomen's engine depended on a great deal of purely mechanical ingenuity, and it is argued that 'the successful fruition of the heat-engine owes virtually everything but the concept of atmospheric pressure to practical engineers'.[15]

The author of this comment goes on in the same passage to minimise the technological significance of Galileo's work and Mariotte's development of it. Their theories were never applied to practical problems, he argues, and were often unrealistic or misleading.

This seems rather to overstate the case, but it is important to realise that the work of Galileo and his French successors had an influence in other ways. Sébastien Truchet (1657–1729), consultant engineer for the Orleans Canal, had at one time been a pupil of Mariotte, and since Mariotte had written a treatise on levelling as well as on hydraulics, this could have been a useful relationship. Certainly the mathematical training which French engineers received was steadily extended to include science of the kind which Mariotte had pioneered.

But to regard clear-cut and successful applications of science to technology as the only real evidence of the influence of the scientific revolution puts the problem in a false perspective. It might be more appropriate to recall the long-standing relationship between mathematics and the 'public works' technologies associated with architecture. Mariotte and Parent had much the same relationship with architects and engineers as Galileo had done almost a century before, and as some Italian theoreticians of architecture of an even earlier time. They taught young men who might later practise architecture or engineering, particularly in its military branches; they occasionally gave advice on practical problems, like the Versailles pipe-lines; and they developed theories about engineering problems which were a stimulus to the following generations – as when Parent's water-wheel calculations helped John Smeaton, in the 1750s, to formulate the requirements for a more practical investigation of water-power (chapter seven).

In addition, the highly successful development of engineering in France during the 18th century resulted partly from the growing application of mathematical sciences to 'architectural' technologies such as hydraulics, bridge-building and fortification. The most important early account of Newcomen's engine to appear in French was contained in an enormous book on canal-building, harbour works and hydraulic machinery which had the significant title *Architecture hydraulique*.[16] Somewhat later, the major developments in technical drawing associated with the name of Gaspard Monge (1746–1818) grew directly out of an interest in the traditional problems of fortification design.[17] Thus the connections between 'science' and engineering which were established during the Renaissance and developed by the scientific revolution did have products of indisputable technical worth.

All this serves to counter the arguments of a number of historians who doubt the relevance of the new science for Newcomen's achievement, who minimise the technological significance of Galileo, Mariotte and Parent, and who then claim that the scientific revolution had very little effect on contemporary developments in 'technology'. It is argued, for example, that 'seventeenth century science still lacked the depth of precise, quantitative information that alone is useful to engineers'.[18] There is much truth in this, but it is also possible to say that: 'The sixteenth and seventeenth centuries mark the transition from complete empiricism to engineering techniques fully grounded in mathematics and applied science.'[19] An able summary and attempted reconciliation of these opposing points of view has been provided by A. E. Musson and Eric Robinson,[20] and it is clear that the divergencies arose partly because the influence of the new knowledge was sometimes indirect. Another difficulty, in the present author's opinion, is that not all historians have recognised the long-standing Renaissance approach to architecture and public works engineering mentioned above. The influence of 'science' on 'technology' did not always occur in

16. By Forest de Belidor; four volumes published 1737 onwards.
17. Booker, in *Newcomen Society Transactions, 34*, 1961–2, pp. 15–36.
18. Hall, in *Technology and Culture, 2*, 1961, pp. 334–5.
19. Usher, in *A History of Technology, 3*, p. 344.
20. *Science and Technology in the Industrial Revolution*, pp. 1–59, especially pp. 26–30.

the particular way we expect it to in the 20th century, but many ideas passed along this more traditional channel of communication between mathematicians and artist-engineers.

A final blind spot in the conventional historians' approach is the assumption that influence always proceeds from 'science' to 'technology'. Interactions of the opposite kind have often been crucially important. In the 17th century, experience with water-pumps stimulated 'scientific' work on the vacuum and on barometers, and Galileo learned much about mechanics in the shipyards of Venice. The practical arts could also influence 'scientific method'. The experimental approach in science owed a great deal to people's growing experience of machines and industrial processes. Accurate weighing, as used in the 16th century by assayers working at silver mines (chapter five below), became an important part of the method of scientific chemistry when this developed much later.

But the scientific revolution did not just consist of the acquisition of new knowledge and the use of new experimental techniques. It also involved a change in people's outlook on the world – a change in what can be called their 'philosophy of nature', a subject about which the men who were responsible for the new knowledge gained at this time held a variety of different views. According to the philosophy of nature accepted by some of them,[21] the universe was in some degree an organic thing, to be studied as one would study the plant and animal kingdoms. Others held that there was something mysterious in nature, which could be understood only by using the concepts and vocabulary of astrology and magic. But the philosophy of nature most strongly associated with the change of outlook which occurred in this period portrayed the universe as being built on the lines of a rather complicated machine. This 'mechanical philosophy' demanded a changed outlook because it banished all sense of there being something mysterious or organic about the universe. The new approach emerged only after 1600, largely in the work of Galileo and a few contemporaries, but by the end of the century it was the predominant philosophy of nature among people with scientific interests in Italy, France and England. It seems worth asking, therefore, whether this mechanical

21. These various philosophies of nature are summarised in Kearney's introductory survey, *Science and Change*, pp. 22 ff.

philosophy had any relationship with contemporary machines or with developments in the mechanical arts.

The mechanical philosophy

Quite a lot has already been said concerning beliefs about the fundamental importance of mathematics, both as a key to understanding nature and as a guide to the builder or craftsman. After being reformulated by Galileo and others at the beginning of the scientific revolution, these beliefs played a major part in the changed outlook of the time.

But while belief in mathematics and enthusiasm for experiments are rather general attitudes, and may be regarded as among the causes rather than the effects of the scientific revolution, two other ideas may be mentioned which belong more specifically to this period. One is the view that problems may be more easily solved if they are broken down into their component parts and studied piece by piece – this may be called 'the method of detail'. The other is the notion of a mechanical philosophy, already mentioned, according to which everything in nature, from the orbit of a planet to the functioning of an animal's muscles, operates in some sense like a well-made machine. In 1644, this view was put into words by the French philosopher René Descartes, who said that he did not 'recognise any difference between machines that artisans make and the different bodies that nature alone creates'.[22]

Galileo never said anything so explicit, but it is worth mentioning that his theory of the strengths of beams was based on a machine theory – the law of the lever – and besides applying this theory to ships and buildings, he also discussed it in relation to animal skeletons, birds' feathers and the stems of plants – in fact, to all the natural beams and struts out of which these living creatures are built. In doing this, he was one of many 17th-century writers to apply mechanical concepts to human and animal bodies. Descartes, however, provides the outstanding example and his writings are of particular interest because they include a description of ornamental water gardens similar to the ones at Versailles for which Mariotte was later to make calcula-

22. *'Principia philosophiae'*, iv, 203, in *Oeuvres de Descartes*, vol. 8, p. 326.

tions concerning pipes and water-wheels. Descartes said that the human body was 'nothing else but . . . a machine'.

'Thus you must have seen in the grottoes and fountains which are in the King's gardens, that the pressure which forces up the water from its source is sufficient to move many machines . . . following the complex arrangements of the pipes which carry it. And truly one can compare the nerves . . . to the pipes of these fountains and their machinery; the muscles and tendons to the various other engines and springs . . . the animal spirits to the water which works them; and the heart to the source of water. . . . Further, respiration and other such actions . . . are like the motion of a clock, or rather a mill which turns continuously with the flow of water.'[23]

This kind of argument recurred in several of Descartes' writings. Henry Power, a physician practising near Halifax in Yorkshire, quoted the 'strong opinion of Des-Cartes' that animals 'indeede are nothing else but engines, or matter sett into a continued and orderly motion'.[24] Power was one of several English authors who discussed the mechanistic ideas of Descartes. He had made a series of studies of small animals, using the newly-available microscope, and these creatures he described as 'Insectile Automata' or 'slow-paced Engines of Nature', even though he had some reservations about how far Descartes' mechanistic view could be pushed. The philosopher Thomas Hobbes probably had many fewer such reservations. In the introduction to *Leviathan* he asked, 'what is the heart, but a spring; and the nerves but so many strings; and the joints but so many wheels, giving motion to the whole body . . .'.

The argument could also be put the other way round, to show how crude a machine was compared with a natural body. This point was made by William Petty, who had been secretary to Hobbes for a short time; he thought that the study of anatomy could 'show proud man that his most mysterious and complicated enginry is nothing to the compounded and decompounded mysteries in the fabric of man. That all . . . mechanics whatsoever, are no more compared to the fabric of an animal than putting two sticks across is to a loom, a clock or a ship under sail . . . nor can any man take a better course to find out curious and useful

23. '*Traité de l'homme*', in *Oeuvres de Descartes*, vol. *11*, pp. 120, 130–31.
24. MS. letter quoted by Webster, in *Ambix*, *14*, 1967, p. 176.

engines than by taking the bodies of animals for his piece and pattern.'[25]

When one considers the motion of man's arm under the influence of the muscles, or the structural strength of a skeleton, machine concepts can be applied with some exactness. But these examples account for only a small fraction of the functions of animal bodies, and there are relatively few other natural phenomena to which the idea of levers, wheels and pulleys can be directly applied. Thus when Descartes compared the universe to a watch, he perhaps only meant this to be taken as an analogy. Such an analogy, acceptable in itself, betrays an attitude of mind which is more open to question. The universe is not operated by celestial gear-wheels. But in a slightly broader sense, Descartes conceived its behaviour to be strictly mechanical in that it could be understood solely in terms of the motions and interactions of solid pieces of matter.

Asked for more details, most of the 17th-century thinkers who held such views would have mentioned the motions of the smallest particles of matter which could possibly exist. The ancient Greeks had discussed such particles and had called them 'atoms'. An account of Greek theories of atoms had been written by the Roman poet Lucretius, and in the 17th century this was being widely read after a long period of obscurity. Many people with an interest in philosophies of nature took up the ideas expressed by Lucretius and adapted them to their own purposes. One of the most influential reinterpretations of the atomic hypothesis was by the French priest Gassendi (1592–1655). Galileo and Descartes both talked about small particles, but not in the sense of indivisible atoms.

What attracted all these authors was that Lucretius used his atoms to draw a somewhat mechanistic picture of the universe, in which the world was created by the random motions and combinations of the atoms, and in which the planets were moved in their courses, 'on the same principle as we see rivers turn water-wheels'.[26]

This ancient work, then, supplied arguments that very neatly supported one of the chief trends in the thought of the scientific revolution. It provided a model of the universe which

25. Quoted by Strauss, *Sir William Petty*, p. 52.
26. Lucretius, *The Nature of the Universe*, p. 18.

was not only mechanical in concept, but which proved to be capable of meeting the particular need of 17th-century thinkers for a world-view that would support and justify the belief that mathematics was fundamental to the understanding of nature; the idea of explaining all phenomena in terms of atoms or small particles fitted in with this because, in principle, everything about the behaviour of an atom could be measured, and expressed in mathematical terms. The only things which had to be specified about atoms in order to explain their behaviour were their numbers, shapes, weights and motions. The many unmeasurable things which people experience – for example warmth, smell, colour – could be explained, again in principle, by the motions of small particles and the reactions of the sense organs to them. Thus Galileo thought that in the *Dialogues* he had explained away musical harmony by talking about the reactions of the eardrums to motions in the air; and elsewhere he wrote that 'tastes, odours, colours and so forth are no more than mere names so far as pertains to the objects in which they reside, [and that] they have their habitation only in the senses'.[27] They were 'sensation' and not 'real qualities'.

The 17th-century authors who discussed such ideas included, in England, Henry Power and Thomas Hobbes, as already mentioned; also John Locke, the philosopher, and many of the people connected with the Royal Society. In their writings, the current outlook was sometimes described as 'the mechanical philosophy' – an appropriate name – although the more specific term 'corpuscular philosophy' was more commonly used. Among the continental authors who were interested in the practical arts as well as in science, Antoine Parent had perhaps the most contemplative turn of mind. His reflections on the changed outlook of the time were expressed in a long commentary on Descartes' *Principia Philosophiae* that was the product, he said, of ten years' experience of teaching Descartes' ideas to his pupils. But while a full account of these and other comments on the ideas of the time would be of some interest, it seems more important to turn instead to another aspect of the changed outlook on nature which accompanied the scientific revolution.

27. *Opere di Galileo Galilei*, 6, pp. 347–8; Drake, *Discoveries and Opinions of Galileo*, p. 274.

The method of detail

In drawing a distinction between 'real qualities', like length and weight, which were measurable, and 'sensations', like tastes, odours and colours, which were to be explained away – a distinction for which Locke later used the terms 'primary' and 'secondary' qualities – Galileo was doing more than argue for a mathematical science of measurable quantities. He was also analysing experience and breaking it down into its parts.

It is this analytical habit of mind which, after the example of the 19th-century author John Stuart Mill, is termed 'the method of detail': a form of thought which operates on several levels. Thus the desire to think of the ultimate particles of matter might be seen as one of its aspects, but its real value and effectiveness was as a means of solving problems. An example has already been briefly mentioned, for when Mariotte was asked to determine the best dimensions for pipes at Versailles, he broke the problem down into several more detailed questions – about how freely the water would flow in pipes of different bore, about the bending-strength of a pipe and about its bursting-strength when filled with water under pressure. Taken as a whole, the problem might have seemed impossible to answer, but its component parts were reasonably simple.

Similar examples can be drawn from the work of Galileo – as when, faced with a question about the strengths of ships' hulls, he avoided discussion of the problem as a whole by analysing instead the strength of a single beam. On another occasion he explicitly acknowledged that the new science of his time was achieving results by turning away from many of the big problems which philosophers had traditionally studied, and looking instead at the details of the natural world. Taken by themselves, such details might seem trivial or uninteresting, but they did at least present problems which could often be solved, while the larger issues were usually baffling. A case in point, thought Galileo, was a question 'relating to pendulums, a subject which may appear to many exceedingly arid, especially to those philosophers who are continually occupied with the more profound questions of nature. Nevertheless, the problem is one I do not scorn'.[28]

28. Galileo, *Dialogues*, p. 94; *Opere di Galileo Galilei*, 8, p. 138.

What was involved in this kind of attitude was neatly summed up a hundred years ago by John Stuart Mill in talking about 'habits of thought and modes of investigation which are essential to the idea of science'. The lack of these before the time of Galileo had made science 'a field of interminable discussion leading to no result'; and the essence of the new method introduced at this time 'may be shortly described as the method of detail; of treating wholes by separating them into parts ... and breaking every question into pieces before attempting to solve it'.[29]

The application of the method of detail in a practical and technical context can be illustrated by the varied career of Sir William Petty (1623–87), who has already been mentioned in connection with Thomas Hobbes. Petty studied medicine at Leyden in Holland, and taught at Oxford; in 1652 he became Physician General to Cromwell's army in Ireland. There, he very efficiently reorganised the army medical service, and at the same time began to take an interest in the country where he was working.

Petty shared the contemporary belief in the value of measurement and mathematics, but applied it in new and original ways. In later life he became a powerful advocate of the need for governments to collect statistics of population and trade, and himself made well-informed estimates of the populations of several countries, including Ireland. Cromwell's military campaigns there had been accompanied not only by terrible destruction, but by outbreaks of plague. Between '23rd October 1641, and the same day, 1652', Petty estimated that the population had fallen from 1,466,000 to 850,000. There were 504,000 Irish and over a hundred thousand English and Scots who 'perished and were wasted by the Sword, plague, famine, hardship and banishment ...'.[30] These figures are probably not greatly exaggerated.

The work of Petty's which is of most importance here arose out of an official policy for confiscating Irish lands and using them to pay debts which the English government otherwise had not the resources to meet. To ensure that the award of lands to creditors would be effectively carried out, it was necessary to

29. Mill, Essay on Bentham, in F. R. Leavis (ed.), *Mill on Bentham and Coleridge*, p. 48.
30. Quoted by Strauss, *Sir William Petty*, p. 52.

make a detailed survey of Ireland in a very short time. This job,
which seemed almost impossible, was undertaken by Petty with
great efficiency, and his map of Ireland, published in 1673, is
said to be the most accurate map of any country produced up to
that time. But the greatest achievement in making the survey was
not so much its accuracy as its organisation. Twenty-two
counties were to be surveyed in fifteen months (December
1654 to March 1656) by a force of about a thousand men. Many
of these were soldiers, unskilled in surveying. The skilled work
Petty reserved for his few experienced surveyors, while the other
work was done by soldiers, who were given some elementary
training for such jobs as taking measurements in the field:

'He divided the whole art of surveying into its several parts,
viz. 1, Field work; 2, protracting; 3, casting; 4, reducing; 5,
ornaments of the maps; 6, writing fair books; 7, examination of
all and every the premisses; withal setting forth, that for the
speedier and surer performance he intended to employ particular
persons upon each species, according to their respective fitness
and qualifications.'[31]

Many of the surveyors' instruments were made in a workshop
which Petty set up for the purpose; he divided 'the art of making
instruments, as also of using them, into many parts' – wiremakers
made the measuring-chains, watchmakers made compasses, and
separate workmen were employed for making the wooden and the
brass parts of instruments. Finally, a more skilled man checked,
adjusted and calibrated them.

In his essays on 'political arithmetic', Petty discussed this
method of organising work. In watchmaking, for example, if
'one man shall make the *wheels*, another the *spring*, another shall
engrave the *dial-plate*, and another shall make the *cases*, then the
watch will be better and cheaper, than if the whole work be put
upon any one man'.[32]

This procedure is an example of the division of labour, the
principle of which was given its classic expression a hundred
years after Petty, by Adam Smith. As a method of organising a
labour force, it is more usually discussed in connection with the
rise of factory industry than with the scientific revolution. But in
the work of Petty, a man fully in touch with the science of the 17th

31. Strauss, *Sir William Petty*, pp. 61–2.
32. Quoted by Strauss, *Sir William Petty*, pp. 62–3.

century and deeply influenced by its mathematical emphasis, one can see that the division of labour, as a concept, sprang from the same source as the method of detail – from the recognition that a job is often done better if broken down into elementary constituent parts.

The disenchanted outlook

Although the method of detail can be thought of as a technique of analysis which does not depend on any particular philosophy of nature, it was closely linked historically with mechanical analogies of the world. The mechanical models of natural phenomena discussed in the 17th century were always based on imagined assemblies of wheels, levers or corpuscles. They therefore always encouraged the study of problems in terms of these basic components.

Such ideas seem highly relevant for understanding some of the difficulties surrounding technology and its applications in the 20th century. The 17th-century mechanical philosophy has persisted, in some of its fundamentals, down to our own time, and may have led us into some of our modern dilemmas.

For example, the idea of the natural world as being something mechanical freed people from any old-fashioned doubts about whether, in making a machine or digging a mine, they might be encroaching on the prerogatives of the Creator. The 13th-century idea of clocks or cathedrals as symbolising heavenly things – the idea of their construction as a reaching-out towards the source of light and life – had been replaced by the notion that the heavens themselves were little better than a piece of well-made clockwork. So there was no particular reason for feeling any humility before nature. It was a machine that one could tinker with. And the machine analogy gave no warning that there were checks and balances in nature which could easily be upset, because 17th-century machines did not incorporate feed-back loops or any other automatic control systems to prevent them getting out of control or running away. The only exception was the escapement mechanism of clocks, but this evidently did not prove sufficiently suggestive.

The mechanical philosophy is sometimes described as a disenchanted view of nature, because it left no room for any mystical appreciation of natural phenomena, and it outlawed astrology and magic. But it would also be appropriate to call it a disconnected world view, in which the links between the different parts of entities were often ignored or broken, and in which subjects were habitually studied in isolation from their broader context. There were, of course, great benefits to be gained by adopting this approach. Problems can be solved far more effectively by concentrating attention on details while ignoring wider complications, and in much academic scientific research these methods have had a long history of success. But with many modern industrial and technical projects, it is now being found that disadvantages sometimes follow from ignoring wider complications.

The dangerous consequences of such disregard are now being recognised. The word 'ecology' has become fashionable as denoting more than the academic subject of that name: as suggesting a quite different approach to nature, in which the interrelatedness of things is fully taken into account. A discipline with comparable aims but with the possibility of a more direct application in modern technology is that known as 'general systems theory'. One of its founders has said that in modern science 'this scheme of isolable units acting in one-way causality has proved to be insufficient. Hence the appearance, in all fields of science, of notions like wholeness, holistic, organismic, gestalt, etc., which all signify that, in the last resort, we must think in terms of systems of elements in mutual interaction.'[33]

Thus terms such as 'holistic' and 'organismic' refer to the art of seeing problems as a whole, instead of taking the fragmented and over-selective view common with conventional science. It is part of the task of systems theorists to make it possible to use this art without losing the genuine benefits brought by the method of detail. If they succeed in this task, and a new, holistic approach to science is at last able to influence the basis of all existing sciences and technologies, then that will be of such value and significance as to be counted as a new scientific revolution.

The disconnected and fragmented view of things which the method of detail demanded has had other implications also. These may be illustrated from Galileo's discussion of music, mentioned in the previous chapter. Music can at times stir the human spirit as deeply as love; it can speak to the source of a person's being and can express things about life for which the prophets and

33. Compare von Bertalanffy's *General system theory*, pp. 9, 29–30.

teachers of the great religions have failed to find words. But for Galileo it was enough to say that the enjoyment of music depended on the eardrum's receiving a pattern of vibrations to which it could easily respond, in contrast to harsh noises which bend the eardrum 'in two different directions in order to yield to the ever-discordant impulses'.[34]

Of course, Galileo was right to think that the deeper things of music were outside the realm of science. But one suspects that because such things were intangible, and neither mathematical nor 'objective', they seemed to him less real. They were even less substantial than 'sensations' or 'secondary qualities' such as colour and warmth, and were perhaps not even worth considering at all. Just as in the world at large the mechanical philosophy produced a science and technology in which the connections of parts and wholes was ignored, so on this more personal level the tendency of the mechanical philosophy was to break the internal balance between thought and feeling, and between the rational and the emotional aspects of human experience.

So it has seemed to one modern commentator, at any rate.[35] But perhaps the point is expressed more clearly in the straightforward language of one professor at the Massachusetts Institute of Technology.[36] The mathematical view of the world, he thinks, has produced an advancement in understanding which is 'quite obviously all to the good. The aim of pure reason, which proceeds upon measurable quantities, is, presumably to introduce in-increasing order and system into the randomness of life. But I have here the apprehension that as time goes by we may begin to lose somewhat our sense of the significance of the qualitative elements in a situation, such things as the loyalties, memories, affections and feelings men bring to any situation, things which make situations more messy but, for men, more real. My apprehension is that the computer which feeds on quantifiable data may give too much aid and comfort to those who think you can learn all the important things in life by breaking experience down into its measurable parts.'

The nuclear physicist Wolfgang Pauli summarised all these issues rather succinctly in 1955: 'Since the seventeenth century the activities of the human spirit have been strictly classified in

34. Galileo, *Dialogues*, p. 104.
35. Bateson, in *The Dialectics of Liberation*, pp. 34–49.
36. Morison, *Men, Machines and Modern Times*.

separate compartments. But in my view, the attempt to eliminate such distinctions by a combination of rational understanding and the mystical experience of unity obeys the . . . imperative of our contemporary age.'[37]

37. Quoted by Jungk, *Brighter than a Thousand Suns*, p. 305.

5

Social ideals in technical change: German miners and English Puritans, 1450–1650

Introduction

In nearly all accounts of the 'scientific revolution', including the one given in the previous chapter, Italians and Frenchmen figure prominently, but, on the whole, Germans are conspicuous by their absence. Otto von Guericke and the astronomer Johannes Kepler are always mentioned by historians, and sometimes also the German Jesuits Kircher and Schott. Yet although von Guericke and Kepler contributed greatly to contemporary understanding of nature, and although Kircher and Schott helped to spread knowledge of recent discoveries, they do not fit easily into the conventional picture of the 'scientific revolution'. In outlook and culture, these men differed markedly from Galileo, Descartes and their associates; and the same was true for other Germans, to be mentioned below, whose interests were in chemistry, mining or metal-working.

One way of describing the approach to 'science' adopted by some of the German school is to mention again the different philosophies of nature which were current in the 16th and 17th centuries. Some people still felt that there was something ultimately mysterious at the heart of nature, and were not averse to talking about magic or alchemy. There were hidden 'virtues' or powers in material things; numbers and geometrical shapes had mystical significance; and invention or discovery was thought to be the result of inspiration or divine illumination.

Such beliefs derived partly from the neo-Platonic ideas which had for long lain dormant in European thought (chapter two), but which had been revived and reinterpreted in Florence just before 1500 (chapter three). Along with other Renaissance ideas, Florentine neo-Platonism had its share of influence in Germany, where current social and religious problems gave it new emphases and applications. Under such influences there developed an approach to 'science' and to the practical arts which contrasted sharply with the mechanistic outlook of Galileo and Descartes.

These somewhat mystical attitudes to the study of nature were clearly *not* 'scientific' in any modern sense. Historians have therefore tended to exclude them from descriptions of the 'scientific revolution', and so to ignore much German work which might otherwise seem relevant to the development of science. The historian of technology cannot so easily dismiss the Germans, however, because from about 1450 they were pre-eminent in the arts of mining and working metals, and their mystical view of nature played an essential part in their practical and technical achievements.

Metal-producing mines were to be found among the mountains of eastern and southern Germany, and metal-using industries in some of the larger towns. Augsburg and Nuremberg were two of the most advanced centres, and printing, clock-making, tin-plate manufacture and gun-casting flourished there, as well as the more traditional cloth manufactures. Augsburg was situated at the northern end of an important trade route opened up in the 15th century. This crossed the Brenner Pass, and gave south German merchants easy access to Venice. There they learned the Italian system of banking and finance, and soon were able to establish their own banking-houses in Augsburg.

The practical arts of the German-speaking countries

One difficulty in speaking about Germany in the 16th century is the lack of any precise boundaries to which that name referred. Most of central Europe was occupied by German-speaking peoples, and there were German settlements far to the east in Poland and Hungary. But Germany as a political unit did not exist. Most places where the German language was spoken were part of the Holy Roman Empire, but the Empire was a hotchpotch of small independent states like Saxony, and self-governing free cities like Augsburg and Nuremberg, with Austria the only 'great power' among them. Saxony was important for its silver mines, and copper, lead and silver were also mined in the Harz Mountains, an area criss-crossed by a bewildering tangle of boundaries defining several small states.

Mining was also important in the Austrian Empire, with many

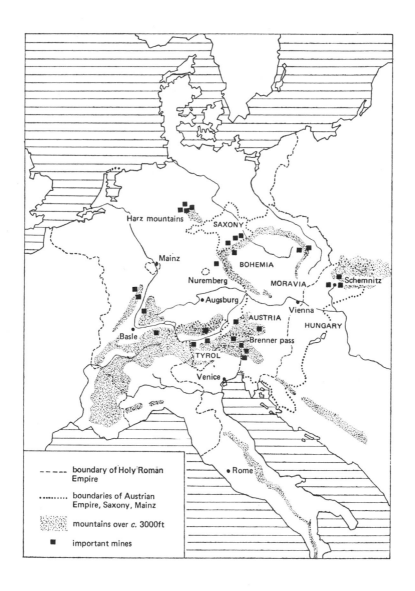

Figure 24
Mining in Europe in the late 16th century.

mines in the Tyrol and Bohemia, and with scattered mining settlements in Hungary, most notably at Schemnitz.

In many of these areas, copper, silver and lead had been worked from a very early date. But there had been a decline during the 14th century, owing to the effects of the Black Death, and because the most accessible ores had been worked out. After 1450, new investment and the introduction of new techniques made recovery possible, and the output of the mines greatly increased.

Before this period, most of the ores had been quarried, or mined in shallow pits, with few real shafts or tunnels. But now shafts could go deep, with water-wheels or horse-gins used to lift material and pump water from the lowest levels. The deepest mines went down to about 600 feet below the surface,[1] with underground workings spreading out horizontally from the shafts. Machinery was applied to crushing the ore, smelting processes were improved, and there was a steady expansion and development up to about A.D. 1530, when something like 100,000 men were employed in mining throughout the Holy Roman Empire.

The rapid development of mining between about 1450 and 1530, and its relative stagnation later in the 16th century, must be understood in terms of the metals that were produced and the ways in which they were used. The two most important were silver and copper. Silver was sometimes found 'native', but in many places the ores of copper, silver and lead were found together, and the metals had to be separated in the smelting process. The actual quantity of silver in relation to other metals was usually very small, but its price was high; for many mines, this was the greatest source of revenue.

The importance of silver arose from its use for making coins. Gold and copper were also used in the coinage of all European countries, but silver coins figured most prominently in ordinary commercial transactions. From about 1450, there was a steady growth of commerce throughout Europe, with a corresponding increase in the amount of silver coin in circulation. Thus mines in the Freiberg district of Saxony, which produced on average about 16,000 ounces of silver each year during the 15th century, boosted production to an average of nearly 150,000 ounces per

1. Lewis, *Early Wooden Railways*, p. 5.

annum by 1530, and continued at that level for several decades.[2] Besides silver and copper, a little tin was also produced in Saxony and Bohemia, and was used to make tin-plate: that is, sheet iron coated with tin by being dipped into the molten metal. A more important use of tin, though, was in the production of bronze, an alloy consisting of one part tin with about eight parts copper. This was much in demand for making gun-barrels, which at this time were either cast in bronze, by means of techniques which had been developed earlier for making church bells, or were fabricated in wrought iron by welding pieces of metal together.

Around the middle of the 15th century, guns began to be far more widely used than before, and the resulting demand for large quantities of copper and tin was an important stimulus to the revival of mining at this time. The growing demand for guns probably also provoked thought about using cast iron, and led to experiments with that material. Casting iron was more difficult than making similar castings in bronze, because of impurities which entered into combination with the molten iron and spoiled its quality. Wrought iron was not subject to this problem, because it was produced in furnaces which were only hot enough to soften the metal, not to melt it. Under these conditions, quality could be more certainly controlled.

However, the quality of the material used to make cannon balls was not too crucial, and they were cast in iron from quite early in the 15th century. Blast furnaces for producing cast iron were in operation by 1464, when one was described by Antonio Filarete, an architect from Florence. But only after 1500 did it become possible to cast iron barrels for cannon, and it was not until much later that cast-iron cannon could rival bronze ones in reliability.

Germans were not prominent in the development of cast iron. Early blast furnaces were to be found in Italy, the Low Countries (Liège) and England (Sussex); and by the mid-17th century Sweden was exporting nearly a thousand tons of cast-iron cannon annually. But in bronze cannon manufacture, German expertise was unequalled. In 1592, it was said that German products were the 'best available' because the Germans 'do things more accurately and more patiently . . . and enjoy a

2. Figures from *Bergakademie Freiberg Festschrift*, p. 9; I am indebted to David Farrar for pointing them out to me.

greater and better supply of copper and tin, with which materials they produce excellent bronze . . . After the castings of Germany, the castings of Venice are considered very good: in Venice the German style and rules are very strictly followed'.[3]

There were many other metallurgical arts at which the Germans excelled. For example, there were the arts of assaying and of smelting metals, knowledge of which contributed to the early growth of chemistry. Smelting provided empirical experience of chemical reactions; but, more important, assayers had to weigh small quantities of metal with great accuracy, and they had to observe the progress of the metal from one process to another, carefully weighing in at each stage. Similar techniques were later used in chemistry, and the assayers' work probably contributed to their development as well as helping to bring out the relevance of assumptions concerning the conservation of matter.

Bankers and assayers

It is possible to illustrate several aspects of this wide range of practical arts by looking at the way in which knowledge of German metallurgical techniques was carried across Europe. In many instances, German craftsmen were sent to distant places as agents of the Augsburg banking firms.

During the 16th century, bankers such as the Fuggers, the Haugs and the Welsers were of major international importance; the Fuggers, indeed, probably had more power and influence than any earlier finance-house in history. And wherever in Europe an Augsburg financier had an interest, there German craftsmen might be sent to improve techniques and the general efficiency of the operation.

Thus, for example, German technicians were sent to mines in Spain by the bankers of Augsburg, and took with them an expertise in pumping-machinery which contributed to the construction of a remarkable but commercially unsuccessful water-pumping station at Toledo. German miners coming to England taught the English the principle of the railway. Simple types of railway had been used in the German mines during the 16th century for moving small wagons of ore in underground

3. L. Colliado, a 16th-century Spanish writer; quoted by Cipolla, *European Culture*, pp. 39–40.

galleries. In England, railways were used principally on the surface, especially for moving coal from mines near Newcastle to boats on the Tyne. Likewise, it was a German, Burchard Kranich (1515–78), who introduced water-powered ore-crushing machinery at tin-mines in Cornwall.

One factor which encouraged German bankers and miners to explore the prospects for mining in places as distant as England was that after about 1550 the mines in Germany were becoming less profitable. Thus the Augsburg bankers possibly hoped, although largely in vain, that richer and more easily-worked ores might be found elsewhere in Europe. The cause of the falling profits was that mining in Germany now faced competition from very rich mines which the Spanish had acquired in Central and South America. After the voyages of Columbus in the 1490s and the conquests of Mexico and Peru, completed in 1535, the Spanish were quick to plunder the wealth of the Aztec and Inca civilisations, and to discover where silver and gold could be mined. Large shipments of gold and silver began to cross the Atlantic during the 1530s, and by 1600, when this traffic reached a peak, Spain was importing 9,500,000 ounces of silver a year:[4] probably about ten times as much silver as all the mines of Europe were producing annually.

This massive import of bullion had much the same effect as the uncontrolled printing of bank notes would have. Spain experienced a rapid inflation, which influenced other countries and added to an already rising trend in prices and costs; in Saxony, prices rose by about 60 per cent between the 1530s and the 1590s.[5] Mining operations in Saxony would become more costly in about the same proportion, while the Spanish imports were keeping the price of silver at a low level.[6] It is not surprising, then, that the bankers of Augsburg were stimulated to look for cheaper sources of silver.

Thus, for example, there was German interest in the ores of copper and lead with traces of silver which existed in the English

4. Hamilton, *American Treasure*, p. 35.
5. *American Treasure*, pp. 206–9.
6. The situation is complicated by the fact that most European currencies suffered a succession of devaluations during the 16th century, i.e. the weight of silver in coins was reduced in relation to their nominal value. However, the price of wheat and many other commodities rose fast while the price of silver rose only slowly. See Braudel in *Cambridge Economic History of Europe*, 4, 1967, pp. 378–486.

lake counties, near Keswick. With the help of finance from the Haugs of Augsburg, the Mines Royal Company was set up in 1568, and worked these ores during the last three decades of the 16th century. This company had 13 of its 24 shares in English ownership, but the remaining 11 were held by the Haugs through their agent in England, Daniel Hochstetter. Skilled in assaying and smelting techniques, Hochstetter had first to experiment with various methods of refining the local ores in order to discover whether their tiny quantities of silver could be extracted economically. He tried ores from several districts – the Newlands valley, Borrowdale and Grasmere – and tested several smelting processes and combinations of processes. It was inevitable that some silver would be lost during extraction, and some would remain mixed with the copper and lead which was also produced, but Hochstetter hoped to discover which process gave the best return for the cost of the fuel and labour employed.

In one set of experiments, carried out in 1567, he investigated a process in which an ore or 'stone' which had already undergone a preliminary smelting was melted with lead and lead ore. During this operation, the silver was expected to become alloyed with the lead, from which it could be separated fairly easily. Hochstetter used six different mixtures of stone, lead and lead ore, with 'sundry ways tried in melting as we might continue the same with profit'. He set out the results of these trials with the quantities of ore and metal expressed in hundredweights (cs.), pounds (lbs.) and half-ounces (lots):[7]

10 cs. *stone* at 1 lot [of silver per hundredweight]   10 [lots]
  3 cs. *lead*
  4 cs. *lead ore*
  3 cs. *Grasmere glance ore* $4\frac{1}{2}$
                                                         ⎯⎯
                                                          $14\frac{1}{2}$ lots of silver
                                                         ⎯⎯

Out of which was made:
Lead. 314 lbs. at 2 lots [per cs.] $6\frac{1}{8}$
Stone. 13 cs. which was dried and brought to 160
  lbs. [crude copper] containing 2 lots per cs.   3
                                                         ⎯⎯
                                                          $9\frac{1}{8}$
                                                         ⎯⎯

7. Donald, *Elizabethan Copper*, p. 202.

The sensitivity of Hochstetter's assays, which could detect one part of silver in 5,000 parts of ore, using quite small samples, is most impressive. But the efficiency of the extraction process seems very poor. Less than half the silver in the 'stone' and the ore was concentrated in the lead, and a third was lost altogether. Smelting techniques which worked well with the ores found in Germany probably needed considerable modification before they could be applied to the poorer and rather different English ores.

Hochstetter's comments and figures were written up from his notebook as letters to his backers in Augsburg; it is very clear from the way they are set out, and from such phrases as '3 cs. stone at $1\frac{1}{2}$ lot the cs.', that his approach to his calculations was derived from accountancy. One is reminded that Hochstetter himself had come from one of the famous Augsburg merchant families, and so would naturally use the numerical methods familiar from commercial practice. His approach also seems to imply some belief in conservation of matter. If the process were perfected, all the silver in the original ore could be extracted – the apparent loss of silver was simply due to its becoming mixed with slag and other waste materials.

Besides making assays of the ores and their products, Hochstetter studied the cost of smelting in terms of fuel and wages. Thus, for example, one bucket or kibble of the mixed copper and lead ore from Caldbeck would cost, he thought, 11d. to dig from the mine, 3d. for carrying to the smelter and 14d. to extract the metals. Much of the latter sum was accounted for by the cost of fuel. So the cost of mining and processing 5,000 buckets of ore: that is, about 400 tons, was likely to be about £590. Hochstetter's tests suggested that the yields and revenues from this ore would be:[8]

30 [tons] of *lead* at 30/-	£ 45
2,187½ oz. of *silver* at 4/11	528
75 [cs.] of *copper* at 53/4	200
	——
	£773

So there should have been a reasonable profit, mainly because of the high value of the small quantities of silver in the ore. But through no fault of Hochstetter, the Mines Royal Company never sold

8. Donald, *Elizabethan Copper*, p. 206; note that 4/11 means 4 shillings and 11 pence (11d.).

sufficient metal to cover its costs during the time he was associated with it, and in 1574 its German backers went bankrupt. After that date, activity in the mines slowed down, and only small quantities of metal were produced. Then in 1602 the continuing un-satisfactory situation led to the appointment of a commission to look into the affairs of the company, and in the course of this investigation, a whole series of new figures was compiled to show the cost of operating the different mines and smelters. In addition, an attempt was made to assess the running costs of some of the machinery. At one mine there was an 'engine' – a water-wheel – which drove pumps and also served for lifting ore and spoil from the bottom of the mine. The cost of running this machine and of pumping water included 'reparation above the wheel, pump shafts, bolts, showing of staffs and like necessaries...', one shilling.[9] There were also payments for 'shoose and oil for the gudgeon at 16d. a week', and for a 'rope for the engine to draw up ore and dead stuff at 6d. a week'.

The literature of mining in the 16th century

Technical literature, in the sense of practical manuals and text-books, scarcely existed before 1450. The introduction of the printing-press brought about a radical change in technology simply by making such literature possible. Handbooks on mining and metals began to appear early in the 16th century; then, a little later, much more ambitious works on the subject were written, most notably by Georgius Agricola.

Agricola was the Latin pen-name of George Bauer (1494–1555), a physician who worked among the miners of Saxony and Bohemia. He came from Saxony himself, and was educated at the local university at Leipzig. His first job was to be master of a school in Zwickau, where he taught Greek and Latin, and wrote a book on Latin grammar. Around 1524 he went to Italy and studied medicine, chiefly at Bologna. His knowledge of Latin and his classical education made him very receptive to the Renaissance culture of Italy, and he quickly developed interests similar to those of the architect-engineers of the period. Thus we find him engaged in typically Renaissance studies which included a scholarly investigation of the weights and measures used by the Romans and Greeks. Based on information gleaned from many

9. Quoted by Donald, *Elizabethan Copper*.

Figure 25

Laboratory scale method of separating silver from gold – a typical illustration from Agricola's *De re metallica*. Various items of chemical equipment are illustrated. On the right is seen an assayer's balance such as Daniel Hochstetter must have used.

(Original published 1556; see English edition of Georgius Agricola, *De re metallica*, trans. Herbert Clark Hoover and Lou Henry Hoover, 1912; new edition, Dover Books, New York, *c.* 1950, p. 446)

classical authors, Agricola's book on this subject was published in 1533. Its close relationship to current architectural scholarship was shown when it was reprinted in 1552 as part of a new edition of Vitruvius.

Ancient authors had written less about metallurgy than about mathematics, and there was no Roman book on mining to correspond with Vitruvius on architecture. But Agricola read a wide range of Greek and Roman literature, noting every small reference to mining, minerals and metals. He noted the Latin technical terms which Roman authors used, because he wished to write in Latin about current mining technology. In some cases he had to devise new Latin terms for techniques which had been unknown to the Romans. He evidently believed that by writing about mining in a good Latin style he could convince learned men that here was a practical art worthy of their attention. The social status of Italian architects had been enhanced by their activities as scholars and mathematicians. Would not mining benefit in a similar way if there was a learned literature concerning it? Agricola argued that 'agriculture, architecture, and medicine are . . . counted amongst the number of honourable professions . . . mining ought not to be excluded from them'.[10]

Agricola's interest in mining had first been aroused when, on completing his medical studies, he began to practise as a physician in the recently-founded mining town of Joachimsthal in Bohemia. With Lorenz Bermannus, a local man who had also had a classical education, he began to tackle the problem of bringing the very practical art of the miners into the scope of Renaissance learning. How well he succeeded in this was affirmed by no less a person than Erasmus, who was clearly impressed by the scholarly style which Agricola brought to his highly technical subject. Erasmus, in fact, wrote the preface to Agricola's first book on mining, which was published in 1530 by the Froben press in Basle, where many works by Erasmus himself had been issued. This first book took the form of a dialogue in which Bermannus was portrayed interviewing two learned physicians about the mines and minerals of Germany.

In 1533, Agricola moved to Chemnitz in Saxony, where he lived for the rest of his life, eventually becoming burgomaster.

10. Agricola, *De re metallica*, Dover Books edn, p. 23. This version, translated in 1912 by Herbert Hoover (later President of the U.S.A.), with his wife, is a major source for the remainder of this chapter.

Here he wrote some half-dozen more books on mining and mineralogy, which appeared from 1544 onwards. His masterpiece was *De re metallica libri XII*: that is, 'twelve books on metals', which was published in 1556, just after his death.

Agricola's writings were careful and objective. He was a good observer, and described assaying and smelting processes with a minimum of 'controversial points of theory'. One author has said that in this respect 'Agricola was the herald of seventeenth century thought'.[11] The comment is an apt one, for in many ways Agricola's outlook and style was typical of the early 'scientific revolution'.

This point, combined with the evident importance of Agricola for the technical arts and 'science' in Germany, helps to underline the paradox of the apparent unfruitfulness of the scientific revolution in Germany. Agricola's approach was less influential than it might have been, because for many mining craftsmen his scholarly Latin was merely an obstacle to understanding. German translations were published, but some of them were of poor quality. The only author in the same field who might be compared with Agricola in style was an Italian, the mathematician Vanuccio Biringuccio, who travelled in Germany collecting material for a book on the metallurgical arts. He was influenced by Agricola's first book on mining, the dialogues with Bermannus, and Agricola in turn benefited from reading Biringuccio's *Pirotechnia* (1540).

The outlook of the miners

Although German miners in the 16th century clearly had a very different outlook from Agricola's, their attitudes are more difficult to document. Most of the information that is readily available was complied by people who, like Agricola, were not themselves either miners or craftsmen. One account concerning an individual miner which is often quoted, however, deals with a man who worked in the copper-mines of the Harz district. First encountered in his twenties and newly married, he lived at Eisleben in Saxony. He probably worked as a labourer, and seems to have been very poor. Two years later he moved to Mansfeld, not far away, but deeper into the mountains. Here the

11. Aitchison, *A History of Metals*, vol. *1*, p. 292.

rewards in mining were greater than in Eisleben; he was still poor, but in 1491 he was evidently rising in the world, for then he was elected to Mansfeld city council. By 1502 he had leased some mines to run on his own account. It was a five-year lease, but it was renewed in 1507, by which date he had become part-owner of six shafts and two furnaces. So it seems that an ordinary workman with some talent could prosper.

This particular miner is well known because his second son was Martin Luther, born at Eisleben in 1483. Martin attended the university at Erfurt, and after completing his course in 1505, he became a monk in the Augustinian house there. In this capacity he later went on to Wittenberg University in Saxony as a teacher; it was there that he developed his criticisms of the Church, and there in 1517 that he launched his attack on it.

The connection of Martin Luther with the mining industry was more than just the accident of his father's occupation; living in Saxony, he was not far from some of the most important mines, and the mining communities identified themselves closely with his teachings. Thus Agricola's personal acquaintances included two Lutheran pastors who wrote books on mining, partly with the aim of popularising Agricola's work. One was Christopher Entzelt (1520–86), whose book on metals, published in 1551, attracted the influence of Luther's friend Philip Melanchthon. The other was Johann Mathesius (1504–65), who had charge of a church at Joachimsthal. His comments on mining and metals appeared in a book of sermons called *Sarepta*, after a town mentioned in the Bible.[12] Mathesius compared this place to Joachimsthal because its Hebrew name, Zarephath, meant 'place of refining'. Another book of sermons by Mathesius, published in 1566, is of importance to historians because it contains the first extended biography of Luther. As a child, Luther had a good home and was well provided for, Mathesius said, because 'God blessed the mining industry'.[13]

Other pastors preached in this way, and there was evidently a tradition of sermons illustrated by mining and metallurgical information which continued into the 17th century.[14] There were even hymns written in this vein; Agricola had noted that the

12. This place was associated with Elijah; I Kings xvii, 9–10; Luke iv, 26.
13. Quoted by Schwiebert, *Luther and His Times*, p. 107.
14. Adams, *The Birth and Development of the Geological Sciences*, pp. 198–9.

miners 'lighten their long and arduous hours by singing, which is neither wholly untrained nor unpleasant'.[15] Luther himself wrote hymns and took immense pains over the musical settings of his German Mass. Indeed, he originated a musical tradition whose 'greatest exponent' was the incomparable J. S. Bach. And he said that whoever 'despises music, as do all the fanatics, does not please me. For music is a gift and largesse of God . . . Music drives away the devil and makes people happy'.[16]

Neither Luther nor Agricola said anything about the words of the miners' hymns and songs, but a hymn published in the 17th century spoke of a great mine-owner, 'born of David's line, a Lord of the whole land', who chose to go down and work in the mines himself. He broke through the rock in a shaft called:

> . . . little Bethlehem,
> looked for a gallery,
> and went to Jerusalem,
> . . . the gallery had
> treacherous stone in it,
> little ore could be seen,
> that was of rich content . . .[17]

This kind of identification of the mining communities with Lutheranism was reinforced on a theological level by Luther's doctrine of 'the priesthood of all believers', first put forward in 1520. This was an attack on the Church's notion that priests had a special 'vocation' or calling from God which people in other occupations did not share. According to Luther, every calling was of God, and a farmer or miner who tried to follow Christ in doing 'his work faithfully . . . is equal to the priest in God's sight. Each man, peasant or cleric, who helps his fellow man in Christian charity, is equally regarded by God's standards'.[18] So however naïve the hymn just quoted, which pictured Christ working in the mines, it did express a thought which was very characteristic of the Lutherans. The clergy needed to know Greek and Hebrew, Luther said, so that they could interpret the scrip-

15. *De re metallica*, pp. 99, 118.
16. Quoted by Schwiebert, *Luther and His Times*, p. 675; on the *Deutche Messe*, see Schwiebert, pp. 663–7; on Bach see Percy Scholes, *Companion to Music*, p. 590.
17. Quoted by Adams, *Geological Sciences*, p. 199.
18. Schwiebert, *Luther and His Times*, pp. 292, 451.

tures for the people, but that did not mean that they were any nearer to God than ordinary craftsmen or labourers.

Luther's idea of the priesthood of all believers grew out of his teachings about the Church and out of other purely theological doctrines. But in so far as it implied that a man's ordinary daily work could be pleasing to God, it had some similarity with the 'work ethic' of the Cistercian monks, which was discussed in chapter one. Since Luther had himself been a monk, he must have known something of the belief that manual work should play a part in monastic life. This was something which St Benedict had taught in the 6th century, and which had influenced most European monastic orders to some degree. A particular stress had been laid on this principle by the leaders of the Cistercian order, especially St Bernard of Clairvaux. Partly as a result of the high value they accorded to manual work, Cistercian monks had built mills, smelted iron and dug mines. Whether Luther knew very much about all this is doubtful, but he certainly 'venerated Bernard',[19] and his theology was influenced by Bernard's writings on St Paul. And although Luther despised the life led by most monks in his own day, he thought that if it was pursued in the spirit of St Bernard, monastic life could be of great value.

Apart from any similarities with Cistercian ideas, Luther's 'work ethic' had implications for Agricola's theories on the social status of mining. If manual work could be the work of God, then mining should be more highly valued. Agricola also wanted mining to be more highly regarded, but mainly in an academic way. He was a scholar with a Renaissance outlook, and he wanted the study of mining techniques to be recognised for its true worth by other scholars.

Thus it was men of learning for whom Agricola wrote; not miners. And it was for that reason that Mathesius found it necessary to tell the miners that he was running 'through the works of Agricola . . . looking for certain things that may be of interest to you'.[20] Here was a cultural gap which Mathesius felt the need to bridge. The degree of his success is uncertain, for by the end of the 16th century, the gap was being filled by a very different kind of technical literature the author of which was principally Paracelsus. These writings began to appear in print

19. Schwiebert, *Luther and His Times*, pp. 405–6.
20. Quoted by Adams, *Geological Sciences*, p. 198.

from the 1570s onwards – that is, more than thirty years after their author's death.

Paracelsus (1493–1541) was a German-speaking Swiss whose real name was Bombastus von Hohenheim; in the course of a turbulent life, he wandered through many of the German mining districts and other parts of eastern Europe. He is said to have served an apprenticeship in a mine as well as receiving a partial education in medicine, and he certainly worked for a time as an army surgeon. The high point of his career came when he performed an apparently miraculous cure for Johannes Froben, the famous Basle publisher associated with Agricola and Erasmus. On the strength of this he was allowed to lecture at Basle University for a year, until his abusive and controversial manner led to his expulsion. Paracelsus wrote extensively on a wide variety of technical subjects, but little of his work was published until after 1570. Then his books drew much attention, and by 1600 they were being widely read. In order to understand the appeal of his works, one need only refer to the many passages where he attacked established learning, like that of Aristotle, or the accepted authorities in medicine, 'who based all their arts simply upon their own opinions . . .'. He explained that this 'has incited us to write a special book concerning Alchemy, basing it not on men, but on Nature herself, and upon those virtues and powers which God, with His own finger, has impressed upon metals'.[21]

The comment about 'virtues and powers' reflects the influence of neo-Platonism, which had earlier enjoyed a renewed popularity in Italy. In other writings, Paracelsus claimed that his theories proceeded from 'the light of Nature'.[22] This too sounds neo-Platonic, but its general tone also coincided with the view of some of the more extreme Protestants who claimed that ordinary people, informed by an 'inner light', had as much access to God's truths as had a priest or a man of learning. This view arose partly from a distortion of Luther's doctrine of the priesthood of all believers, for where Luther had merely said that all vocations could be equally worthy, it was now being claimed that all men had equal access to knowledge, through inspiration, the inner light, and, in technical matters, through the intuition and experience acquired by craftsmen.

21. Waite, (ed.) *The Hermetical and Alchemical Works of Paracelsus*, I, pp. 72–3.
22. *Works of Paracelsus*, I, p. 20.

Such views were held by the Anabaptists and by some of the leaders of the Peasants' Revolt of 1524–5, who thought that ordinary people, with no theological training, could take the reform of Church and State into their own hands. Luther was appalled by this; he valued scholarship and was in many ways conservative in his approach to reform. But his sharp condemnation of the Peasants' Revolt led to much bitterness among people who had thought of him as their leader.

It was the persistence of these more extreme kinds of Protestant opinion which provided a receptive audience for the books of Paracelsus as they came from the presses at the end of the 16th century. There were plenty of people ready to be told that conventional learning had 'to have its ineptitude propped up and fortified by papal and imperial privileges',[23] and that knowledge of chemistry was 'graven … in the metals', and was to be acquired not from books, but by craftsmen as they worked, and through inspiration stimulated by experiment. Technical knowledge was the product of a spiritual process and of manual work, and did not arise from intellectual or scholarly researches.

Paracelsus wrote about the diseases of miners, but not about the mines themselves. His main interests were in medicine and chemistry. He had theories about salt, sulphur and mercury, the three chemical 'principles'; and he had opinions as to how the influence or virtue of the planets could act through metals. His ideas were thoroughly mixed up with alchemy, so for the modern reader it may seem disappointing that they should have had greater influence than the careful scholarship and the balanced empiricism of Agricola. But in contrast to Agricola's learned Latin style, Paracelsus wrote in the German vernacular, and in an idiom which touched the imagination and idealism of ordinary craftsmen. He identified himself with the 'lower social groups' and with some of their Protestant attitudes, although he himself was always nominally a Catholic. He was 'a man with Anabaptist sympathies, taking his stand with the oppressed'.[24]

Agricola had more in common with the intellectuals of Lutheranism than with the ordinary miners, and he lived as a highly respected citizen of the predominantly Lutheran mining town of Chemnitz. None the less, he remained staunchly Catholic, though his churchmanship was of a very different

23. *Works of Paracelsus*, I, p. 20.
24. Kearney, *Science and Change*, p. 114.
6

stamp to that of Paracelsus. In the 1520s he had written some tracts on religious topics.[25] He was at that time a critic of the papacy, and like his friend Erasmus he may have sympathised with Luther's early demands for reform. But with the widening breach between Luther and the Church, and in 1524 with the emergence of the Anabaptists, many of those who thought like Erasmus turned away. They disliked Luther's vehemence and apparent sacrifices of reason to faith, and wanted instead a moderate and tolerant Church which stressed morals more than mysticism.

But despite his disagreements with them, Agricola was greatly appreciated by the Lutheran leaders. When he died, one of them wrote to Luther's close friend, Philip Melanchthon, in very warm terms: 'I know that you loved the soul of this man, although in many of his opinions he . . . differed from our own. For he despised our Churches, and would not be with us in the Communion of the Blood of Christ . . . I have always admired the genius of this man, so distinguished in our sciences and in the whole realm of Philosophy – yet I wonder at his religious views.'[26] Unfortunately, this admiration did not give Agricola's books an influence as great as the writings of Paracelsus.

Developments after 1600: Germany and England

Some of the trends described in the preceding pages came to a head in what has been termed 'the general crisis of the seventeenth century'.[27] The Thirty Years War (1618–48) in central Europe and the Civil War in England (1642–9) were merely the best known in a series of conflicts which arose from religious as well as political causes. To the devastation of war was added a series of plagues which killed many people in Italy and Germany from the 1620s onwards; according to one authoritative estimate, the German lands as a whole lost 40 per cent of their population in the three decades up to 1650.[28]

During this period of war and other disruption, there was a significant degree of similarity between English and German ideas about technical progress. German refugees came to England

25. Agricola, *De re metallica*, pp. viii, 605.
26. Agricola, *De re metallica*, pp. x–xi.
27. Trevor-Roper, *Religion, the Reformation and Social Change*, p. 46.
28. *Cambridge Economic History of Europe*, *4*, p. 41.

and made common cause with Puritans who fought under Cromwell against the English King. They brought with them an interest in chemistry, medicine and agriculture, and an enthusiasm for the writings of Paracelsus. The latter, translated into English, had a special appeal for certain groups of people, particularly apothecaries who could make direct use of medical remedies he had suggested.

But apart from limited technical reasons for studying Paracelsus, there was the imaginative appeal of his mystical approach to knowledge. At this time of upheaval, when rational order in human affairs seemed to have broken down, the 'mystical, anti-rational aspect' of Paracelsus aroused a warm response in many people's minds, and there was a considerable enthusiasm for studies of medicine and chemistry along the lines he had laid down.[29]

There has been considerable confusion among 20th-century historians of science who have attempted to assess these developments. Some have stressed the persistence of alchemy among the followers of Paracelsus, and have observed the mystical attitudes of many English Puritans and their German contemporaries. On these grounds they have dismissed the work of these people as non-scientific, and have tended to minimise the contributions to knowledge made by such Germans as Rudolph Glauber, Joachim Becher and G. E. Stahl, who will be mentioned again below, and by J. B. van Helmont, a Flemish Catholic who supported a Paracelsian approach to chemistry. Neglect of these contributions has supported the mistaken view that Germany was largely by-passed by the 'scientific revolution'.

Other historians, though, have noted the genuinely technical content of work done by English Puritans who were interested in Paracelsus. They have equated this technical content with 'science', and have argued that the Puritans provided much of the leadership for the 'scientific revolution' in England. The aim of historians who put this point of view, most notably R. K. Merton,[30] is usually to support a more general argument about a 'Protestant Ethic' which is alleged to have originated with John Calvin a little after Luther's time. This 'ethic' is said to have influenced Dutch businessmen as well as English

29. Rattansi, 'Paracelsus in the Puritan Revolution', in *Ambix*, 2, pp. 24–32.
30. See his *Science, Technology and Society*.

Puritans, and is supposed to have had a beneficial effect on commerce, industry and technology as well as on science. The views of Marx, Weber and Tawney on this subject are well known; and so, more recently, is the very convincing criticism of their case offered by Hugh Trevor-Roper.[31] Among historians of technology, Friedrich Klemm has been particularly emphatic about Calvinist influence.[32]

These opposing points of view among historians are both usually presented in a misleading way, by the misapplication of modern definitions of 'science' to 17th-century thought. The Paracelsians were studying nature in quite a different way from that adopted by Galileo and Descartes, but not even Galileo, the most modern-minded thinker of the period, can be accurately described as a 'scientist'. His natural philosophy and our science, however similar, were by no means identical in aims and method.

The argument about the 'Protestant Ethic' is also misleading. The work ethic which has been mentioned elsewhere in this book was by no means the original creation of Protestants, let alone Puritans, and Calvinists played no unique role in the development of technology. With regard to the growth of science, indeed, continental Roman Catholics such as Galileo, Torricelli, Fr Mersenne, Fr Gassendi, René Descartes and the Abbé Mariotte contributed as much as any group of Protestants, even when full weight is given to the work of the Paracelsians. And as was implied in the previous chapter, the case for a constructive Jesuit contribution to the 'scientific revolution' is at least as good as the case for a Puritan one. During the 17th and 18th centuries, Jesuit efforts in education helped to spread knowledge of new discoveries, and helped also in the exchange of technical information between Europe and the Far East. Jesuits taught Copernican astronomy in China, they helped to start a clock factory in Peking, and they sent back to Europe accounts of Chinese porcelain manufacture and engineering which were not without technological significance.

Social ideals for education and technology

What seems to have been especially distinctive among 17th-century Protestants was not so much the 'work ethic' as a

31. Trevor-Roper, *Religion, the Reformation and Social Change.*
32. See *A History of Western Technology*, pp. 191–7.

socially-orientated approach to the use of technology. Here Calvinists were considerably less important than Lutherans and various other sects from eastern Europe. Their ideal was that the practical arts should be used for the welfare of mankind; they wanted to develop a 'philanthropic' science.[33] And the sense of work being a worthy vocation grew out of this deeper idea of helping humanity.

The wars and devastation of the period emphasised the need for this approach, as is illustrated in the career of Rudolph Glauber (1604–70), a German who travelled widely in Europe during the war period. He wrote about chemistry and medicine, discovered the medicinal properties of sodium sulphate (Glauber's salt) and became interested in the works of Paracelsus. The poverty of war-torn Germany impelled him to study the practical arts in relation to the reconstruction of trade and agriculture and the better use of the metals from German mines. With regard to agriculture, he was interested in the use of saltpetre as a fertiliser; 'fruits will then ripen much earlier and have a much pleasanter taste than if stinking cow-manure had been used . . .'. Elsewhere he commented that although Germany had many mines, it lacked 'experienced persons who know how to use them properly, and then to find timber and sufficient of all other necessities'. This indicates how far the German metal industries had declined during the war, as does Glauber's comment that unworked metal produced in Germany was being exported to Holland, France and Venice. There it was used in the manufacture of various goods and materials, some of which were being bought back by Germans at greatly enhanced prices. Germany had all the raw materials it needed for any sort of manufacturing. 'Why are we so bad at it?' Glauber exclaimed.[34]

Glauber's writings on 'Germany's welfare' are filled with a concern to help his fatherland. He discussed alchemy, quoting Paracelsus. A large number of his ideas were highly speculative, but his aims were not in doubt. Many other people at this time studied technical subjects with similar objectives. Among them there grew up a sense of the importance of useful knowledge, and, accompanying this, an appreciation of the need for new kinds of education, in which practical subjects were given more attention. One of the leading exponents of the ideal of practical education

33. Ravetz, *Scientific Knowledge and its Social Problems*, pp. 434–6.
34. Quoted by Klemm, *A History of Western Technology*, pp. 186–8.

was J. A. Komenský (1592–1671), better known by his Latin name, Comenius. He was a minister and bishop of the 'Unitas Fratrum', a small sect with ideas somewhat like the Lutherans', but with a longer history. Known in more modern times as the Moravian Church, this body had been formed in Bohemia during the 1450s, and had survived in that part of Europe until 1621, when the advance of Catholic armies during the Thirty Years War almost wiped it out. Before 1621, Comenius worked in a school at Fulnec[35] in Moravia, but with invasion impending there, he fled to Leszno in Poland where he again took up his work as a teacher.

Comenius believed that knowledge, mastered and shared, could change the world. Hence the aim of much of his work was to improve education. He also believed in the unity of all knowledge and wrote books of an encyclopedic kind to illustrate this. Knowledge was to be gained both from the study of nature and from the scriptures. In a treatise on 'Natural philosophy reformed by divine light' (the significant title of its English translation), he argued that science should be based on experience, reason and scripture; in particular, he thought, the creation of the world as it was described in Genesis gave support to the ideas upon which Paracelsus had founded his chemistry.

The books which Comenius wrote on subjects connected with education and the extension of useful knowledge attracted wide attention. They were welcomed enthusiastically by English Puritans, and were published in English translation from 1631 onwards. England and Sweden were the countries most admired by the Comenians – Sweden was thought well of because its military power was the most effective force on the Protestant side during the Thirty Years War. In addition, Swedish mines and industries were developing in an exemplary way under the management of Louis de Geer, a Calvinist banker who himself greatly admired Comenius and sought to put his educational ideas into practice. England, a country where the Protestant cause seemed secure, and where Protestant refugees from eastern Europe were settling, was also admired because it had been the home of Francis Bacon (1561–1626), the most eloquent and influential of all the advocates of 'philanthropic' science and socially useful technology.

35. The Fulneck Moravian settlement near Leeds was named after this place.

Although Bacon had died in 1626, his ideas were studied with renewed interest in the 1630s and 40s. He had believed that advances in knowledge would lead inevitably to an improvement in the practical arts by which the lot of man was eased. But while Bacon, like Paracelsus, Glauber and the Comenians, gave an enlarged philosophic scope to the practical knowledge of the artisan, unlike them he did not encourage the wilder forms of magic and Paracelsian mysticism.

The link between Englishmen who admired Bacon, and eastern Europeans like Comenius, was provided by Samuel Hartlib (1592–1662) and John Dury (1596–1680), both of whom had lived at Elbing in Polish Prussia until forced to leave by the advance of the Catholic armies. Hartlib came to England in 1628 and for two years ran a school on Baconian principles in Chichester. It was not a success, and he soon moved to London, where he applied himself to helping refugees from Germany and eastern Europe. One of these was Johann Christoph de Berg, an inventor who had worked on mine-drainage problems in Moravia. Dury meanwhile travelled widely in Europe, campaigning for the unity of all Protestants, and carrying messages for Hartlib. Dury's function was partly to oil the wheels of Hartlib's vast European correspondence. The latter wrote so many letters and his contacts were so wide that he became known as 'the great intelligencer of Europe'. He put himself forward as a universal secretary who would link good men in many countries in an 'invisible college'. This body would improve agriculture, teach languages, forward inventions, compile statistics, educate the poor, and generally work for the good of all.[36] Much could be achieved in this way if a united, tolerant Protestant society could be established. Hartlib's ideas revolved around Baconian 'science' and Protestant unity, but perhaps his greatest concrete achievement consisted in the promotion of many 'manuals of general improvement'. As a result of his encouragement, several important books were published, including works by John Milton on education, and by William Petty on population statistics. Many other proposals for the improvement of the country's welfare were discussed among Hartlib's friends, including 'A short and ready way For the extraordinary Facilitation & Dispatch of RECKON-

36. Trevor-Roper, *Religion, the Reformation and Social Change*, pp. 249–251.

INGS. By meanes of Two or Three NEW DECIMAL COINES'.[37] This idea, put forward in 1655 or 56, was to replace the shilling, penny and farthing with coins equal to a tenth, hundredth and thousandth of a pound.

The campaign for educational reform supported by Hartlib and many of his Puritan friends came to a head when Parliament debated the proposals in 1653. Among those outside Parliament who were provoked into discussing the question was John Webster, a former chaplain in Cromwell's armies. Webster's ideas were less realistic than Hartlib's, but well illustrate the educational ideals of the more radical Puritans. In a series of sermons preached in 1653, Webster criticised the traditional teaching of the universities. 'The Apostles and Disciples', he said, 'bad us beware of Philosophy, which is after the rudiments of the World, and not after Christ.' Philosophy at the universities is carnal and frivolous; 'they have atomised the unity and simplicity of . . . truth . . . accumulating a farranginous heap of divisions and sub-divisions, distinctions, limitations, axioms, positions and rules, [which] do chanel & bottle up the water of life . . .'.[38] In the study of 'natural philosophy', Webster argued, Aristotle's works should be forgotten, except for his 'History of Animals', but new material should be introduced from the works of Descartes, Paracelsus, van Helmont and Gassendi. Webster seemed to be unaware of any possible incompatibilities in the syllabus which this recommendation would produce!

In all this, he emphasised, the knowledge to be encouraged was that which could be used for 'the general good and benefit of mankind, especially for the conservation and restauration of the health of man'.[39] At the beginning of another of his works, *The Saints' Guide*, Webster actually said that learning by itself was a sin, 'but if it be sanctified . . . the providential wisdom of God doth . . . make use of it for the good of his People'. So, for example, academic mathematics was to be condemned, but the universities should teach accountancy, the mathematics of navigation, and the geometry which a carpenter might use.

But the stress on useful and practical studies was made most fully in relation to the chemical arts. Students should 'learn to inure their hands to labour, and put their fingers to the furnaces,

37. Quoted by Charles Webster, in *Nature*, 229, 1971, p. 463.
38. John Webster, *Academiarum examen*, pp. 5, 12, 14.
39. *Academiarum examen*, p. 19.

that the mysteries discovered by *Pyrotechny*, and the wonders brought to light by *Chymistry*, may be rendered familiar unto them; that so they may not grow proud with the brood of their own brains, but truly be taught by manual operation, and ocular experiment, that so they may not be sayers but doers. . . .'[40] Webster went on to talk about 'nature's hidden secrets', and he was clearly reflecting the Paracelsian view that knowledge was to be acquired through the light of nature, which was made accessible in the course of working at a trade or making a practical experiment.

Hartlib was 'not sympathetic with the widespread puritan antagonism to secular learning'[41] which people like Webster expressed, but he did share the ideal of providing a more practical form of education. To some extent this ideal was realised with the foundation of a college at Durham in 1657, based on plans made by some of Hartlib's associates, and made effective by the personal support of Cromwell. The college was to teach languages, chemistry, agriculture, medicine and the practical arts. Language teaching was to be based on the methods of Comenius and there was a workshop for teaching the practical subjects. The college was forced to close after the death of Cromwell in 1659: that is, after only about eighteen months of operation. But its ideals survived to some degree in the Dissenters' Academies of the late 17th and 18th centuries; and the general emphasis on practical and useful sciences was shared to a limited extent by the Royal Society, chartered in 1662.

Since much of the impetus for these ideals concerning practical education had come from eastern Europe, it is not surprising to find a similar educational movement developing there. The ideas of Comenius were taken up with enthusiasm by the Pietists, a group within the Lutheran churches which, from the 1670s onwards, emphasised a 'religion of the heart' and the inward spiritual life. One of the Pietist leaders, August Francke (1663–1727), was closely involved with the foundation of the university of Halle in 1693–4 and became a professor there. Halle was the first German university 'to introduce studies in the sciences on a really large scale',[42] and Francke's former students founded

40. *Academiarum examen*, pp. 105–6.
41. Charles Webster (ed.), *Samuel Hartlib*, p. 3.
42. Merton, *Science, Technology and Society*, p. 125; also Klemm, *A History of Western Technology*, p. 266.

secondary schools which taught practical subjects at Halle (1708), Berlin (1747), and other places. The teaching of science at Halle also influenced its adoption soon after at other universities, of which Göttingen is one example.

But as with other 17th-century movements which emphasised practical education, abstract mathematical studies were often suspect at Halle; the rationalism of the 'scientific revolution' was sometimes regarded as irreligious; and there was a tendency to adopt a somewhat spiritual view of chemistry and the practical arts. The first professor of chemistry at Halle, appointed in 1693, was G. E. Stahl (1660–1734). He had believed in alchemy while in his twenties, but although he became more sceptical later, his phlogiston theory of combustion is regarded by many historians as one of the last phases of 'pre-scientific' chemistry. The phlogiston theory was of considerable importance in the 18th century, however, when it affected the ideas which most chemists held about the processes of burning.

The distrust of too much abstract science which was sometimes expressed at Halle was also shown towards Christian von Wolff (1679–1754). A friend and follower of Leibniz, Wolff was one of the leaders of German rationalism. But he lost his professorship at Halle because of his rationalist views, and in 1723 was banished from Prussia. Happily, though, he was able to return in 1740.

Social ideals or mechanical philosophy?

If social and religious idealism has predominated in this chapter over any technical analysis of what was actually achieved in the practical arts of this period, it is perhaps because the ideals which have been mentioned had little practical effect. Their most concrete expression was in the realm of education. Chemistry was of central interest, but historians of this subject differ in their estimate of how much it developed. Other practical arts evolved slowly, and the people who have been mentioned here often had more to do with spreading knowledge than with developing it. Agricola in 1556 portrayed mine machinery such as pumps, hoists and ore-crushers which were already very sophisticated. In the succeeding century such machines were more widely adopted, especially in Britain, but few further inventions appear to have been made in this field until the end of the 17th century.

Thus, during the war-stricken years of the mid-17th century, the range of subjects discussed by English Puritans and their German contemporaries reflects intended directions for technical progress rather than anything invented or built. But there is a sharp and significant contrast to be drawn between these intentions and the kind of technical progress into which the Italians and Frenchmen of the 'scientific revolution' put their best efforts. In the northern lands, where Comenian influence was important, chemistry, medicine, agriculture and certain social arts were given greatest stress. Indeed, the specially valuable feature of this approach was that the relationship of technical and social problems was kept in sight. The 'social arts' which were emphasised included not only education itself but also modern languages and statistics. Hartlib believed that governments should have proper statistical information about population and trade; with Hartlib's encouragement Petty estimated the population of Ireland (chapter four) and used official information about deaths in London to try to decide how many people lived there, and whether the number was increasing.

The difference in emphasis between Italy and France and the north had a great deal to do with prevailing ideas about the social status of technology. In Italy the most respected of the practical arts were those which could be brought within the scope of scholarship or mathematical learning – architecture, machines, hydraulics. This Agricola tried to do for mining; and this is what architects and architect-engineers in Italy and France largely succeeded in doing. But in the north, over-sophisticated mathematics and even Agricola's scholarship did not really help to increase the status of the practical arts. The work of craftsmen, miners or assayers came to be valued in its own right. Such men were regarded as having a worthy vocation; and there was much respect for the insight and knowledge which only their experience could provide. This attitude was particularly valuable in relation to chemistry and metallurgy, fields in which mathematics and classical scholarship were of little relevance, and where only long experience and careful practical work could yield an increase in knowledge. So the chemical arts developed rapidly in Germany, while in Italy and France they were relatively neglected.

It is perhaps not surprising, therefore, that there turned out to be almost total opposition between the mathematical view of technology which accompanied the south European 'scientific revolution', and the philanthropic, social view in the north. At first sight it seems that some common social objectives ought to have been possible; there seems to be no reason why mathematically-inclined engineers should not have been moved by social ideals in carrying out their work. But to apply mathematics consistently to the world, one had to take a selective and deliberately partial view of the world. The technical and social aspects of human problems could not be seen together in their wholeness, because the very power and effectiveness of the mathematical approach depended upon the exclusion of the messy personal and social factors which cannot be measured. And while this did not matter very much for an engineer whose job was to design bridges or pumps, too much concentration on this kind of engineering led to a complete neglect of more socially orientated branches of technology.

This contrast between attitudes in different parts of Europe becomes more concrete and specific when one compares the works of Galileo with those of Comenius, Hartlib or Glauber. Galileo's discussion of technical matters is far more progressive and 'modern' than anything to be found in the northern writers. It was Galileo's hard-headed, 'no-nonsense' practicality rather than Hartlib's idealistic educational or agricultural schemes which future generations developed most successfully. Galileo wrote about machines and he applied mathematics to practical problems, but he never spoke of the humanitarian ends which could be achieved with the aid of the practical arts. He made a careful and brilliant analysis of the advantages to be gained by the use of machines, but in one case it ended with the conclusion that if a machine allowed eight men to be replaced by one horse, then that was good because it was cheaper – not because the men could be more happily employed elsewhere, nor because of any other benefits that would accrue to them.

Perhaps this is to cast Galileo in a role which he does not deserve. It is none the less true, however, that he stood for an ideal very different from that of 'philanthropic' science, and that from about this time, and among his followers, technology began to take a different course from the one which the northerners advocated. The woolly-minded, mystical approach of Comenius and his associates was effectively overwhelmed by the more rigorous thought and the more successful treatment of practical problems developed by Galileo. But perhaps only Bacon in this period managed to combine hard realism with compassion.

6

The State and technical progress: 1660–1770

French policies under Colbert
'Seven or eight years ago I showed to Monsieur Colbert an engine which I had built . . . It worked as follows: a tiny quantity of gunpowder, about a thimbleful, was able to raise some 1,600 lb. . . . with a moderate and steady power. Four or five servants, whom Monsieur Colbert ordered to pull the rope attached to the engine, were quite easily lifted into the air.'[1]

So wrote Christian Huygens in 1686, describing experiments which have already been discussed here in chapter four. The incident illustrates the close interest in science shown by one of the most important ministers in the French government, Jean Baptiste Colbert.

Colbert served Louis XIV as *Contrôleur général des finances* from 1661 until his death in 1683, and in this office he had a general responsibility for the economic welfare of France. A problem which concerned him particularly was the inadequacy of French shipping in relation to the huge expansion of overseas trade which some nations were enjoying, and he seized every opportunity for making improvements not only in the number and size of ships, but also in the training of their officers, in the preparation of charts, and in the art of navigation.

Colbert probably first became interested in Huygens's work because of a possibility that pendulum clocks designed by Huygens might be adapted for use as chronometers on ships. These would have been of the greatest value in navigation, because they would have provided an easy way of determining longitude. But despite many ingenious designs and much experiment, Huygens was not, in the end, successful in his attempts to make a chronometer for use at sea.

1. Quoted by Klemm, *A History of Western Technology*, p. 219.

For Colbert, though, navigation was just one of many practical subjects where mathematics and science seemed potentially useful to the State. For this reason he encouraged mathematical and experimental studies in France as a matter of government policy. Colbert knew that in London the Royal Society had been chartered in 1662, and that one of its aims was to try to improve trades and the practical arts. In 1666, he founded a somewhat similar body in Paris, the *Académie Royale des Sciences*. Huygens was well known in France, although his home was in Holland, and Colbert encouraged him to take office in this body. Huygens accordingly did so, and 'was indisputably the one who chiefly guided the affairs of the Académie'.[2] From 1666 until 1681 he lived almost continuously in Paris, returning home to The Hague only for short visits.

In most respects this was in no way remarkable, for Huygens was the son of a diplomat, and the family had been used to living away from home. Descartes had been a regular visitor to his father's house; there were many family friends in Paris. But as the policies of Louis XIV and Colbert developed, they became increasingly hostile to Holland, and Huygens was criticised to some degree for appearing to help an enemy.

The point which was the greatest cause of tension between France and Holland was the pre-eminence of Dutch shipping. Much of France's trade was being carried in Dutch vessels, and it was felt that the prosperity of the country was being endangered by the concentration of so much traffic in Dutch hands. In 1669 Colbert himself drew up a memoir to underline the point. He estimated that European owners altogether possessed about 20,000 ocean-going ships – that is, ships of 60 tons burden or more. Of these, 15,000–16,000 were owned by the Dutch, 3,000–4,000 by the English and only about 500 belonged to French owners. Colbert believed that there was little scope for increasing the total volume of sea-borne trade, so if France was to increase the size of her merchant fleets, as was necessary for her prosperity, the size of the Dutch fleet had to be reduced. Commerce was a form of warfare, and the Dutch were the principal enemy. Whatever Huygens could teach the French about navigation would be an asset here; with regard to shipbuilding, Colbert persuaded a number of Dutch carpenters to work in French shipyards and teach the local craftsmen by their example.

2. Bell, *Christian Huygens*, p. 61.

He commissioned a scientific analysis of hulls of different shapes with a view to finding the best combination of factors relating to speed, manoeuvrability and the positions of gun-ports. In addition, he founded schools of naval construction at Brest and Rochefort, and at the same ports established academies for training naval officers (a three-year course) and artillery officers. Rochefort and Dieppe were also given schools of hydrography. Thus technical education played a major part in naval policy.

Another aim of Colbert's was to promote the formation of trading companies. In 1670, he was able to claim that by competing with the Dutch for trade between France and the West Indies, these companies were depriving the Dutch of eight or ten million livres a year (the equivalent of something like £2 million a year in modern currency).

Huygens was far more interested in mathematics than in national rivalries, and Paris provided him with the best available environment in which to study. But he continued to live in Paris even when Colbert's policies led to war between France and Holland in 1672. 'Huygens could have secured a position of eminence under the Prince of Orange at this time, but he had a deep repugnance for political activity and remained in Paris, suspected by some, but protected throughout by the minister Colbert. It is not surprising, therefore, that he came in for some criticism from his fellow countrymen.'[3] And although Huygens returned to Holland in 1681 as a result of ill-health, he only ceased to be welcome in Paris after the death of Colbert in 1683, and after official toleration of Protestants and Jews was ended in 1685 by the Revocation of the Edict of Nantes.

Colbert's policies for the economic prosperity of France had far-reaching implications for the whole internal economy of the country. There was an effort to promote new industries and to reorganise existing ones. An edict of 1674 forced all trades to be administered by guilds, on which taxes were levied, and which had to enforce regulations about book-keeping, company formation and apprenticeships. Many businessmen hated Colbert for his interference, but others recognised his fair dealing and genuine support for their work, and called him 'the protector of merchants'.[4]

Amongst Colbert's most successful and lasting work for the

3. Bell, *Christian Huygens*, p. 61.
4. Cole, *Colbert*, vol. 1, pp. 360–62.

French economy was the improvement of inland transport. He initiated several small road-building projects, but no funds were available for roads after the start of the Dutch war in 1672, and it was with river and canal transport that most was done. France was well endowed with naturally navigable rivers, which had been extensively used from a very early date, but by building weirs and locks, by digging new channels for some lengths of river, and by dredging others, it was now made possible for sizeable boats to navigate the upper reaches of streams previously impassable. Work of this kind was undertaken on the Rivers Seine, Aube, Loire, Rhône, Marne, Somme and several others, and the Orleans Canal was made between 1679 and 1692 to provide a link between the Loire and the Seine.

But all these schemes were on a very small scale compared with the project to build a 'canal of the two seas', which would be some 175 miles long and would link a river which flowed into the Atlantic with one flowing into the Mediterranean. By this means, traffic for Mediterranean ports would be saved the long journey via Gibraltar, and the Dutch would lose even more of their sea-borne trade. The idea of such a canal had long been discussed, but it became possible only when Pierre-Paul Riquet demonstrated how water could be supplied to the canal's summit-level, which was about 600 feet above sea-level. Riquet performed experiments to test the feasibility of his ideas, and eventually designed a water-supply system which included a large impounding reservoir and water channels extending for some miles.

Riquet wrote to Colbert about his scheme in 1662, suggesting that the Crown should buy the land needed for the canal and finance its buildings; when it was finished, he would operate the waterway and maintain it with money raised in tolls. Colbert greatly approved of the scheme, not only for its economic value, but as a monument to French achievement under Louis XIV. With this in mind, he wrote to Riquet stressing that the works should be built to the highest standards.[5] Riquet certainly did build well, and proved himself also an expert in organisation, for at times he was using a labour force of nearly 10,000 men. About a third of the cost was borne by the Crown, about a fifth by Riquet himself, and the rest by the provincial authorities. The

5. Cole, *Colbert*, vol. I, p. 381.

canal was completed in 1681, and was soon carrying a considerable traffic. But the cost of trans-shipping cargoes from sea-going ships to canal boats prevented it from becoming a real alternative to the sea route via Gibraltar.

Developments in England

It was another century before England had a waterway which could compare with the Languedoc Canal, as the 'canal of the two seas' was more properly called, but contemporary with the improvement of navigable rivers under Colbert, there were comparable, if smaller, river-schemes being promoted in England. Shortly after the Restoration, Parliament passed Acts to allow a number of small rivers to be made navigable – the Stour in Worcestershire (1662), the Medway (1665), the Wiltshire Avon passing through Bath (1665) and others.[6] But after 1665, few further river-improvement schemes were begun until the end of the century. Then in 1699 there was the important scheme based on the River Aire to link the Yorkshire towns of Leeds and Wakefield with the sea at Hull. The Trent was made more effectively navigable up to Burton, and a link with Derby followed. In 1720, an Act was passed to make the Rivers Mersey and Irwell navigable up to Manchester.

There were several similar projects at this time, and altogether a great deal was done during the two or three decades before 1730. The period was one of vigorous material progress in other ways as well. The output of tin from the mines of Cornwall was rising fast, and the smelting of Cornish copper, previously a very small operation, was increasing even faster. This in turn helped to stimulate the improvement of pumps for use in mines. From 1712, Newcomen's engines were available for this purpose, but these machines found their most extensive applications in the coalfields where fuel was cheap. By 1733, there were 70 or 80 Newcomen engines in Britain – about six in Cornwall, 50 at coal mines in the Midlands and North, and others elsewhere.[7] By the 1730s also, Abraham Darby's coke-fired blast furnaces, first used in 1709, had helped to establish Shropshire as a major iron-producing region.

The river navigation which linked Derby with the Trent was

6. Willan, *River Navigation in England*, appendix.
7. Allen, in *Newcomen Society Transactions*, 42, 1969–70, pp. 169–90.

surveyed by an engineer named George Sorocold, a central figure in other improvements of the period. He was one of the engineers for the construction of Liverpool's first dock (*c.* 1709–20), and before that had gained a reputation for the installation of piped-water systems in many provincial towns. Like similar water-supply schemes in Paris, Sorocold's installations used water-wheels to pump water out of rivers into a cistern, from where it was distributed to the basement kitchens of individual houses.[8] Towns where Sorocold installed waterworks of this kind included Derby, Leeds, Norwich, Portsmouth, Sheffield and Newcastle in the 1690s, with the famous London Bridge water-works following in 1701, and a smaller scheme at Bridgenorth in 1702. His partner in many of these projects was John Hadley, who in 1699 became engineer for the scheme to make the River Aire navigable to Leeds.

These water-supply schemes were usually operated by private companies, and at this time served only small parts of the larger towns. In London, apart from the London Bridge waterworks, there was the New River Company which brought water into the town from Hertfordshire by means of a canal constructed in the 17th century, and yet another company had a Newcomen-type steam engine at York Buildings near the Strand. The latter engine served houses in an area which not long before had been mostly green fields separating the Cities of London and West-minster. Lincolns Inn Fields and Covent Garden had been built up in early 17th-century town-planning schemes, but now digni-fied squares and streets were extending farther to the north and west, around the new churches of St George's, Bloomsbury (1720) and St-Martin-in-the-Fields (1721). Previous to that, the orderly rebuilding of the City after the Great Fire of 1666, and the completion of St Paul's around 1710, had likewise added to the Londoner's sense of prosperity and well-being.

But a venture which was less in the public eye, though more significant for the future, was a water-powered silk-twisting mill at Derby. Sorocold had built a water-wheel for it in 1702, and then in 1717 he was involved in extending and adding to it. By this time it belonged to John Lombe, a man who had experienced the early difficulties of the scheme, and had travelled to Italy to look at the silk-twisting mills being used there. By 1721, the

8. Williamson, 'George Sorocold of Derby', in *Derbyshire Archaeological and Historical Journal*.

Derby silk-mill was a success, and soon there were several similar establishments in Derbyshire and Staffordshire.

Much of what took place during this period of rapid technical change must be understood in terms of the discussions about technology which took place in England during the 1640s and 50s. In the next decade, too, lofty objectives concerning the improvement of trades and manufactures were discussed in the Royal Society, but whether this body provided any real stimulus to

Figure 26

Fodder crops in the 17th and 18th centuries. A hay-barn built in 1775 in the Yorkshire Pennines; and crop plants typical of those regularly sown in the Midlands and south-east England from 1640 onwards. Left to right, the plants are Cocksfoot, Meadow Fescue, Rye-grass, Sainfoin, and two kinds of Clover.

the practical arts is difficult to assess. However, the discussions of the Civil War period definitely had some influence. For example, agriculture was a particular interest of Samuel Hartlib; while he was encouraging its study in England, Royalists fleeing from Cromwell's rule travelled the continent, observing agricultural techniques, and thinking of applying them to their own lands at home. A major problem in English agriculture earlier in the 17th century had been that a lack of winter feed severely limited the number of sheep and cattle which could be kept. Travellers in the Low Countries saw clover and other legumes being sown to provide fodder crops, and also improved strains of grass, such as cocksfoot, rye-grass and meadow fescue. Clover made good hay for animals and added to the fertility of the soil (by nitrogen fixation); the increased herds of cattle produced more manure and so provided a more effective re-cycling of organic material. The theory of all this was not understood, but the improvements to both soil fertility and cattle-rearing were readily appreciated, and proved to be particularly effective in East Anglia. Thus, 'at the beginning of the eighteenth century, improvement was already much more widespread than we once believed'.[9] Several people introduced these crops to England and began to import Dutch clover seed – the best-known of them being Sir Richard Weston, who was in the Low Countries in 1644. Hartlib's interest was immediately aroused, and he too made enquiries about the continental fodder crops and helped to spread knowledge of them.

This was a period when the English were learning fast from apparently less backward European countries – from Italy about silk-twisting, from France about canals, and from the Low Countries about agriculture. There were also the locally-invented steam engines and iron-making processes. And the net result was that already, in the first decades of the 18th century, England was probably the wealthiest country in Europe in relation to its size,[10] although France, with three times the population, was more powerful. To put it in a somewhat different perspective, England at this time was wealthier than almost all the so-called developing countries of the 1970s. The criterion of 'per capita income', which modern economists have estimated for early 18th-century England,[11] suggests that prosperity then was at least *twice* as great as for most of modern Africa or Asia.

The mood of the improvers in England

The authors of travel-diaries in England at this time, such as

9. Chambers and Mingay, *The Agricultural Revolution*, p. 61.
10. Landes, *The Unbound Prometheus*, p. 13.
11. Deane, *The First Industrial Revolution*, p. 6. Of course, some countries, such as India, were little better off in 1970 than in 1700, and may even have been poorer; see chapter nine below.

Celia Fiennes (1698) and Daniel Defoe (1720s), recorded a
wide range of industrial activity, including coal-mining in Yorkshire and the silk mill at Derby. But river navigation, water-
supply projects and civic improvements – new houses, roads and
churches – probably attracted the most general attention. The
progress being made was obvious and visible, but there was also
much cause for dissatisfaction. In the 1730s, roads were still very
bad throughout most of the country, and there were a number of
delays about building the new bridge over the Thames at
Westminster which was eventually begun in 1739. So there was a
considerable need for public works of many kinds; and the lack
of skilled men in the relevant branches of engineering was becoming obvious. These points were alluded to by Alexander
Pope in 1731, in a poem addressed to the Earl of Burlington.
Its closing lines give a strong impression of the sense of prosperity
and well-being which the construction of new roads, churches
and bridges would bring.

> Bid Harbours open, public Ways extend,
> Bid Temples, worthier of the God, ascend;
> Bid the broad Arch the dang'rous Flood contain,
> The Mole projected break the roaring Main;
> Back to his bounds their subject Sea command,
> And roll obedient Rivers thro' the Land;
> These Honours, Peace to happy Britain brings,
> These are Imperial Works, and worthy of Kings.[12]

Pope wished to stress the benefit to the community arising from
public works such as these, and elsewhere he picked out for
commendation men who used their own resources to promote
projects for the public good. A prime example was John Kyrle
of Ross-on-Wye,[13] who, around 1700, had provided his home
town with a water-supply on the Sorocold model, and also a
public park. The two things were connected, for the water pumped
from the river by the water-wheel was used to work fountains
in the park before it was piped to various points in the town for
domestic consumption.

Another man whom Pope admired was his friend Ralph Allen,
improver of postal services, owner of quarries near Bath, and one

12. 'Epistle to Burlington', lines 197–204, *The Poems of Alexander Pope*,
ed. Butt, 3 (ii), p. 151.

13. *The Poems of Alexander Pope*, 3 (ii), pp. 113–16.

of those responsible for the Avon navigation in the vicinity of Bath. Allen made a fortune from these activities, but his private gain was the product of public improvement, and he used his money for many charitable purposes.[14] From 1725, Allen actively exploited building stone from his quarries for the construction of the famous squares and crescents of Bath. The quarries were celebrated in the technical literature of the time: partly on account of the railway or wagonway with wooden rails by which the stone was carried from the quarry-face to a wharf on the River Avon. The wagons on this railway had flanged wheels with good brakes, which were necessary because of the steep hillside down which loaded wagons descended to the wharf by gravity, empty ones being hauled back to the quarry by the use of horses. Specially-designed cranes lifted the stone from the wagons on to boats, which carried it a short distance down river to a point near the building-sites in Bath. In the 18th century, this was thought to be a 'great Improvement on some Carriages and Waggonways made use of at the Coal Mines near Newcastle'.[15] It was also celebrated in verse – though not Pope's – as the

> ... *New Made Road*, and wonderful *Machine*,
> Self-moving downward from the Mountain's height.[16]

Alexander Pope's rather general comments on such things are relevant here because he had many friends among public men in England, including among those, like Allen, who commissioned public works or in other ways contributed to the material progress of the nation. To some extent, then, his poems express the aims of these people, and describe social ideals which were capable of influencing engineering projects. Englishmen at this time were prone to use the language of the Renaissance to discuss such ideals. They even, in their most confident moments, talked about a golden age that had just dawned or was about to dawn, and described its qualities in terms of the cultivated grandeur and noble civilisation of the Roman Empire. The achievements of

14. Epilogue to the 'Satires', lines 1235–6, *The Poems of Alexander Pope*, 4, pp. 308, 344.

15. Desaguliers, *A Course of Experimental Philosophy*, 3rd edn, 1763, vol. 1, p. 283; Ralph Allen's railway is illustrated by Lewis, *Early Wooden Railways*, plates 56, 62, 63.

16. Mary Chandler (1734), quoted by Klingender, *Art and the Industrial Revolution*, p. 68.

ancient Rome, they thought, were being equalled, and could be surpassed in modern times. And those writers, like Pope, who had an interest in classical literature thought particularly of the literary civilisation of Rome at the time of its first Emperor, who from 27 B.C. was known by his title 'Augustus'.

'Awareness of the achievement of Augustan Rome, and of the great preceding period of Hellenistic and Greek culture, provides, in post-classical times, a challenge and a model for Renaissance endeavour. The goal of this endeavour, and its fulfilment, was the achievement of a new Augustan Age.' From the early 17th century, poets 'in different ways and to different degrees, saw themselves as emulating the poets of the Roman Augustan Age. Contemporaries of Pope clearly felt that the English Augustan Age was either about to reach its zenith or was but a little way declined from it. Alexander Pope himself, one may conclude by strong inference, thought of himself as an English Augustan.'[17]

When writers on technological matters wished to show that modern Europe had achieved as much as, or more than, ancient Rome, they had been in the habit of citing inventions such as printing, firearms and the magnetic compass. A century and more before the time of Pope, the habit of listing inventions continued to be quite common, but now attention was directed more towards harbours, roads and bridges, and who could say that 18th-century Europe possessed roads or aqueducts to compare with those of the Romans? These were 'Imperial Works', wrote Pope, and worthy of Kings, meaning that they were works which an English ruler or English nobleman could worthily promote. Pope addressed many of his poems to contemporary noblemen, discussing in them the proper use of wealth. He held that magnificent palaces like Versailles, or like some of the larger country houses in England, were of little worth if unregulated by 'sense', and of much less value than the projects of the philanthropic John Kyrle, 'the Man of Ross'. In Rome, Pope claimed, the 'pompous buildings once were things of Use',[18] and public improvement was far more to be valued than private but useless opulence. What Pope was advocating was exactly what some Italians of the period of Palladio and Galileo had done (chapter three). They too wished to emulate the splendours of

17. Erskine-Hill, in *Journal of the Warburg and Courtauld Institutes*, 28, 1965, p. 274.
18. Pope, 'Epistle to Burlington', line 24.

ancient Rome, and concentrated much of their effort on canal and river works or civic improvements. Their leading technological skills were those concerned with machines, hydraulics, architecture and public works of all kinds.

Pope would not have been displeased by such a comparison with 16th-century Italy, for he linked the name of Palladio with that of Vitruvius, the Roman architect. Palladio had provided a fine example of the emulation of Roman architecture in 16th-century Venice, equalling what Vitruvius and other architects had done for Augustan Rome. Lord Burlington, to whom Pope addressed the lines quoted above, was an accomplished amateur architect who advocated the adoption of Palladio's style of building in England. Pope encouraged him to 'be whate'er Vitruvius was before',[19] and observed with interest the 'Palladian' villa which Ralph Allen of Bath built near his quarries. The architecture of Bath itself contains many adaptations of Palladio's style, but at the same time Bath was planned with Roman examples in mind. The clearest mark of this was the Circus, whose curved terraces of three-storied houses were given fronts modelled on the Colosseum in Rome. And partly because it was in building towns, roads, harbours and water-supply systems that the Romans had excelled, not in manufactures or metallurgy, it was works of the former kind that were most often stressed in Renaissance Italy, in Colbert's France, and now in England.

English country gentlemen with their large estates were also often conscious of the need for agricultural improvement. Here Palladio was a more appropriate ideal for them than perhaps they realised, for it will be recalled that many of his houses were built for gentlemen farmers who were developing newly re-claimed land around Venice. Probably Pope did not know much about the agricultural background to Palladio's architecture, but he did criticise gentlemen who surrounded their country houses with vast lawns, ornamental gardens, fountains and avenues. For him, the ideal country gentleman was one

> Whose ample Lawns are not asham'd to feed
> The milky heifer and deserving steed;
> Whose rising Forests, not for pride or show,
> But future Buildings, future Navies, grow . . .[20]

19. Pope, 'Epistle to Burlington', line 194.
20. Pope, 'Epistle to Burlington', lines 185–8.

As the 18th century progressed, more landowners were moved by similar sentiments and steady progress was achieved on the basis of the agricultural improvements introduced in the later 17th century. More fodder crops, such as clover, were grown, more hay was harvested, and more animals were kept. On the village level, small farmers gradually abandoned, or were forced to abandon, traditional methods of farming small strips on open fields. Land was enclosed, and larger, more efficient, farms were formed.

In many ways, England at this time was catching up with what had been done on the continent many years before; but besides catching up, the English were taking new initiatives and outpacing their European rivals. Among many English people, there was a marked sense of optimism and confidence. It was felt that the glories of ancient Rome were being recaptured and surpassed. To do this had long been the aim of Italians and Frenchmen as well, and the literary notion of Augustanism was merely a latter-day expression of a Renaissance sentiment. One important difference, however, between the way in which the English put these things into practice as compared with the French, or earlier with the Venetians, was that in England matters were usually left to the initiative of individuals or small groups of men, and government was relatively inactive.

Fifty years before Pope, Colbert had certainly thought that harbours, roads and bridges were 'Imperial Works', and had organised their construction under government supervision. When Colbert promoted such schemes, he was thinking not only of the economic development of France, but also of the imperial splendour of Louis XIV. Indeed, Colbert's aim in his economic policies has been characterised as 'to glorify the King' and to create 'the grand style that was to signalise the reign of Louis XIV'.[21] Thus Colbert tolerated the grandiose building scheme at the Palace of Versailles which drained away much of the wealth he had so carefully husbanded. The Languedoc Canal, too, was intended to be a monument to the King as well as an economic improvement. 'Take care that your works are constructed in such a way that they will last for ever,'[22] Colbert commanded, no doubt recalling the Roman aqueducts which indeed seemed capable of lasting for ever.

21. Cole, *Colbert*, vol. 1, p. 314.
22. Cole, *Colbert*, vol. 1, p. 381.

Mercantilist economics and the Eastern trade

The imperial splendour about which 17th- and 18th-century Europeans talked was not conceived on an international scale, but in terms of individual nations. Pope wrote:

> Oh when shall Britain, conscious of her claim,
> Stand emulous of Greek and Roman fame?[23]

This nationalist emphasis had also been characteristic of Colbert. In his time, he was the outstanding exponent of the economic theory known as 'mercantilism', and this has been described as 'the economic phase of nascent nationalism'.[24]

Mercantilism influenced the policies towards technology adopted by several European states during the 18th century. It was a theory which pictured trade as a savagely competitive struggle between nations. Wealth was defined in terms of the possession of gold and silver bullion, and unless a nation owned gold or silver mines, it could only become wealthy by trading at the expense of others. The French could increase their prosperity only by reducing that of the Dutch, because if the bullion reserves of France increased it would most likely be because French merchants traded to the disadvantage of Dutch colleagues. Prosperity depended on having a favourable balance of payments, so that gold flowed into the Treasury. But since it was impossible for every nation to achieve this at once, the gains of one must come from the losses of others. A nation pursuing mercantilist policies would aim for self-sufficiency in its industries, so that no imports were necessary. Then foreign trade need be pursued only in circumstances where it led to a net gain in the nation's bullion.

This view of economic life was given a peculiar twist in the 18th century by the increasing volume of trade between Europe and the Far East. Spices grown in the East Indies, cotton goods from India, and silk, porcelain and tea from China loomed large in the import trade of most European countries. At this time, 'India was the greatest exporter of textiles the world had ever known, and her fabrics penetrated almost every market of the civilised world. The extent to which Western Europe shared in

23. 'Epistle to Addison', lines 53–4; *The Poems of Alexander Pope*, 6, p. 204.
24. Cole, *Colbert*, vol. 1, p. 24.

this trade is reflected in language itself: "chintz", "calicoe", "dungaree", "gingham", "khaki", "pyjama", "sash", "seersucker" and "shawl" are all Indian words . . .'[25]

During the 17th century, the majority of these goods were carried to Europe in Dutch ships. The Dutch had been active in this trade since the end of the 16th century, and a number of trading companies were grouped together under government auspices in 1602 to form the Dutch East India Company. The English also had an East India Company founded at about the same time but although it operated with some success it was not at first so large or powerful as the Dutch concern.

Trade with the East was a somewhat dubious undertaking from a mercantilist point of view, because there was very little that Europeans could export to India and China. Most of the porcelain, silk or cotton had to be paid for in gold or silver. The quality of European textiles and pottery was markedly inferior to what was available in the East, so it is understandable that European wares of this kind could not be exported in any quantity.

What is more difficult to understand is why the mechanical devices made in Europe – even firearms – could not be sold more widely in China or India. Certainly clocks and optical instruments were bought by the Chinese, and around 1700 a workshop for the manufacture of clocks was set up by the Emperor K'ang Hsi, with the help of Jesuit missionaries. But these European gadgets were regarded as toys or curiosities, not as objects of use, so their sale was always limited.

Thus while wealthy people in Europe bought Chinese and Indian goods in large quantities because of their high quality, there was no corresponding demand on any large scale for European goods in the East. For that reason, European bullion was steadily drained away to India and to the treasury of the Chinese Empire, and it was only by using the gold and silver of Central and South America that European nations were able to maintain this trade. Another difficulty was that European textile manufactures were suffering as a result of competition from Indian products, and the import of cotton cloth from India was prohibited in France in 1686 and in England in 1701.

However, these prohibitions were short-term measures. The proper mercantilist solution to this imbalance in trade was to promote the development of industries in Europe which could

25. Irwin and Brett, *Origins of Chintz*, p. 1.

produce goods of the same quality as those from the East. With regard to textiles this object was not secured until the 19th century, when competition from the British cotton industry at last virtually destroyed the textile trade of India. But the problem of producing something comparable with Chinese porcelain was solved earlier in the 18th century in Saxony, largely as a result of researches provoked by mercantilist policies.

Chinese porcelain began to come to Europe in significant quantities during the 1640s. Fairly soon, Europeans were investigating the technique of making porcelain, which was so much finer and whiter than their traditional earthenware. There were problems about the kinds of raw materials to be used, and problems too about the very high temperatures at which the pottery was fired. By a long series of experiments with materials that seemed likely to give the required white pottery, and by trial and error with various firing-temperatures, a satisfactory imitation of Chinese porcelain was eventually produced at Dresden in 1708. Tschirnhausen, the man mainly responsible for this breakthrough, set up a pottery at Meissen in Saxony which remained the leading manufactory of porcelain during most of the 18th century.

The importance of trade with the East for European technology during this period was that techniques and processes unfamiliar in the West provided a very considerable stimulus to Western inventors and experimenters. Historians often mention the debt which Europe owed to China in the 12th and 13th centuries for such things as paper and the magnetic compass. Few have recognised, however, that the 17th and 18th centuries mark a second phase of Chinese and Indian influence on European technology. It was not, as in the earlier period, that the technologies of the East were always more advanced than those of Europe, but merely that they were different. In most branches of engineering Europe had developed further than the East by this time, but in most manufactures, Eastern methods and products were superior. And while some new techniques were introduced to Europe in the 18th century by copying the practical arts of the Indians or Chinese, a different kind of influence was of greater importance: this was that Europeans saw things demonstrated in the East whose possibility they had not fully considered before. Having once appreciated the possibility, though, they did not have to copy the Eastern technique, but could devise their own methods for achieving the same result. The point is true both for some kinds of manufactured goods, and for the unusual construction of bridges, ships and other items of engineering interest which were to be seen in the East.

The way in which Europeans learned how to make porcelain is a good example, but there were many other cases. The cotton cloth brought from India was not only of finer quality than that produced in the West, but it was patterned with printed designs in faster and more brilliant dyes. Iron made in India was of a high quality too, even though Indian furnaces were operated inefficiently as compared with those of Europe. Samples of Indian iron were sent to Sheffield, because it was 'excellently adapted for the purpose of fine cutlery',[26] and it was difficult to obtain such good iron in England, except through imports from Sweden.

Travellers in India and China wrote books about what they had seen, and these provided other sorts of challenge to European technology. For example, the iron suspension bridges which spanned river gorges of great width in the mountainous areas of south-west China were described by Jesuit writers, including Athanasius Kircher (1667) and J. B. du Halde (1735–9), as a result of missionary journeys made by them or their colleagues. These bridges were discussed by architects such as Fischer von Erlach (1726) and Sir William Chambers (1773), and they attracted the attention of engineers (including Thomas Telford). No major suspension bridges existed in the West until late in the 18th century, when the Chinese examples clearly became a stimulus to American and European engineers. These men devised their own form of construction, but undoubtedly owed a debt to China for demonstrating the novel possibilities which the suspension principle offered.[27] Chinese naval architecture and seamanship also impressed Europeans. The British Admiralty conducted tests on Chinese sculling oars in 1742, and at the end of the 18th century six vessels were designed for the Admiralty with water-tight bulkheads modelled on those used in Chinese boats.[28]

26. Comment made by B. Hayne in 1814, quoted by Dharampal, *Indian Science and Technology*, pp. L–LI.

27. See Pevsner, *Pioneers of Modern Design*, p. 126; Needham, *Science and Civilization in China*, vol. 4, part 3, pp. 194 ff.; Pacey, in *British Journal for the History of Science*, 6, 1972.

28. Needham, *Science and Civilization in China*, vol. 4, part 3, pp. 420–21.

In India, agricultural implements attracted attention. One innovation during the so-called agricultural revolution in 18th-century Britain was the seed drill. This allowed seed to be sown in neat rows so that later in the season weeding would be easier. After this had been introduced, Englishmen were surprised to find that machines which performed the same function had been in regular use in India for a very long time. Several implements, including a plough and a seed drill, were sent from India to the British Board of Agriculture in 1795.[29]

Mercantilist policies in Europe

Although mercantilist thinkers were much troubled by the imports coming into Europe from the East, and by the loss of bullion which this entailed, they did have other interests as well. Following the example of Colbert, they were also anxious for the improvement of canals, roads, mines and manufactures in their own countries. Again following Colbert, there was a tendency to think that governments should intervene directly to promote such projects.

Yet to the British, this was distasteful. They were already feeling their way towards the *laissez-faire* approach in economics which was advocated by Adam Smith in 1776, and which became the dominant orthodoxy of the 19th century. But in France, Saxony, the Austrian Empire and some other European states, mercantilist policies which have been characterised as 'the opposite of *laissez-faire*' were extensively practised. It was believed that 'the state could, should, and would ... act in the economic sphere'.[30]

Colbert, the great 17th-century practitioner of mercantilism, had thought that ordinary manufactures and commerce should be left in private hands, but where difficult or risky ventures had to be undertaken in France, like the Gobelin tapestry factory or the French East India Company (founded 1664), it was advisable that they should be run by the State. However, he thought that State enterprise was nearly always preferable when it came to the construction of roads, canals and other public works, and his policies here benefited France enormously. Roads and canals were built ahead of economic need and probably

29. *Communications to the Board of Agriculture*, vol. *1*, 1797, pp. 352–6.
30. Cole, *Colbert*, vol. I, p. 20.

to higher standards than would have been the case had they been purely commercial concerns, as in England. But more than that, French policies led to the gradual development of a professional corps of civil engineers – the *Corps des Ponts et Chaussées*. And just as Colbert's improvements to the French Navy had demanded the development of a whole range of schools for ship-building, hydrography and artillery, so later the government organisation for road-building and public works called into being a school for the training of civil engineers – the *École des Ponts et Chaussées*, founded in 1747. Taking its place alongside existing military and naval schools, this gave France a more complete system of technical education than had existed anywhere before. The result was that during the 18th and much of the 19th century, France had the best-trained and most effective engineers in the world.

A century after Colbert, an interesting exposition of mercantilist theory was given in a masterly textbook on mining published in Vienna in 1773, with a French translation following almost immediately. Its author was Christoph Traugott Delius (1728–79), and it provided a comprehensive and detailed account of the mining arts: sinking shafts, cutting rock, mine ventilation, lifting-gear, pumps and the treatment of ores. The discussion of mercantilist economic theory cropped up in a discussion of the finance of mines.[31] The prosperity of a nation, Delius said, was directly dependent on the amount of money circulating within it. If each country produced all the goods necessary for its welfare, including luxury articles, then its prosperity would neither grow nor decrease. But if a country was able to produce goods or materials which other countries needed, then it could trade favourably with its neighbours. Bullion would flow into its treasury, and its wealth and general prosperity would increase.

Delius wrote his book while teaching at the Schemnitz Mining Academy, which was situated in the Hungarian lands of the Austrian Empire. He remarked that Austria had a considerable advantage over many other nations, for within its Empire several mines produced silver and a little gold. Thus by regulating not only its trade but also its mines, Austria could readily control its 'balance of commerce', and ensure that its

31. Delius, *Anleitung zu der Bergbaukunst*, trans. Schreiber vol. 2, pp. 323 ff. I am indebted to D. M. Farrar for allowing me to use translations and notes made by him from the French edition.

bullion reserves, and so also its wealth, were always increasing. Between 1740 and 1772, the mines of Hungary and Transylvania had provided the Royal Treasury with gold and silver worth a total of 150,000,000 florins, equivalent to about 60,000,000 ounces of silver.[32] A measure of the significance of this sum is that it seems to have provided something like 10 per cent of the total revenue of the Austrian Crown during the period.[33] But even with this large supply of bullion, the imports of the Austrian Empire could only just be paid for. Until 1775, when exports at last exceeded imports, there was a chronic imbalance of trade, and most of the silver from Hungary was used to make up the deficit. Thus, Delius explained, there was an urgent need to establish new industries within the Empire so that imports could be cut. There were some people, he said, who disputed the value of mining and who cited Holland and France as nations which had become rich while lacking mineral resources. But these nations had no certain source of wealth, and had become wealthy only through the weakness and idleness of others. If neighbouring countries developed their own industries more effectively, he argued, they could become less dependent on France and Holland, and keep their own wealth within their boundaries. It was assumed in this argument that if Holland failed to sell its imports from the Indies, if France could not sell its wine, and if neither could sell their cloth and other manufactures, then they would be as nothing.

The weakness of mercantilist theory is apparent. There was a failure to see that the growth of manufacturing or agricultural production could result in an increase in wealth, even if it was all consumed within the country and there was no in-flow of gold. Gold and silver constitute wealth only if there are products which they will buy. If manufactures increase, it can come about that the same amount of bullion will buy more goods, or that more goods are bought on credit. Thus the wealth of nations can increase by their industry and not only by trade conducted to the disadvantage of others.

Because of the special importance of gold- and silver-mining in

32. That is, 1·9 million ounces per year over the 32-year period; elsewhere, Delius gives figures which imply 1·2 million ounces a year for silver production alone.

33. Macartney, *The Habsburg Empire*, pp. 48–9; Marczali, *Hungary in the 18th Century*, p. 319.

the mercantilist scheme of things, it is not surprising to find that like road- and canal-building in France, mining in the Austrian Empire was largely a government enterprise. There was provision for the private ownership of mines, but if the production of a private mine declined, it could be taken over by the Crown.

The State-owned mines were administered by professional civil servants who needed to combine some technical knowledge and practical skill with the ability to keep the detailed written records required by a distant government administration. At first the officials who ran the mines were trained by a system of apprenticeship, but in 1733, attempts were made to organise some part-time formal education for trainee officials. Courses of this kind were begun in 1735 at Schemnitz[34] in Hungary, the centre of one of the most important mining areas within the Austrian Empire. In 1763 a more ambitious school of mining was established at Schemnitz and in 1770 this was reorganised as the Royal Hungarian Mining Academy. For a few years it had a high reputation throughout Europe as a kind of technological university. Its courses in practical chemistry were particularly well known, and in 1770–72, while Delius was there, the course on mine machinery must also have been very good. But in many ways the kind of education provided at Schemnitz had been anticipated by the small technical schools founded in France from Colbert's time onwards. The military schools at Mézière (founded 1749) and at La Fère (1720) were probably the best academically, but, more to the point, the *École des Ponts et Chaussées* had begun teaching mining engineering on a small scale in the 1750s. There were also mining schools elsewhere, notably at Freiberg in Saxony, where the *Bergakademie* was founded in 1765. This institution was comparable with the academy at Schemnitz, but had the advantage of being less isolated. It was not far from either of the two universities in Saxony: Wittenberg and Leipzig; and the geology lectures given at Freiberg at the end of the century by A. G. Werner attracted students from far and wide.

The mining districts of Saxony figured prominently in the previous chapter because of their association with Agricola. Since then, mining, like other local industries, had been badly disrupted by the Thirty Years War (1618–48), but at the

34. Schemnitz is now within the boundaries of Czechoslovakia, and is known as Banskà Stiavnica.

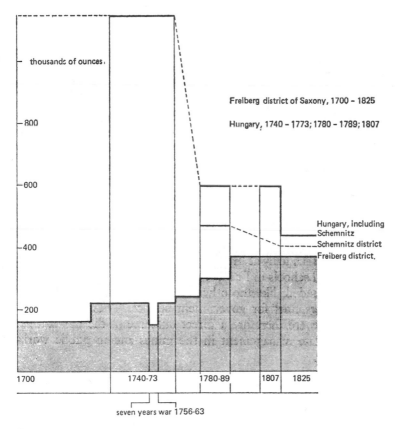

thousands of ounces

— 800

— 600

— 400

— 200

Freiberg district of Saxony, 1700 - 1825

Hungary, 1740 - 1773; 1780 - 1789; 1807

Hungary, including
Schemnitz
Schemnitz district
Freiberg district.

1700   1740-73   1780-89   1807   1825

seven years war 1756-63

Figure 27

Average yearly output of silver from the Freiberg district of Saxony and
from the Hungarian mines.
(Based on figures compiled by D. M. Farrar using data from the *Bergakademie
Freiberg Festschrift 1765–1965*, Freiburg, 1965 and from Delius, Héron de Villefosse
and other authors)

beginning of the 18th century, silver output in Saxony had
regained its pre-war level. As the century proceeded, Saxon
output steadily rose, while from about 1780 the much larger
output of the Schemnitz mines began to fall. The most important
mining area in Saxony was centred on Freiberg; at the end of the
century, production there was about 400,000 ounces of silver per

year. This was about the same as the output at Schemnitz (see fig. 27).

This seems to reflect a somewhat healthier state of economic affairs in Saxony than in the Austrian Empire. Saxony was a country of about 2,000,000 people which, by 1800, had 'acquired many of the characteristics of an industrial region'.[35] Between 1756 and 1763 it was again badly affected by war, but a government commission for reconstruction helped to establish 70 new industrial enterprises in the twenty years up to 1784. Coal was mined on a scale that was still very unusual in central Europe, and production was 60,000 tons in 1807. There was a thriving textile industry and the famous Meissen china factory as well as mines which produced copper, silver, lead and iron.

Mercantilist thinking predominated in the policies of the Saxon government. The mines were subject to close government control. The academy at Freiberg, like that at Schemnitz, and like the technical schools in France, was financed by the government, and was founded, like the other schools, to provide technically qualified personnel for government service. These educational institutions were therefore a direct outcome of the mercantilist policy of State management in the mines and in public works engineering.

Steam power in the Austrian Empire

The use of atmospheric steam engines in the Austrian Empire not long after their first application to English mines indicates how well the practical arts fared under the influence of mercantilist policies. By 1735 there were already at least three engines in the Schemnitz area: two at the Windschacht mine and one not far away at Königsberg. Two further engines seem to have been installed at Windschacht in the next two or three years.

These engines, employed to pump water from the mines, were built by the Austrian architect-engineer Joseph Emmanuel Fischer von Erlach (1693–1742) whose father was mentioned above as writing about Chinese bridges. Fischer had visited England, studied Newcomen engines there, and engaged a certain Isaac Potter to return to Hungary with him. Potter helped

---

35. Smith, *An Historical Geography*, p. 575; see also Henderson, *Studies in the Economic Policy of Frederick the Great*, pp. 114–22.

particularly with the Königsberg engine, but died in 1735, before Fischer's later engines were begun.

A few years later, a further atmospheric steam engine was erected by Joseph Karl Hell (1718–85), an engineer trained at Schemnitz in the 1740s. Hell pioneered the use of water-pressure to drive a hydraulic piston engine, again for working pumps. He also invented a most unusual pneumatic engine for raising

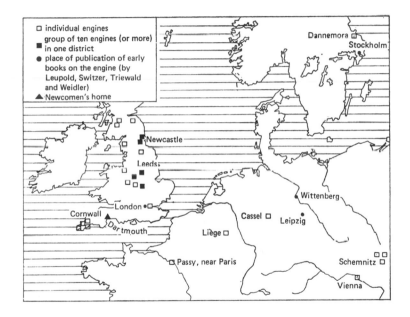

Figure 28
The Newcomen engine in Europe up to 1734.

water from the mines. Both types of engine were powered by water supplied from a high-level reservoir, and nine of the hydraulic engines were built between 1749 and 1768.

Other Newcomen engines on the continent were few and far between. There was one in the coal- and iron-working district around Liège, near Brussels, and one had been built at a Swedish mine by Marten Triewald, another foreign engineer who had visited England. In Saxony, people had been interested in the use of steam-power for pumping out mines even before Newcomen's engine had proved to be successful, although no Newcomen engines were used there until much later. In 1690 Denis Papin, Huygens's former assistant, had described his ideas for such engines in the journal *Acta Eruditorum*, which was published in Leipzig. Shortly afterwards, he wrote to Count Philip Ludwig von Zinzendorff, assuring him that a steam engine would be 'very advantageous' for pumping out mines. Zinzendorff was an influential man in Saxony, and held office in the government for a time.[36] In the 1690s he had written to Papin inviting him to visit a mine in Bohemia 'which had become unworkable owing to the extent of underground flooding'. Papin replied excusing himself from this duty, but describing his engine at length. Water-wheels might have been used to work pumps at the mine, except that 'Your Excellency's mine is far removed from the rivers'.[37]

Two books published in Saxony in the 1720s show that there was continuing interest in the subject. One was written by Jacob Leupold, a Leipzig instrument-maker and mathematics teacher, who in 1725 became a commissioner of mines in Saxony. In the first volume of a remarkable encyclopedia or 'theatre' of engineering, which appeared in twelve volumes from 1724 onwards, Leupold described the Newcomen-type engine which Isaac Potter had helped to erect near Schemnitz, and quoted letters from his 'good friend' Fischer von Erlach. Another book, a 'treatise on hydraulic machines' which was written in Saxony by Johann Friedrich Weidler, a professor at Wittenberg University, gave more details of early Newcomen engines. It illustrated one erected at York Buildings, London, in 1726, that was designed to pump water for the supply of houses in the Strand.

Weidler wrote in Latin, thereby setting himself the intriguing task of devising Latin technical terms for the components of Newcomen's engine, the 'English machine'. He said that the first such engine in Germany was erected at Cassel in 1722 by Fischer von Erlach. Cassel had been a place where much work had been done on steam engines since the time, around 1700,

36. Zinzendorff's son was of some importance as a religious leader of evangelical persuasion; see Lewis, *Zinzendorff the Ecumenical Pioneer*.
37. The text of Papin's letter is given by Klemm, *A History of Western Technology*, pp. 220–23.

when Papin lived there, but it is doubtful whether a Newcomen engine *was* ever erected there. However, it is quite possible that Fischer von Erlach visited Cassel on his way back to Austria, and he may have provided a small engine or model for Landgrave Charles, ruler of Hesse-Cassel and former patron of Papin.

Apart from this, and apart from the mine engines near Schemnitz, Fischer von Erlach was responsible for a steam engine erected in Vienna in 1727. This pumped water needed to work fountains in a garden, and was commissioned by Prince Francis Adam of Schwarzenberg. It had a 2-foot-diameter cylinder, and was notable chiefly for a novel boiler designed by Fischer. 'The round copper boiler was surrounded by many closely spaced cells . . .', Weidler wrote. The smoke from the fire passed through these cells before going up the chimney; it 'went round the boiler twice, was passed back and forth, and any heat remaining in the smoke, even that was drawn out of it . . .'[38]

Directions of technical progress under mercantilism

The fact that this novel engine in Vienna was built in connection with an ornamental garden and not for an industrial purpose helps to explain why economic and technical development in the Austrian Empire was lagging by the end of the 18th century. Magnificent palaces and gardens were built by aristocrats, and very advanced technology was applied to the particular tasks in which the government and the nobility were interested. But much of the countryside remained very backward, and basic industries like textiles were underdeveloped. The vast sums which were spent on imperial magnificence in Vienna, and the expenditure on mine machinery and on the academy at Schemnitz, probably drained resources away from more mundane but more urgent tasks, and certainly contributed to Austria's chronic balance of payments difficulties. Delius said that because of the demand for food and other materials it created, the mining community at Schemnitz had a beneficial influence on the agriculture of the surrounding area. But his comments on the difficulty which Austria faced in maintaining its bullion reserves, despite its rich silver mines, suggest that agriculture and manufacturing production was really very inadequate.

The situation in most of the territory ruled by Austria was in

38. Weidler, *Tractatus de machinis hydraulicis*, p. 91.

some ways similar to that which is found in many underdeveloped countries in the modern world, and which economists call a 'dual economy'. That is, advanced technology and good technical education are to be found in a small sector of the economy, with a few people benefiting, while the majority of the population live mainly by agriculture, using traditional techniques with low productivity. Austria used Hungary as a source of food and raw materials, and allowed the industries of Hungary to decline. Only in the mining towns was there a technically advanced industry, and this had stronger links with Vienna and western Europe than with the immediate needs of people in the surrounding area.

Backward conditions in agriculture or industry were of course by no means unusual in 18th-century Europe, but in some countries they were less accentuated. In England, less power and money was concentrated in the hands of the monarch than was the case with the Austrian Emperor, and in English society generally, wealth was more widely diffused among members of a fairly large middle class, many of whom were active in trade and industry. And while large-scale projects as ambitious as the Languedoc Canal or the Schemnitz mines were scarcely attempted in England before 1750, a great number of more modest schemes provided a larger volume of work for craftsmen and engineers, and ensured a more balanced development of the country as a whole.

The effect on technology can be illustrated by comparing the Schemnitz mine engineer J. K. Hell (1718–85) with his English contemporary, John Smeaton (1724–92). In their work on Newcomen engines and horse-gins for mines, and in their interest in piston engines worked by water-pressure, Hell and Smeaton were engineers of very similar calibre. But while in Hungary there was little an engineer like Hell could turn to outside the mines, in England John Smeaton drew plans for harbours, bridges, canals and land-drainage works, and the half-dozen mine engines he designed occupied only a fraction of his time. By the end of the 18th century, the Austrian Empire's shaky finances seem to have inhibited investment at the mines to the point where maintenance was neglected. Thus while the young men who worked under Smeaton became the civil engineers of a new generation, Hell's pupils were faced with a declining industry and few openings for engineering work elsewhere. So the brilliance of engineering at Schemnitz in the time of Fischer, Potter, Hell and Delius was not developed further.

It is easy to criticise this state of affairs, but it should be remembered that 18th-century governments did not envisage their objective as economic development in the modern sense. Their aim was the acquisition of wealth and power; but more than that, they wished to express the achievement of their civilisation in a display of imperial magnificence which would rival the grandeur of Rome – and outshine the Empire of China, of which they were newly conscious. Thus the prudent and austere Colbert, who did so much to build up the wealth of France, did not object to the expenditure of 50,000,000 livres[39] on the palace, gardens and water-supply at Versailles, even though this strained the country's economy. For what was the object of possessing wealth, if not for a display such as that?

In Austria, the Royal House and the nobility also built great houses, churches, gardens and palaces. An example is the Palace of the Prince of Schwarzenberg, where steam-powered fountains were installed in the 1720s, as was mentioned above. These were designed by Fischer von Erlach, whose father had been the architect of the palace itself, which was built between 1705 and 1720. Every minor princeling wanted his own Versailles, and the two Fischers did much to satisfy their demand. Indeed, the elder one nicely expressed his aspirations by publishing a book of pictures 'in the representation of the most noted buildings of foreign nations, both ancient and modern'.[40] The palaces and bridges of contemporary China were shown, along with those of ancient Rome, Greece and Egypt. Then palaces and churches in Vienna were illustrated, all of them designed by the author, and the reader could not but feel that these were the equal of anything that other civilisations had achieved.

The English shared the ideal of emulating the splendour of ancient Rome, but interpreted it with a somewhat utilitarian emphasis. Roman grandeur was the result of Roman skill in building roads and aqueducts. Magnificent architecture was not just an empty show, but the product of wise government and a concern for the public good. As Alexander Pope put it;

39. Cole, *Colbert*, vol. I, p. 315. This sum might be equivalent to about £10,000,000 at 1970 values, and about one-seventh of it was accounted for by the Marly machine.

40. Part of the title of *A Plan of Civil and Historical Architecture*, by John Bernhard Fischer of Erlach, English translation by Thomas Lediard.

> 'Tis Use alone that sanctifies Expence,
> And Splendour borrows all her rays from Sense.[41]

And as another poet, the Reverend John Dalton, explained in 1755, it seemed right to celebrate the growing prosperity of England in the same kind of language as Roman poets had used in describing the achievements of their own civilisation. Thus Dalton employed 'classical allusion' and 'parody' of Roman poets to describe the progress of agriculture, mining and forestry in his native Cumberland, and to portray a Newcomen engine at Whitehaven (which he wrongly attributed to Savery).

> Sagacious Savery! Taught by thee
> Discordant elements agree,
> Fire, water, air, heat, cold unite,
> And listed in one service fight,
> Pure streams to thirsty cities send,
> Or deepest mines from floods defend.
> Man's richest gift thy work will shine;
> Rome's aqueducts were poor to thine![42]

In these ways, then, the English had their own ideas about the emulation of Rome. Landowners were enthusiastic 'improvers' as often as they were palace-builders. The King was not an absolute monarch, and rarely indulged in such extravagant royal expenditures as those of the Austrian or French rulers. Parliament set limits on the King's powers, and supported a form of government in which policies like Colbert's, or like those of the Austrian Crown, were almost unthinkable. One disadvantage of this was that technical schools like those of France, Saxony and the Austrian Empire were never established in Britain. In the 19th century, this neglect of technical education came to be sorely felt. But in the 18th century, Britain gained by avoiding the defects of mercantilist policies.

So English agriculture and trade quietly prospered, while canals, harbours, aqueducts and pumping-engines could be seen as symbolic of the practical achievements of this golden age – this period when the public splendour and civilised values of Augustan Rome had been regained and perhaps surpassed. What

41. 'Epistle to Burlington', lines 179–80; *The Poems of Alexander Pope, 3* (ii), p. 154.
42. Rev. John Dalton, *Descriptive poem*, p. 12, and introduction. Dalton's poems are among the earliest to describe the scenery of the Lake District at first hand. See Klingender, *Art and the Industrial Revolution*, pp. 19–20, etc.

lay in the future? Would there be further steady improvement, or a lazy decadence? There were people, including Pope, who sometimes felt that the latter was the more probable. The one possibility that was not foreseen was the series of revolutionary technical and industrial advances which was soon to occur.

7

Technology in the industrial revolution

Economic incentives in technical change

When Newcomen's atmospheric steam engine was first introduced into the mining areas of Britain, horses were the most common source of power in the mines. They hauled wagons of coal along short lengths of railway; or, walking in a circle around a horse-engine or 'gin', turned winding-gear and worked pumps. So when a mine-owner thought of installing a steam engine to drive pumps in his mine, he needed to compare its promised performance with what his horses were already doing.

One comparative study of horses and a steam engine was made in north-east England during 1752, at a coal mine 240 feet deep. It cost 24 shillings a day to keep horses for driving the pumps. They worked two at a time, in eight 3-hour shifts, and they lifted 67,200 gallons in a full day. The steam engine, on the other hand, cost only 20 shillings a day, and in that time it could pump 250,560 gallons of water from the mine.[1]

Episodes of this kind, repeated many times in England around this date, illustrate two of the major themes of technical progress during the industrial revolution: the drive to cut costs and produce raw materials or manufactures more cheaply – and the search for new or improved sources of power. By studying the industries which were developing most rapidly at this time, particularly cotton-spinning and -weaving, and the production of iron, other characteristic forms of technical innovation might be identified. But in all industries a growing unwillingness to accept existing levels of costs would be observed, and also a growing recognition that existing sources of power were inadequate for any further significant progress.

The new atmospheric steam engine was at first used almost

1. Quoted by Raistrick, in *Newcomen Society Transactions*, *17*, 1936–7, pp. 153–4.

solely in the mines. Windmills provided a source of power for grinding corn and for pumping water in land-drainage works. But for most industrial applications water-wheels were the most important source of power, with horses quite widely used where water-supplies were inadequate.

One engineer who made systematic studies of all these sources of power was John Smeaton (1724–92). In 1768–9, for example, he collected an enormous amount of information about the atmospheric steam engines being used in the Northumberland and Durham coalfield. He analysed the performance of fifteen of these engines in some detail, comparing the amount of water pumped with the weight of coal burned under the boiler. He also built a small steam engine whose performance he could study at leisure, and carried out many experiments with it. The result was that new engines designed by Smeaton incorporated many detailed improvements. In some cases, coal consumption was less than half of what was expected from similar engines of earlier design. Indeed, the improvement in performance which Smeaton achieved can be expressed in modern terms by saying that a typical engine designed by him might work with more than twice the efficiency of one of conventional design – about 1·5 per cent instead of 0·6 per cent.

Smeaton's engines did not differ in either principle or function from earlier types, but only in detail. Their advantage was simply that they used less coal and were therefore cheaper to run. Smeaton's work in this field illustrates the direct influence of economic pressures on innovation; and the fact that several engines of his design were built reflects the operation of the profit motive among mine-owners whose money they would save. This is understandable enough, and it is tempting to regard economic motives of this kind as the principal force behind the inventions and technical improvements which occurred during the industrial revolution. In other industries the economic pressure was often directed towards increasing output or speeding up production rather than just towards cutting costs. Nevertheless, the innovator's keen appreciation of current economic circumstances was usually the key to the improvements which he introduced. In the major industries of the time – textiles and iron-making – 'it was in large measure the pressure of demand on the mode of production that called forth the new techniques in Britain'.[2]

2. Landes, *The Unbound Prometheus*, p. 77.

This being so, it might seem that there is little to be said about the industrial revolution in a book such as this which aims to trace the influence of non-economic ideas and impulses in the development of technology. But of course, to say that most engineers and inventors at this time were acutely conscious of the financial profit which might result from their work is not to say that they thought of nothing else. Many of these men must have been enthusiastic about machines for their own sake, as many people still are. Some of them certainly believed that life would be improved by their inventions. And John Smeaton showed many signs of a certain intellectual idealism in his approach to engineering. His attitude, indeed, seems to have been that the old intuitive methods of the craftsmen who had previously been responsible for most engineering work in Britain should be replaced by methods that were more exact and more systematic. Smeaton expressed his views by example rather than through explicit statement, but what he was aiming at can perhaps be fairly characterised as a *rational* approach to engineering.

Rational methods and civil engineering

In order to understand the background to Smeaton's rationalised engineering, it is necessary to recall that in most conventional branches of the art, the English had lagged behind badly during the early part of the 18th century. In the 1730s, for example, it had proved impossible to find an English engineer to build Westminster Bridge. The job was given to Charles Labelye (1705–62), a Swiss engineer who had been educated in France. J. T. Desaguliers, the author of the only worthwhile English book on practical mechanics, pointedly remarked that England lacked 'Ingénieurs of a proper Education for the Science'.[3] He used the French word to denote a breed of men which did not then exist in England.

John Smeaton did more than anybody else to remedy this situation. His own career in engineering began in the 1750s, and included all the usual branches of the subject: bridges, canals, harbours, land drainage and mine machinery. His work, in fact, was mainly in engineering of a traditional kind, not greatly different from what had been common practice in the France of Colbert's time or the Italy of Galileo's. Among contemporaries on the continent, J. K. Hell (chapter six) was Smeaton's equal as

3. Desaguliers, *A Course of Experimental Philosophy*, ii, 1763 edn, p. 415.

an engine-builder, and J. R. Perronet, the first head of the Paris *École des Ponts et Chaussées*, employed more advanced techniques in the design of bridges and masonry work.

Smeaton came from Leeds, where his father was a lawyer, and it was originally intended that Smeaton himself should enter this profession. But from an early age he was interested in mechanical things, and he eventually prevailed upon his father to let him go and work for an instrument-maker. He was, indeed, one of several contemporary engineers who gained their initial practical experience in this way. The instrument-making trade flourished in Britain. Sextants, compasses and telescopes for mariners were in demand, and clocks and surveyors' instruments sold well both at home and on the continent.

By 1750, Smeaton seems to have had his own instrument business in London. He was particularly interested in astronomical instruments, but he also became known as the maker of an unusually effective air-pump, which his scientific friends used in their experiments. But already Smeaton was becoming interested in engineering on a larger scale, and about 1754 he decided to devote himself entirely to this kind of work. He travelled to Holland to study canals, windmills, land drainage and harbour works. Then in 1755 he was given his first major commission, which was the rather formidable one of rebuilding the Eddystone Lighthouse on its tide-swept rock near Plymouth.

This project goes a long way to illustrate Smeaton's ideal of rationalised engineering. Firstly, in building on the Eddystone Rock he had to find a cement which would set despite being submerged by the tides twice a day. He collected samples of lime and sand from different sources, mixed them in varying proportions, and subjected the resulting mortar to standard tests of setting and strength. The result was the first fully successful hydraulic cement since Roman times; and Smeaton's systematic experiments are a good and clear example of a rational approach to a baffling practical problem. But not every aspect of the project could be treated by rational methods; at one point Smeaton admitted that he had to rely on intuition. The most desirable shape for the lighthouse tower, he said, could not be 'accurately solved', but 'I have endeavoured to do it, so far as my feelings, rather than calculations, would bear me out'.[4]

4. Smeaton, *Narrative of the Building . . . of the Eddystone Lighthouse*, p. 136.

The lighthouse was finished during the summer of 1759, but during May and June of that year Smeaton found time to give five lectures to the Royal Society. They were mainly concerned with the working of water-wheels and windmills, and Smeaton demonstrated a model water-wheel, two feet in diameter. He had constructed the model in 1752, when he had found that books did not give consistent information about water-wheels. It seemed that experiments with a model would be one way of settling the question. The chief authority on which the books based their remarks was Antoine Parent, who in 1704 had calculated the maximum efficiency that could be achieved by an undershot water-wheel (chapter four). But Parent had reached his conclusions on entirely theoretical grounds, and since he was not an engineer the question of his using the theory in practice did not arise. Smeaton's experiments were designed specifically to test Parent's theory. And they showed that undershot water-wheels could develop much more power than Parent's theory had predicted.

But apart from providing better data about the performance of water-wheels, Smeaton's work was outstanding as an example of experimental method in science, and how it could be used to shed light on engineering problems. And in this respect Smeaton's studies of water-power made an important contribution to the adoption of rational methods in engineering.

Much of Smeaton's work was characterised by a close attention to accurate measurement, a habit he had acquired partly as a result of his experience in making and using precision instruments, and partly through his interest in astronomy. He built himself a small observatory at his home near Leeds. He wrote papers on astronomy for the Royal Society. And he was interested in making precise and accurate observations of such things as the slight wobble in the earth's orbit about the sun which is due to the moon's gravitational pull.[5]

Measurement in engineering was not often as precise as that needed in astronomy. Smeaton took as much care as possible, but there were still discrepancies between his conclusions about the performance of water-wheels and his measurements of their actual behaviour. His conclusions were expressed as principles or 'maxims' about water-wheel performance, and he remarked

5. See Smeaton's Royal Society paper of 1768 on the 'menstrual parallax', in his *Miscellaneous Papers*, pp. 111–19.

that 'in comparing different experiments, as some fall short, and others exceed the maxim, and all agree therewith, as near as can be expected ... we may, according to the *laws of reasoning by induction*, conclude the maxim true'.[6]

This sentence is referring to Isaac Newton's 'rules of reasoning' about 'propositions inferred by general induction'.[7] Newton had discussed these rules in his great book *Principia* (1687) as a preliminary to comparing a large number of astronomical observations with calculations based on his theories of planetary motion. Smeaton, as an astronomer, was familiar with Newton's book. He possessed a copy (in Motte's translation), and his writings show knowledge of it in several places. In the work on water-wheels, he clearly saw that the comparison of his maxims with experimental measurements involved the same methodological problem as Newton's comparison of theory and observation in astronomy.

Principia was a mathematical book with very little obvious relevance to the extremely practical observations which Smeaton was pursuing. But another book by Newton, his *Opticks* of 1704, described many experiments with glass prisms and lenses which are more closely comparable in method with Smeaton's investigations. It has therefore been assumed[8] that Smeaton's experimental method derived from this. Smeaton must have known of *Opticks*, but his writings do not show any evidence that he was interested in the book. For Smeaton, *Principia* was more important, because his approach to science was through astronomy, not through the conventional 18th-century studies of 'experimental philosophy', of which *Opticks* was a forerunner.

Smeaton's experiments established a number of important points about the design of water-wheels. Following Parent's example, he had at first considered only undershot wheels – that is, wheels driven by the impulse of moving water on flat blades or paddles (see fig. 29). But he then went on to consider overshot water-wheels, which were worked by the weight of water falling into buckets attached to the wheel's circumference. Smeaton established that the overshot wheel worked with about twice the efficiency of the undershot type, and he worked out the

6. Our italics; Smeaton's *Experimental Enquiry*, p. 17; also his *Miscellaneous Papers*, p. 39.

7. Newton, *Principia*, book III, 4th rule of reasoning.

8. For example, by Cardwell, in *History of Science*, 7, 1968, pp. 119-20.

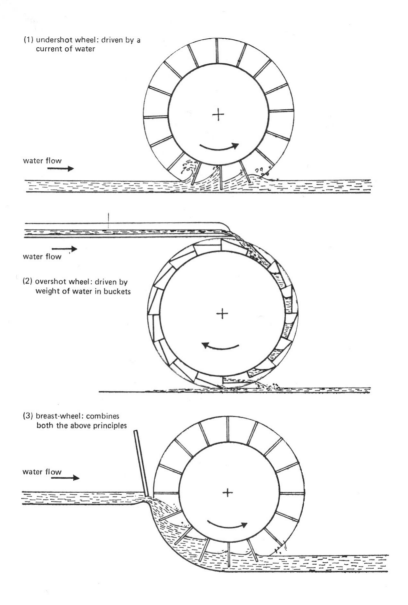

(1) undershot wheel: driven by a
current of water

water flow

(2) overshot wheel: driven by
weight of water in buckets

water flow

(3) breast-wheel: combines
both the above principles

water flow

Figure 29

The different types of water-wheel discussed by John Smeaton.
(Diagram specially drawn for the author by D. M. Farrar)

speed of rotation at which the undershot wheel gave its best performance. He also advocated the use of breast-wheels. These were a compromise between overshot and undershot types which could be used when the available fall of water was insufficient to allow overshot wheels to be used. It is perhaps significant that many of the large water-powered factories erected during the industrial revolution were equipped with breast-wheels, although this type had rarely been used previously.

The technical details of Smeaton's work are less important than his method of investigation, however. In his studies of water-wheels, his approach derived partly from Parent and partly from Newton. For although Smeaton rejected Parent's theory, it none the less contributed to his work. Parent had given the problem a mathematical shape, which had shown how an experiment might be done to measure the power and efficiency of the water-wheel.

Smeaton's account of these experiments was the most important of his published works. After appearing in the *Philosophical Transactions* of the Royal Society in 1759, it was reprinted in 1760, 1796, 1814 and 1826. Through it, many engineers acquired something of Smeaton's approach to engineering problems. In the middle of the 19th century, Robert Stephenson remarked that 'To this day there are no writings so valuable ... in the highest walks of scientific engineering; and when young men ask me what they should read, I invariably say, "Go to Smeaton's philosophical papers; read them, master them thoroughly, and nothing will be of greater service to you".'[9]

However, it was not only Smeaton's scientific approach which helped to provide a sound basis for the development of engineering in Britain; there was also his awareness of what engineers on the continent were doing, and how they benefited through being members of a recognised profession. The editor of Smeaton's *Reports*[10] commented, in 1812, that about fifty years earlier, the 'general situation of things gave rise to a new profession and order of men, called Civil Engineers. In all the polished nations of Europe, this was, and is, a profession of itself, and by itself. – Academics, or some parts of such institutions, were appropriated to the study of it, and of all the

9. Quoted by Smiles, *Lives of the Engineers*, 2, 1874 edn, p. 177.
10. *Reports of the late John Smeaton*, preface to the first edition.

preparatory science and accomplishments necessary to form an able artist.'

In Britain, however, there was 'no public establishment, except common schools, for the rudimental knowledge necessary to all arts, naval, military, mechanical and others', and the education of engineers was 'left to chance'. In order to give some shape to the emerging engineering profession in the absence of any systematic training, a 'Society of Civil Engineers' was formed in 1771. Meetings were at first held in the King's Head Tavern in London on Fridays when Parliament was in session. Bills to allow the construction of canals and other public works had to be passed by Parliament, and when these were under consideration, the engineers responsible had often to be present in London. So Parliamentary sessions provided a good opportunity for meetings of men who at other times were widely dispersed throughout the country.

Smeaton is said to have been the first person to call himself a 'civil engineer', using the term to include mechanical as well as constructional work. In England, the term 'engineer' was coming to have a purely military connotation. Smeaton seems genuinely to have felt that he owed 'a debt to the common stock of public happiness or accommodation',[11] so he would wish his work to be clearly distinguished from that of military engineers. The members of the Society founded in 1771 showed the importance they attached to Smeaton's example by formally calling themselves 'Civil Engineers' and informally 'Smeatonians'. And they adopted a motto which expressed the ideal of rational methods and measurement in engineering. It consisted of words from the book of the Wisdom of Solomon (xi, 20), in the Apocrypha, where God is described as having ordered 'all things in measure, number and weight'. In like manner should engineers order their work.

James Watt (1736–1819)

Twelve years younger than Smeaton, Watt had a similar and almost parallel career, beginning in the instrument trade. But unlike Smeaton, Watt came of a family which already had instrument-making connections. His uncle was a surveyor, and his

11. Mary Dixon (Smeaton's daughter), in a preface to *Reports of the late John Smeaton.*

father's business in Greenock probably included a little instrument making. After gaining some initial experience, partly in London, Watt set himself up as an instrument-maker in Glasgow in 1756. Part of his work was to repair some astronomical instruments belonging to the university there. Soon after, other work was given to Watt by the university, including the repair of a model Newcomen engine which Professor John Anderson used to illustrate his lectures. The model caused Watt to think about atmospheric steam engines to such effect that, after 1764, engines became his chief concern.

When Watt had repaired Anderson's engine, he found that although it now worked quite well, it would run for only a very short time before the boiler ran out of steam. It seemed that the model engine was using a disproportionate amount of steam in relation to its size. In fact Watt found that to perform one stroke, several cylinderfuls of steam had to be supplied to the engine. Yet the cylinders only had to be filled once.

The problem may be understood by recalling that in Newcomen's engine, steam was condensed in the cylinder, producing a vacuum, and the piston was pushed downwards into this empty space by atmospheric pressure. The trouble was that the jet of cold water which condensed the steam also cooled the metal walls of the cylinder. Then, when steam was let into the cylinder to start the next stroke, much of it immediately condensed on the cold metal cylinder walls.

Watt considered various expedients for dealing with this problem, and finally realised that there was no need to have jets of water condensing steam inside the cylinder. He could have a 'separate condenser' linked to the cylinder by a pipe. This would be sealed off while the cylinder was being filled with steam. But when a vacuum was required in the cylinder, steam would be allowed to pass along this pipe. Meeting cold metal surfaces in the condenser, it would revert to water, and more steam would flow from the cylinder to take its place. If this was done, the cylinder could be kept hot all the time, while a low temperature and pressure could be permanently maintained in the condenser.[12]

Watt had the idea for the separate condenser in 1765, and

12. For a fuller account see Dickinson, *A Short History of the Steam Engine.*

patented it in 1769. But in the meantime, Smeaton had encountered the same problem in the studies he made of steam-
engine performance. To a remarkable degree his work followed
the same lines as Watt's, and he came to similar conclusions
about the waste of steam through condensation on the metal
surfaces of the cylinder. With the small experimental engine he
had built at his home near Leeds, he found that in each stroke
nearly four times more steam was being used than was needed to
fill the cylinder. Thus almost three-quarters of the steam had
condensed on the cylinder walls.

Smeaton saw that the amount of steam wasted in this way
would depend on the volume of the cylinder in relation to the area
of its internal surfaces. In a large engine, or in an engine whose
cylinder was more carefully proportioned, the ratio of volume
to area would be larger than in his small experimental engine.
Thus a smaller proportion of the steam would come into contact
with the cold metal of the cylinder walls. By attention to detail
in this and in many other parts of engine design, Smeaton was
able to make a very significant improvement to the conventional
Newcomen-type engine. Unfortunately, though, he did not
realise that Watt had already eliminated the problem of steam
wasted by condensation on cylinder walls, and that this was
already leading to greater improvements in engine performance.
Thus Smeaton's work was very largely outdated before it began.

The methods adopted by Smeaton and Watt in their studies
of the Newcomen engine were in some ways remarkably similar.
The approach of both men was certainly 'scientific' and systematic. But there were important differences as well. Smeaton
expected to make only detailed modifications to engine design.
In contrast to Watt, he was an improver, not an inventor. For
although Watt did not invent the steam engine, as some people
seem to think, he radically transformed it, and his separate
condenser was a clear-cut invention. Watt said that the idea came
to him suddenly on a Sunday in May 1765, when he was walking
on Glasgow Green. One cannot help thinking that Smeaton's
approach was too rigorously systematic and methodical to permit
such flashes of insight. He examined the engine part by part,
looking for ways to make detailed improvements. He employed
what, in chapter four, was called the 'method of detail', and used
it with a thoroughness one cannot help but admire.

Watt had a more flexible mind. He could look at the engine as a whole as well as in detail; and he could therefore envisage improvements affecting its whole principle of working. It was men with an outlook like Smeaton's who were responsible for the evolutionary development of technology as it was taking place in many parts of Europe at this time. Watt's turn of mind was more unusual, but it was that which produced revolutionary changes in technology.

Many years were to pass before all the technical difficulties involved in Watt's invention were solved. In 1774 he entered into a partnership with Matthew Boulton (1728–1809), a Birmingham businessman whose factory employed the kind of craftsmen Watt needed to complete the development of his engine. In the next two decades, the firm of Boulton and Watt was responsible for the construction of many engines of the new type for use at mines and in factories all over the country. However, Boulton and Watt did not at this time build complete engines. They furnished drawings from which other firms could make the parts; they supplied technicians to erect each engine at the site where it was to be used; and they were paid for their services on the basis of a royalty levied for the use of the patented separate condenser.

The industries of the 'industrial revolution'

For a while, Boulton and Watt were responsible for some of the most advanced engineering work being done in Britain. But they can hardly be regarded as having taken the lead in the process of industrial change, because without the prior existence of other large industrial concerns, there would have been nobody to buy their engines. During the last thirty years of the 18th century, large units of this kind were to be found most notably in mining, the iron industry and in textiles. But how novel was large-scale industry such as this?

In the last decades of the 17th century, and during nearly all the 18th century, the prosperity of Britain had been steadily increasing, and many trades and industries had seen considerable advances. Between about 1680 and 1730, there had been a period of particularly fruitful technical advance (chapter six), covering the first Newcomen engines and Abraham Darby's first coke-fired blast furnace. Why, then, has it become common to pick on a period beginning in 1760 or 1770 and call it 'the industrial revolution'? What sense does it make to use this name?

Very often, the word 'revolution' is used to refer to change which is mainly of a social or political kind. Taking that meaning, one could justify the term 'industrial revolution' by pointing out that during the period so denominated, there was a radical change in the economic and social relationships of various groups of people in Britain, marked particularly by the emergence of the working class in its modern sense. However, the more basic meaning of 'revolution', as a period of especially rapid, if not discontinuous change, is really all that is indicated here. Thus the question of why we should regard the industrial revolution as beginning about 1760 or 1770 can be answered mainly in terms of the rapidity of industrial change, as it may be expressed by percentage growth rates, or by means of graphs. For example, it is estimated that the production of pig-iron in Britain increased significantly between 1660 and 1760, possibly by as much as 50 per cent.[13] This is quite impressive; but a much bigger percentage increase, amounting to a growth of 100 per cent, took place in a mere ten years between 1796 and 1806.[14]

There was thus a very considerable acceleration in the rate of increase towards the end of the century, and it is this which justifies the term 'industrial revolution'. The first two-thirds of the 18th century had been a time of very significant change, but the pace was slow enough for us to describe it as 'evolutionary'. It is by contrast with this that the very rapid industrial growth which occurred at the end of the century may seem to be 'revolutionary'.

The transition between evolutionary and revolutionary phases of development can be quite clearly distinguished for the cotton industry in Britain, and seems to have been completed a little earlier than in the iron industry. An accurate record of the quantity of raw cotton imported was kept by the Customs authorities. Because this represents the whole of the raw material used, the growth of the industry can be measured with some precision. Soon after 1770, a rapid expansion very clearly began, and during the following decade raw cotton imports increased by an average of about 30 per cent each year.

This phase of rapid growth may, perhaps, be dated from 1774,

13. Flinn, *Economic History Review*, series 2, *11*, p. 146.
14. Mitchell and Deane, *Abstract of British Historical Statistics*, tables for pig-iron production.

when government restrictions on the use of cotton were lifted. These had been imposed at the beginning of the century to protect wool manufactures. More important, though, were a series of technical inventions related to the spinning of cotton yarn. The most significant was the machine patented in 1769 by Richard Arkwright (1732–92). Before the 1760s, spinning had been something of a bottleneck in all the textile industries. The

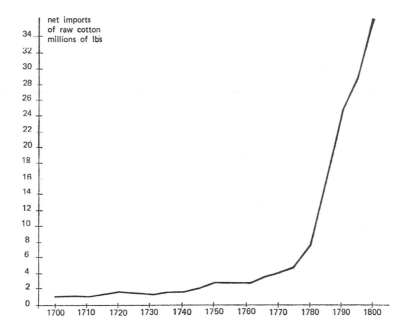

Figure 30

Raw cotton used in the British textile industry during the 18th century. (Source: Phyllis Deane and W. A. Cole, *British Economic Growth 1688–1959*, Cambridge University Press, 1962, p. 51; figures are ten-year moving point averages)

full-time work of five or six spinners was needed to keep one loom supplied with yarn, and the production of cloth could only be increased if spinning was in some way speeded up. Many people were aware of this, and many attempts were made to devise new spinning techniques.

James Hargreaves of Blackburn made his famous 'spinning jenny' in 1764 or soon after. This, however, was a simple hand-powered machine; what excited Richard Arkwright was the prospect of spinning by mechanical power. The example had been set by the silk mill at Derby, opened in 1721 (chapter six). Driven by a water-wheel, this produced silk thread by the use of machines not greatly different from the type invented in Italy around 1300.

When the Derby silk-mill proved to be successful, the question seems to have arisen as to whether a similar kind of machinery could be designed for the spinning of woollen or cotton thread. Several features from the machines used in the silk-mill were adopted by Paul and Wyatt in a cotton-spinning machine which they devised in 1738. Then comparable ideas were developed further in the 1760s by Thomas Highs of Leigh in Lancashire and his associate John Kay, a Warrington clock-maker. Arkwright was also a Lancashire man. He had worked as a barber and wig-maker at Preston and then at Bolton. Little else is known of his early career, but he evidently heard of the work of Highs and Kay, and enlisted Kay's help in the construction of a similar machine. This was successfully completed by 1769, when Arkwright obtained his patent for a spinning-machine.

At this stage, Arkwright set up the first factory in which cotton-spinning was carried on by means of power-driven machinery. This was at Nottingham, where the hosiery industry promised a good market for Arkwright's yarn. Power was provided by horses. Probably six were used at a time; they were harnessed to a horizontal wheel, 27 feet in diameter, which was housed in a ground-floor room of the factory. Wooden shafts and pulleys took the drive from this wheel to the spinning-machines on the floors above.

Arkwright raised the capital needed to start this factory by entering into a partnership with two local stocking manufacturers. The firm prospered; in 1771, a larger factory, powered by water-wheels, was set up at Cromford, two miles south of Matlock in Derbyshire, and within a short time 600 workers were employed there.

One of Arkwright's partners in these early ventures was Jedediah Strutt of Derby. In the late 1770s, Strutt and Arkwright collaborated to set up new mills at Belper and Milford, a few miles north of Derby, both with water-wheels driven by the

River Derwent. By means of other partnerships, Arkwright became associated with four more cotton factories in Derbyshire, and others in Lancashire and Scotland. All these were in operation by 1790, and their construction so soon after Arkwright's first invention gives a measure of how quickly the cotton industry grew.

Rational methods in mechanical invention

A clear and definitive account of the machines used in these early cotton-mills has recently been provided by R. L. Hills,[15] so it seems unnecessary to go into detail about their working principles. However, it is worth considering the background to the introduction of these machines in a slightly different way. Arkwright's spinning-machine and many other of the new devices seem to have depended for their invention solely on the mechanical ingenuity of a succession of fairly ordinary craftsmen. It would appear that most of these people had no special scientific or theoretical knowledge, but were simply 'mechanically-minded'.

If we ask, how did people become mechanically-minded without being taught any of the theoretical principles of mechanics, the answer would seem to be that as more and more machinery came into use, so people's experience of mechanism was enlarged, and their insight into what a machine could do increased. Mechanical invention advanced in a kind of geometrical progression. The more machines there were, the more a man picked up by experience about their working principles, and the greater, therefore, was his capacity to imagine and devise new kinds of machine. The mechanically-minded craftsmen of 18th-century Britain were the product of several previous generations of instrument-makers, clock-makers, millwrights and machine-builders.

John Smeaton never had to deal with the new textile machinery, nor was he connected with any of the notable mechanical inventions of the period. Therefore he never had the stimulus to apply his rationalising impulse to machine design or to the processes of mechanical invention. In the course of time, however, the ideas involved in the invention and design of machines did

15. *Power in the Industrial Revolution.*

come to be rationalised and codified, and textbooks were written about them. When this happened, it could be seen that there were general principles involved. Earlier craftsmen had learned these by experience, and had put them into practice without being able to state them in words, but in the 19th century they could be formalised in terms of the science which is now called 'the kinematics of machinery'.

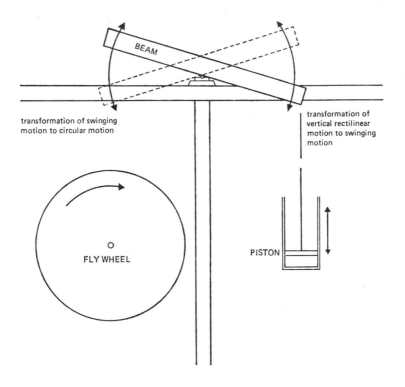

Figure 31
The kinematic problems in Watt's rotative engine.
(Diagram specially drawn for the author by D. M. Farrar)

Some of James Watt's work helps to illustrate how the intuitive ingenuity of a mechanically-minded man was capable of being rationalised. In the 1780s he introduced a rotative steam engine which was extensively used to drive machinery in cotton-mills.

This was made possible by two particular inventions in the field of kinematics. On the face of it, these were based on the same kind of intuitive mechanical ingenuity as many of the textile inventions. But a closer examination shows that Watt was capable, to some degree, of rationalising the general principles which they involved.

These two inventions were both related to the problem of transforming the reciprocating motion of the steam engine's piston into the rotary motion of a fly-wheel. Watt retained an

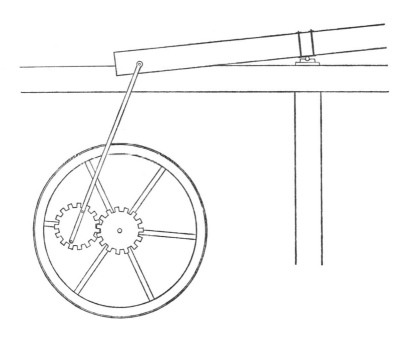

Figure 32

Solutions to kinematic problems (1): transformation of a swinging motion into a rotary motion – the 'sun-and-planet motion' used on Watt's engines. (Diagram specially drawn for the author by D. M. Farrar)

overhead beam in his engine like the beam of the Newcomen engine. Thus the motion of the piston had first to be transformed into the swinging motion of the beam; then the swinging beam had to turn the fly-wheel (fig. 31).

The connection between the beam and the fly-wheel could

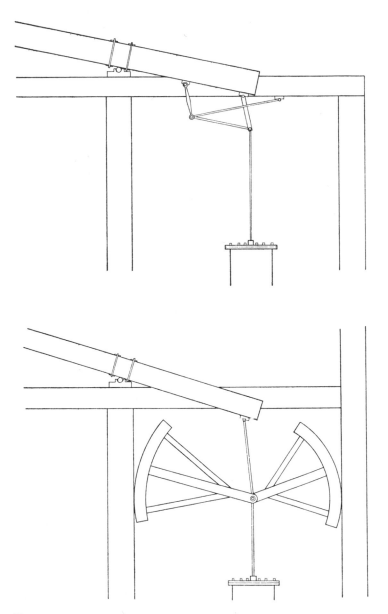

Figure 33
Solutions to kinematic problems (2): transformation of a vertical reciprocating motion into a swinging motion: two of the several methods proposed
by Watt, the top drawing showing the 'parallel motion' actually used.
(Diagram specially drawn for the author by D. M. Farrar)

most obviously be made by means of a rigid connecting-rod and a crank. However, Watt thought that his use of the crank would be restricted by a patent that had been taken out by somebody else. Wishing to avoid trouble over this, he considered four other methods for linking a connecting-rod to a fly-wheel without using a crank. In 1781, he patented all four of these methods, although only one of them, the 'sun and planet' motion, was used regularly on his engines (fig. 32).

The other kinematic problem was how to transform the straight-line reciprocating action of the piston into the swinging motion of the beam. Watt found several different solutions for this too. Eventually, only one method, which became known as the 'Watt parallel motion', went into regular use.

Watt's capacity to think of several solutions to each problem shows that he had formulated the problems in generalised terms.[16] It suggests an intellectual interest in the rational basis of the mechanism. Of course, Watt had other motives as well. He wanted to secure patent rights that would exclude other inventors in the same field, and he had therefore to try to anticipate the alternative methods which they might suggest. Watt used his patents in a very restrictive way to discourage other inventors, and to maximise the business of his own firm. But that should not blind us to the exceptional way in which he explored the principles on which his patents were based.

The need to rationalise the procedures involved in designing machines became more urgent when this aspect of engineering had to be taught to students. The origins of the 'kinematics of machinery' as a science must therefore be sought partly in early attempts to provide formal technical education. In France, during the later 18th century, the most interesting technical schools from this point of view were the *École des Ponts et Chaussées*, and a school for army officers at Mézières, the *École du Génie*. In 1794–5, the *École Polytechnique* was founded in Paris as part of a scheme for enlarging and co-ordinating the work of the other technical schools. It is clear that some form of machine kinematics was taught at this new institution as part of a course on descriptive geometry. The syllabus was devised by Gaspard Monge (1746–1818), the former teacher at the *École du Génie* who is celebrated for his innovations in the field of technical drawing.

16. See Ferguson, *Kinematics of Mechanism from the time of Watt.*

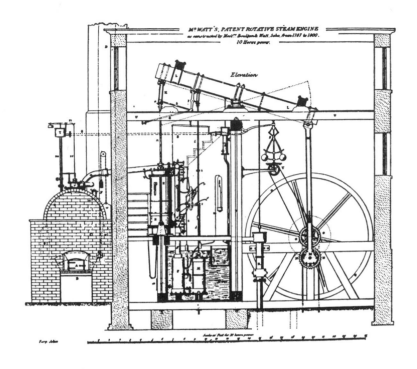

Figure 34
Watt's double-acting rotative engine, showing the cylinder with condenser
below, the parallel motion and the sun-and-planet motion.
(Original in John Farey, *A Treatise on the Steam Engine*, London, 1827; also
reproduced as fig. 14 of H. W. Dickinson, *A Short History of the Steam Engine*,
Cambridge University Press, 1939, p. 81)

He classified the motions of machines using two pairs of basic categories: circular or rectilinear motion; and continuous or reciprocating motion.[17] A little later, two other authors writing in Paris, took much the same line: 'The motions which are used in the arts are either rectilinear, or circular, or determined by some given curve; they can be either continuous or reciprocating. . . . All machines have as their object the transformation or communication of these motions.'[18]

At the end of their book, these authors gave a diagram illustrating their classification of the motions of machines; and this included some mechanisms which were clearly derived from a knowledge of Watt's engines.

In the 1820s, polytechnic schools were founded in many German cities following the example of the *École Polytechnique*, though usually on a more modest scale. Once again one finds that the science of kinematics developed in parallel with the growth of engineering education. Karlsruhe Polytechnic and the Freiberg Mining Academy became well known for their courses in this field. But the classic book on the subject was written at Berlin by Franz Reuleaux. First published in 1875, its English translation appeared in the following year and was entitled *The Kinematics of Machinery*.

It may seem out of place to mention these French and German authors here, but it was a feature of the industrial revolution that Germans, or more often Frenchmen, wrote the best books about the new technologies which had been pioneered in Britain. Watt and Smeaton had both found it necessary to study French books on engineering because there were so few English works on the subject. Even in the next generation it was French and German authors who succeeded most in formulating a rationalised approach to engineering.

Perhaps the only exception to this statement is John Robison, a professor at Edinburgh who wrote a good account of Watt's steam engine for the *Encyclopaedia Britannica* in 1797. But even on this subject there was an earlier French author. He was Riche de Prony, director of the *École des Ponts et Chaussées*, whose book *Nouvelle architecture hydraulique* (1790–96) also gave some

17. Booker, in *Newcomen Society Transactions*, *34*, 1961–2, pp. 15–36, especially the appendix to the paper.
18. Lanz and Bétancourt, *Essai sur la composition des machines*, opening sentence.

account of Smeaton's work on water-wheels. One of its readers in England commented: 'I am out of all patience with Prony in the second volume—such a parade of Algebraical Formulae and total want of Candour and Justice to Mr. Watt.'[19] Rationalised engineering in France was certainly often more mathematical than it needed to be, but this quotation reflects chiefly on the abysmal ignorance of algebra and the calculus which prevailed among even well-read engineers in Britain at this time.

Engineering materials

One point about the new textile machinery of the 18th century which is not often discussed is the very elementary one of the materials out of which the machines were made. In fact, machinery of this period was made principally of wood, sometimes strengthened with iron brackets and ties. Iron and brass were used in bearings, and for the cylinders and pipes of engines and pumps, but for little else. Arkwright's spinning-machines had wooden frames and were driven by wooden pulleys; the large gear-wheels used in mills and in much industrial machinery were constructed of timber, with apple-wood the favoured material for the teeth.

In the first generation of cotton-mills, traditional materials, traditional building techniques and traditional mechanical design were brought together for an entirely new purpose. Inherited from generations of craftsmen, the old methods were adequate while Arkwright's machines were still in the experimental stage. But serious problems occurred as soon as intensive industrial production was begun. Water-wheels which might serve a country miller for many years deteriorated rapidly when run for twenty-four hours a day in mills working a night shift. Wooden-floored factories lit by candles or oil-lamps represented an alarming fire risk. Many mills were burnt down, including in 1781 Arkwright's first one in Nottingham.

William Strutt, a son of Arkwright's former partner Jedediah Strutt, was particularly concerned by these fires. He had heard of a theatre in Paris which was said to have a 'fireproof' structure. It had been built between 1785 and 1790, and a friend visiting Paris sent Strutt a description of how the floors in this building were made from hollow bricks. These bricks were built up into

19. MS. letter, George Lee to James Lawson, 5 March 1798.

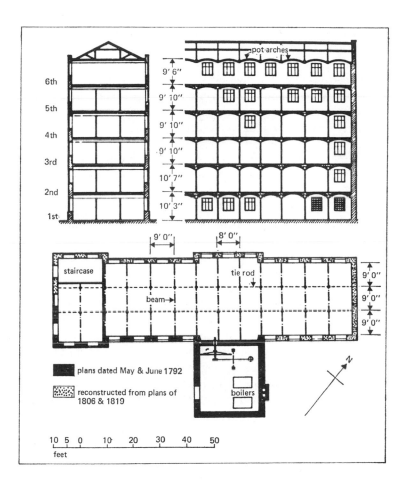

Figure 35

William Strutt's fireproof structure. This six-storey cotton-mill designed by Strutt was erected at Derby in 1792-3, and was the first multi-storey fireproof building. The floors consisted of brick arches carried on heavy timber beams, which themselves were supported by two rows of cast-iron columns.

(Source: H. R. Johnson and A. W. Skempton, 'William Strutt's cotton mills', in *Newcomen Society Transactions*, 30, 1956)

arches and supported by wrought iron bars; no timber was used in the construction.

Strutt immediately adapted the idea of the brick arches for use in cotton-mills. He devised a floor structure in which timber floorboards were eliminated, while the main beams, which were still of wood, were well protected from any outbreak of fire. Between 1792 and 95, three cotton-mill buildings were erected on this principle for the Strutt family firm. Cast-iron columns were used to support the very heavily constructed floors, and one of the buildings, erected at Belper in 1795, needed 148 columns, costing about £2 each.

One of Strutt's friends, Charles Bage, took things a little further in 1796. The owners of a flax-spinning mill in Shrewsbury took him into partnership at a time when they were planning to erect a new building. Bage acted as architect, and designed a structure in which no timber was used at all either for the floors or the roof. Cast-iron columns were used, as in Strutt's mills, but the novel feature was that the main floor beams were of cast iron also. In 1802, Bage began to build another factory on the same principle at Leeds. He wrote to Strutt at this time, seeking to persuade him of the virtues of his designs for cast-iron beams. With the aid of geometrical figures, he explained how he had calculated the strengths of the beams in the Leeds mill, making use of what seems to be a straightforward adaptation of Galileo's theory of the strength of beams (chapter three).

After Bage's time, iron beams and columns and fireproof floors came into fairly widespread use, at least among industrialists who could afford this somewhat expensive form of construction. At the same time, water-wheels and many other kinds of machine were made increasingly of iron. In the 1790s, for example, even steam engines contained a large amount of wood in their construction, but very soon all-metal construction became standard. The great beam, which swung to and fro, transmitting the motion of the piston to the pumps or the fly-wheel, was the most prominent timber component. About 1801, Boulton and Watt began to make these engine-beams of cast iron. But some four or five years earlier, iron engine-beams had been pioneered by the little-known Yorkshire firm of Aydon and Elwell. They seem to have got advice on the theoretical aspects of the design of engine-beams from John Banks (c. 1740–1805), an itinerant lecturer on mechanics and 'natural philosophy'. It is clear that

Banks, like Bage, made use of Galileo's theory.[20] This at first seems surprising, because far better theories had been developed during the 18th century by Antoine Parent and other continental mathematicians. The difficulty was that French mathematics was simply not intelligible to English readers. Galileo's theory had serious defects, but it could be used in such a way that these did not affect conclusions drawn from it. Thus in 1806, one English author said that French theories were 'certainly very ingenious; but . . . we prefer the comparatively simple theory of Galileo'.[21]

The use of iron in the construction of cotton-mills and their machinery provided the growing cotton industry with equipment far more adequate to its needs than the makeshift adaptations of traditional techniques and materials which had characterised the Arkwright period. Strutt and Bage had made many of the essential innovations in the remarkably fruitful ten years between 1792 and 1802. A very clear-cut second generation of textile factories had emerged, based on a markedly more advanced technology than the first generation of Arkwright's time, and this also marked a new phase in the industrial revolution generally.

John Banks remarked, in 1803, that 'Of late cast iron has been used in various cases, in place of stone or wood, as in bridges, engine beams, pillars, rail ways. . . .'[22] He was thinking of the pioneer iron bridge near Coalbrookdale in Shropshire, completed in 1781; of the iron bridges and aqueducts which Telford had been building since 1795; and of the cast-iron rails currently being used on colliery railways in Yorkshire.

The use of cast iron for these many engineering purposes increased very rapidly indeed during the 1790s. This is especially significant because it seems that the iron industry at this time had only just moved from the evolutionary to the revolutionary phase of its development. The demand for iron machinery, and for iron columns and beams for building, contributed greatly to this transition, and it could be said, just after 1800, that 'For this improvement we are perhaps indebted to those who are engaged in cotton manufacture'.[23]

20. Banks, *On the Power of Machines*, pp. 73-4.
21. Olinthus Gregory, *A Treatise of Mechanics*, vol. I, p. 104.
22. Banks, *On the Power of Machines*, p. 89.
23. Buchanan, 'On the shafts of mills', in *Practical Essays on Mill Work*, pp. 252-4.

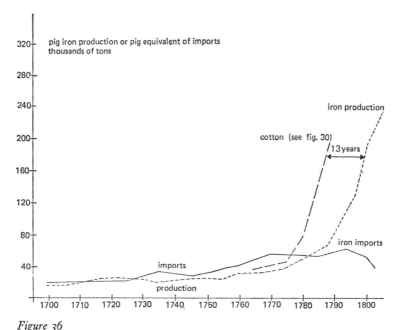

320— pig iron production or pig equivalent of imports
thousands of tons

280—

240—   iron production

200—   cotton (see fig. 30)

160—   13 years

120—

80—

40—   iron imports
             imports
                        production

1700 1710 1720 1730 1740 1750 1760 1770 1780 1790 1800

Figure 36
Iron production and imports during the 18th century (England and Wales).
Dashed lines represent the author's estimates, based on analysis of all
available figures for imports, exports and consumption.
(Sources: for imports, Phyllis Deane and W. A. Cole, *British Economic Growth*, p.
51; for production [marked o], B. R. Mitchell, *Abstract of British Historical
Statistics*, Cambridge University Press, 1962)

It is difficult to say exactly when the iron industry entered its
revolutionary phase of growth. During most of the 18th century,
about half of the iron used in Britain was imported from Sweden
and Russia, and while accurate records were kept of the quantity
imported, figures for home production are extremely sparse and
difficult to evaluate. There seems to have been some increase in
production around 1760, stimulated by a demand for cast-iron
gun-barrels from the belligerents in the Seven Years War
(1756–63). By 1775, home production was increasing, while
imports remained the same, but the kind of rapid growth which
justifies the term 'industrial revolution' was not in evidence
until almost 1790 (see fig. 36). By then, English iron-making was

competing very successfully with the Swedish industry, and imports soon began a rapid decline. This reflects an increasing technological expertise in Britain which can be studied in greater detail in standard works by T. S. Ashton and others.[24]

The fact that the iron industry entered its period of revolutionary growth some twelve or fifteen years after the cotton trade illustrates the way in which cotton effectively led the whole of the British economy into the industrial revolution. The cotton industry grew quickly because cloth made from factory-spun yarn was so cheap that working people could buy it – people who had never been able to afford cotton before. At one time a lady could be distinguished from her maid because she wore cotton and the maid wore wool, but that particular kind of class distinction now began to disappear.[25] British merchants also found that cloth made from Arkwright's machine-spun yarn could be sold in Europe, in Africa and in the Americas. So Arkwright's spinning-machine catered for a market of enormous size, and one which had scarcely existed before. The consequence was that the cotton industry could grow very rapidly – and as it grew it created a greatly-increased demand for steam engines, machines, transport, dyes, fuel and building materials. The almost explosive development of the textile trade therefore led to a rapid expansion in the industries which produced these things, most notably the iron industry. Without the prior development of textiles, these other industries would certainly all have developed very much more slowly.

Motives and ideas during the industrial revolution

If there was space here to analyse the innovations which occurred in the cotton and iron industries at this time, it would be clear that most of them were intended to meet quite explicit economic objectives. There were cost-saving improvements aimed, for example, at economising in the fuel consumed by steam engines, and there were innovations like Arkwright's which were designed to speed up particular parts of a productive process; there were also inventions aimed at specific markets or to meet particular demands.

24. See Ashton, *Iron and Steel in the Industrial Revolution*, and Schubert, *History of the British Iron and Steel Industry . . . to 1775*.
25. Edwards, *The Growth of the British Cotton Trade*, chapter 3.

However, there were many people whose efforts in technology were in addition related to social and intellectual ideals. In correspondence about iron columns and fireproof floors, William Strutt and Charles Bage also found time to discuss their social ideals. Occasionally they designed iron-framed buildings to house schools as well as spinning-machines. And it has been suggested here that Smeaton's use of the term 'Civil Engineer' reflected an ideal about engineering's being used for the public good.

Whether people acted on social ideals such as this, or whether their motives were always really aimed at private profit, is a difficult question, of the sort being discussed by the professor of moral philosophy at Glasgow University during the time when Watt was repairing instruments there. It is doubtful whether the distinguished professor and the young instrument-maker ever met, although they certainly had friends in common. But whether Watt heard about it or not, the point that the professor was making in his lectures was that men had both social and selfish propensities; and although at times a social impulse such as 'fellow feeling' for another person could cause a man to act unselfishly, his economic behaviour was chiefly a matter of pursuing his own self-interest. It was futile simply to deplore the predominance of self-interested behaviour in trade and commerce, for such behaviour was a natural part of life and often had a constructive effect. Benevolence might be the greatest virtue, but self-interest could lead to lesser virtues such as thrift, hard work and discretion.

This analysis of human motivation was begun in a book called *The Theory of Moral Sentiments* (1759), and was extended into the economic sphere in *An Inquiry into the Nature and Causes of the Wealth of Nations* (1776). The author of both these works was Adam Smith (1723–90); he was professor at Glasgow between 1751 and 1764, then travelled on the continent for a while, meeting French intellectuals and 'economists', before settling down to write his famous *The Wealth of Nations* in the seclusion of his home at Kirkcaldy.

Although Smith had little to say in his books about technical change, his propositions about human motives can very appropriately be used to illuminate the part played by ideas and idealism in the development of technology. To the extent that the practical arts – or later, technology – were purely economic activities, they were subject to the motives of self-interest which, according to Smith, predominate in economic life. Idealism would then hardly be relevant to technical change. But in fact, technology belongs only partly to the economic sphere; there have always been some fields in which the impulse towards technological innovation could arise from what Smith classed as the social rather than the selfish propensities of man. During the Thirty Years War, people like Rudolph Glauber (chapter five) had clearly been moved by fellow-feeling for those who suffered, and had proposed all sorts of projects for restoring the trades by which they had formerly earned their living. In earlier times, the impulse to innovate had sometimes arisen from intellectual ideals which whole communities had shared. Clocks and cathedrals had been the physical realisation of symbols which had excited many people in 13th-century Europe (chapter two). The mathematical trend among architects and engineers during the Renaissance was the result of a neo-Platonic idealism about the use of mathematics. In all these cases, the motives of the practitioners of the arts can be more readily understood in terms of social rather than self-interested inclinations.

It can, of course, be argued that the cathedral-builders in the 13th century, or the engineers of the Languedoc Canal in the 17th, were all affected by the need to keep costs within certain limits. Their personal incomes and financial security would also depend on the progress of the work. But they were, to some degree, protected from the direct force of economic pressures; what they finally achieved was judged on other grounds than purely economic ones. The size and grandeur of the works, the quality of the craftsmanship, and the way in which the construction symbolised the aspirations of those who had commissioned it – all these could be more important than strictly financial considerations. The ever-present pressure to cut costs would be greatly modified by non-economic demands, and innovation would only to a limited extent be influenced by the profit motive.

To use Smith's distinction between social and selfish inclinations in making this point is to use his ideas 'to promote an end which was no part of his intention'. For one thing, he was most concerned to demonstrate the possible constructive social influence of economic self-interest. He would probably have felt it unrealistic to give too much stress to the non-economic motives mentioned here, and he also tended to minimise the importance of technological change in industrial progress. It seemed to him that to organise industrial production on the principle of the division of labour[26] would lead to a far greater improvement in output than would the introduction of machines. But despite his apparent lack of interest in technology, Adam Smith's ideas appealed strongly to some technically-minded people – and it is they who form the subject of the next chapter.

26. William Petty discussed the division of labour a century before Smith – see p. 140 above.

8

Liberty, Utility and Socialism: social ideals during the industrial revolution

Peter Ewart, engineer

In October 1790, Boulton and Watt appointed an agent to represent their interests in Manchester. His name was Peter Ewart; he was the youngest son of a Church of Scotland minister, and he was then about twenty-three years of age. His job was to seek orders for steam engines, supervise their erection, and undertake what ancillary engineering work he liked on his own account.

Ewart represented Boulton and Watt in this capacity for less than two years, although he worked for them again later; but he maintained a close and friendly contact with James Watt and his son throughout their lives. In sending Ewart to Manchester, Watt may have thought of himself as launching him on a career within the firm of Boulton and Watt. But as it turned out, it was a very varied career which Ewart followed, embracing many aspects of the industrial and intellectual life of Manchester. And because that town was by now very clearly at the centre of the industrial revolution, Ewart's career illustrates some of the most important developments of the period.

Throughout most of the forty-five years which he spent in Manchester, Ewart was connected with the cotton industry in one way or another. He erected Watt engines at cotton-mills, designed water-wheels for them, and devised new types of machinery for spinning and weaving. When he ended his agreement with Boulton and Watt in 1792, it was with the purpose of entering more fully into the world of cotton manufactures. He had accepted an offer of partnership from Samuel Oldknow, the owner of cotton-mills near Stockport. This arrangement was to prove short-lived, however. After it had ended, and after a few months of working at Birmingham for Boulton and Watt,

Ewart returned to Manchester in 1796 as partner of another mill-owner, Samuel Greg. Eventually, at the end of eighteen years with Greg, Ewart acquired a small cotton-mill of his own in the centre of Manchester. But even this did not exhaust the variety of his career in the textile industry. In 1824, while continuing to run his own mill, Ewart entered into a third partnership, this time with Charles Macintosh, the pioneer of rubber-coated cloth. Macintosh was setting up a factory in Manchester, and Ewart negotiated the purchase and erection of a steam engine for him – a 20-horse-power one from Boulton and Watt.

Ewart's outlook on engineering may have owed quite a lot to the writings of John Smeaton, whose work he admired,[1] and it is perhaps significant that he became a member of the Smeatonian Society in 1822. In other matters, Ewart was influenced by the period of about a year, around 1782, which he spent at Edinburgh University. Ewart's cousin John Robison, professor of natural philosophy at Edinburgh,[2] was actively interested in most branches of physical science, and in practical mechanics, including steam engines; Ewart undoubtedly attended his lectures. But he must also have gone to lectures on other subjects, and some clue as to what these were is perhaps provided by the interest he later showed in the work of several Scottish philosophers. At the end of his life, one of Ewart's 'most favourite authorities' was Adam Smith's *Theory of Moral Sentiments*. Ewart evidently marked his copy of the book with numerous pencil notes.[3]

On settling in Manchester, he found an outlet for these wide-ranging interests in the Manchester Literary and Philosophical Society, of which he became vice-president in 1812. At various times he read papers to the Society, setting the tone of his contributions in 1808 with one paper on economics and another 'On the Measure of Moving Force'. The latter was of some importance in establishing the concept of energy in mechanics, but the paper on economics was never published. However, it is

1. Peter Ewart, in *Memoirs of the Manchester Literary and Philosophical Society*, 1813, p. 160.
2. Robinson and McKie, *Partners in Science*, pp. 112–3; John Ewart, *Biographical Sketches*, p. 14.
3. W. C. Henry, in *Memoirs of the Manchester Literary and Philosophical Society*, 1846, pp. 132–4.

of interest that in 1817 Ewart again spoke to the Society on economics, this time under the title: 'Dr. Adam Smith's distinction between Productive and Unproductive Labour'.[4]

Although no details of Ewart's views on Adam Smith survive, a reasonable surmise can be made about the aspects of Smith's work which interested him. In their economic behaviour, Smith said, men tended to act solely on the basis of their own self-interest. 'It is not from the benevolence of the butcher, the brewer, or the baker that we expect our dinner, but from their regard of their own interest.'[5] There was no disadvantage in this, because there was no essential conflict between the butcher's self-interest and that of his customer. The latter was satisfied if he got a good piece of meat at a reasonable price, while the butcher attracted more customers and made bigger profits by consistently supplying good meat. The natural order of things in society ensured that in a free market everybody got the fairest possible treatment. The problem was that governments could prevent the 'natural' law of the free market from working for the common good by introducing arbitrary rules and regulations.

When Adam Smith visited France during 1764-5, he found similar arguments being used by a group of people who used the term '*laissez-faire*' to describe the policy of allowing economic life to develop freely without government interference. These men were sharp critics of the mercantilist policies then being pursued by France (which were described above in chapter six), and they wished to see a more 'natural' form of development in agriculture and trade, less hampered by cumbersome regulations.

Towards the end of the 18th century, arguments of this sort were put forward with real conviction. They were not just cynical attempts to whitewash the selfish actions of factory-owners and traders, or to protect them from government intervention. They were, rather, the product of a genuine belief in a 'natural' order in society, accompanied by a remarkable and optimistic expectation that if 'nature' was allowed to take its course, there would be steady social improvement. Taxes, subsidies, regulations and Customs dues were all criticised as 'artificial' constraints on the natural processes of improvement.

The background to these ideas was the growth of science since the time of Galileo, Descartes and Newton. This had created a

4. *Manchester Literary and Philosophical Society*, 1846, p. 136.
5. *The Wealth of Nations*, Book I, chapter ii.

widespread enthusiasm for the discovery of laws of nature in other fields, and had given an example of how a rational ordering of knowledge was possible in the study of society, in economics and even in religion. In England, rational attitudes to religion were shown most strongly in Unitarianism, the liberal nonconformist creed which developed among the Presbyterian and Independent Churches during the 18th century. Many of the people among whom Ewart moved in Manchester were Unitarians, and Ewart himself attended the Moseley Street Unitarian Chapel. In the sphere of morals and religion, the Unitarians took as optimistic a view of mankind as Adam Smith and his like took in discussing economics. Like them, they felt that man's natural impulses, enlightened by reason, would tend to work for the good; they felt, too, that the mind of God was seen in the laws of nature more clearly than in the traditional sources of revelation. These views may have appealed to Peter Ewart, but his father, the Scottish minister, most strongly disapproved:

'The Unitarians do not see that they require any revealed religion; they think that the unaided wisdom of mankind is able to understand the principles of piety towards God. Full of their own wisdom, they have not felt nor understood the weakness and sinful propensities of human nature.'[6]

Unitarian beliefs were rooted in the same kind of rationalism as *laissez-faire* economic philosophy, and were influenced by the same view of nature and the natural order. But as Ewart's father pointed out, this set of ideas implied a very optimistic view of man and society. And when one reflects on the cruelty of much 19th-century industrial life, which was often justified or excused by later versions of the *laissez-faire* argument, one tends to agree that in this respect also, people had 'not felt nor understood the weakness and sinful propensities of human nature'.

The philosopher-manufacturers

Ewart never made a fortune by Manchester standards, partly because his interests were so diverse. It seems that he never stayed in one line of business for long enough to grow rich by it. None the less, he gained a degree of social standing and the leisure to pursue all these interests through his partnership with the important local cotton-mill owner, Samuel Greg.

6. John Ewart, essay on Isaac Newton, *Biographical Sketches*, p. 18.

This was a considerable advance, for when Ewart had first come to Manchester it was as an engineering craftsman of the type known as a millwright. He worked for Boulton and Watt, but they allowed him to undertake some millwright work on his own account. In this capacity he would do jobs for various mill-owners, charging something like four shillings a day for time spent at their factories. With his particular background and interests, though, Ewart could aspire to a better social position than that. And on several occasions, mill-owners who were conscious of this point and who wished to retain his services on a long-term basis offered him partnerships in their firms. In 1792, Ewart accepted such an offer from Samuel Oldknow of Stockport. The arrangement did not last for long, owing to financial difficulties in the firm, but in 1796, Ewart joined the liberal-minded Samuel Greg, owner of cotton-mills in Manchester and at Styal, to the south of that city. Ewart had no capital to contribute to Greg's enterprise.[7] He was made a partner simply because of the technical knowledge and skill he could contribute to building a new weir and water-wheels at Styal, and to ordering and erecting steam engines and other machinery in the mills.

Peter Ewart's combination of technological and philosophical interests was shared by a group of like-minded men who may appropriately be called the 'philosopher-manufacturers'. These were the intellectuals of the manufacturing community, and it is significant that several of them, like Ewart himself, owed their positions as members of the mill-owning class to partnerships in which they contributed technical knowledge rather than capital. Thus in the Salford firm of Philips and Lee, George Lee had been taken on for his technical ability. He had little money to contribute, but he designed machinery, planned new buildings with fireproof floors and experimented with steam engines. He was also a close friend of Peter Ewart, and married his sister Mary in 1803.

A somewhat different case was that of Robert Owen, who came to Manchester in 1789 and tried his hand in various small textile businesses, starting with £100 borrowed from his brother. After two years with little success, he became manager of the large Manchester cotton-mill owned by Peter Drinkwater. His predecessor in that post had been George Lee, who had supervised the construction of a new mill building and its machinery,

7. Greg and Ewart partnership agreement.

but had left before the job was complete, to enter into partnership with Philips in Salford. In April 1792, Lee reported to the younger James Watt that: 'We expect to begin working the Salford Mill next week when I shall quit Drinkwater – he is at last compelled to advertise for a manager after having in vain hawked it about privately – Ewart had an offer but I suppose you know he had made an Engagement with Oldknow.' (18 April 1792.)[8]

Robert Owen answered Drinkwater's advertisement, and was appointed manager almost as a last resort. He at first felt over-awed by the task which Lee had left him, for as he said, Lee was 'one of the most scientific men of his day, who was considered a man of very superior attainments, having been highly educated, and being a finished mathematician'.[9] There was also the problem that Owen knew very little about the machinery in Drinkwater's mill, and Lee had left before he started there. So he 'inspected everything minutely, examined the drawings and calculations of the machinery as left by Mr. Lee and said very little'. But at the end of six weeks, he felt himself very much the master of his position and 'ready to give directions in every department'. He was, in fact, so successful that Drinkwater proposed to make him a partner, although in the end this offer did not come to anything.

Lee and Owen, in very different ways, had intellectual interests comparable with Ewart's. Among other 'philosopher-manufacturers' outside Manchester, they may also be compared with William Strutt of Derby, the inventor of the 'fireproof' cotton mill, and his friend Charles Bage. Strutt had inherited his share in the family firm, but Bage was taken into partnership by much richer men for the sake of his technical knowledge. His partners were the Benyon brothers, owners of a flax-spinning mill in Shrewsbury, who had just then joined their business with the famous Marshall flax-spinning concern in Leeds. Bage was taken on in 1796, specifically, it seems, so that he could act as architect for the mill at Shrewsbury in which he introduced the first cast-iron beams ever to be used in Britain (chapter seven above).

8. Dates given in this way on subsequent pages refer to manuscript letters in the Boulton and Watt Collection, Birmingham Reference Library.
    9. Quoted by Cole, *The Life of Robert Owen.*

Liberty and laissez-faire

Men like Bage, Strutt, Lee, Owen and Ewart, the intellectuals of
the manufacturing class, found an outlet for their wider interests
in Literary and Philosophical Societies, like the one in Derby in
which William Strutt was active, or the much more famous one
in Manchester. These bodies may be compared with the more
informal and short-lived Lunar Society in Birmingham, in which
Matthew Boulton and James Watt met their more scientifically-
minded friends.

Owen joined the Manchester 'Lit and Phil' in 1793 and Ewart
followed in 1798. In later years, one of this society's most
prominent members was John Dalton, who introduced the idea
of atomic weights into chemistry. Both Owen and Ewart knew
him well – Owen was one of those who proposed him for member-
ship, and one volume of Dalton's book *A New System of Chemical
Philosophy* was dedicated to Ewart and another friend. But when
Ewart first came to Manchester, one of his closest friends was
James Watt's son, also called James, who was then enlarging his
experience by working for a textile firm in Manchester.

During the 1790s, the younger Watt was probably the most
politically conscious of all Ewart's associates. He belonged to the
Manchester Constitutional Society, which was a body dedicated
to the cause of Parliamentary reform on the basis of universal
suffrage. It believed in 'liberty', was very much influenced by the
writings of Tom Paine, and was sympathetic to the ideals of the
French Revolution.

Now the ideal of liberty in politics was very much the counter-
part of a belief in *laissez-faire* economics. Both were based on the
view that the power of governments should be limited, and that
the most desirable and most natural order in society was one in
which everybody enjoyed the minimum of restraint upon his or
her activities. It is not surprising to find that Peter Ewart, with
his interest in Adam Smith, was also sympathetic to Watt's
radical views. However, Ewart did not join the Constitutional
Society. Its principal members in 1791 included Samuel Greg
and George Philips, the mill-owners who later took on Ewart and
Lee as their respective partners. There was also Thomas Walker,
who in 1794 was tried on a charge of 'conspiracy to overthrow the
Constitution and Government'. Even earlier, in May 1791, it was
unwise to be known as a supporter of radical opinion, and the

young Watt thought it advisable to leave Manchester. He went first to Edinburgh, and then travelled on the continent for about three years. During this voluntary exile, he was kept in touch with Manchester affairs by letters from Lee and Ewart. One such letter, written in a humorous mood, was sent to Watt in Paris, where he was staying with 'your friends the Jacobins' and observing the French Revolution at close quarters. Lee described how he and Ewart had sat down after dinner one evening to write a joint letter, but their 'different Species of Wit' prevented it. (8 December 1792.)

Other letters show that while Lee and Ewart sympathised with Watt's politics, they were neither of them so radical as he. Watt's views were 'in danger of being biass'd rather by the State of Politics', Lee thought, and did not take sufficient account of other kinds of progress. Lee believed in the improving condition, 'of Society in other respects in Europe – on that Subject you and I have always agreed and differ'd in part – you take the heroic and I the prudent side of the question – you will all at once accomplish everything . . . and I with opinions not materially different deem it expedient to weigh the Risque of a Violent Convulsion. . . . Affairs have been lately untoward but not particularly so with us and consistent with a convenient system I deem it all for the best – pray what are your views? do not be too romantic, value everything for what it is worth, and do not disregard your Expectations in this country . . .' (September, 1793).

The French Revolution lost a great number of its English sympathisers once the guillotine began its work, and we may guess that Ewart, Lee and Watt ended their flirtation with radical politics about then. Attitudes were also influenced by the fact that England was almost continuously at war with France between 1793 and 1815. Thus of the reformers of the 1790s, not many remained true to the cause in 1815. They were 'a little circle of men, faithful, amongst the faithless, to liberal principles . . . There were few remaining of those who had been reformers at the commencement of the French revolution . . . Mr. George Philips . . . frightened at the atrocities of the revolution, had retreated into the ranks of the whigs . . . [but] Mr. Samuel Greg remained true to his early principles.'[10]

With their optimism about 'natural' social progress eroded, it

10. Prentice, *Historical Sketches*, p. 73.

was not so easy for generous-minded people to support a *laissez-faire* economic order; and Watt, Ewart and Lee seem to have been less generous and more hard-headed in their continued support for *laissez-faire* policies. Two issues which illustrate their opinions were the Corn Laws and the employment of children in factories. The Corn Laws had existed since the 1770s and were designed to stabilise the price of grain. However, the system had not worked well during the wars with France, when prices had sometimes risen to about twice the pre-war level. A new Corn Law was passed in 1815 in an attempt to maintain a better control of prices by prohibiting imports of corn when home prices were low. The trouble was that this arrangement favoured not the consumers, but the farmers who produced the corn, and it attempted to stabilise the price at a very high level.

Naturally, this was an unpopular measure in Manchester. The high price of corn meant that factory workers had to pay more for food, and many people were so poor that they were brought near to starvation. Among the mill-owners, including Peter Ewart and George Lee, there was also a campaign against the Corn Law, because they thought that the high price of food would force wages up and add to their costs.

The leaders of the factory-workers saw the problem in terms of Parliamentary reform. Parliament only represented the land-owners, and had approved the Corn Law because high prices would bring landowners a bigger income. If everybody had been allowed to vote in elections, and if all classes were represented in Parliament, this kind of law could never have been passed.

Ewart, Lee and the other mill-owners based their arguments on their *laissez-faire* attitude to economic matters. To restrict imports of corn, or to try to control prices, was an interference with the 'natural' economic order. By pushing up food prices, the new law might affect the level of wages and disturb the 'natural' equilibrium of the labour market. But as it happened, wages did not rise, so although the suffering of the working class increased, the manufacturers began to forget their objections.[11]

William Strutt of Derby, the pioneer of 'fireproof' factory buildings, seems to have felt greater sympathy with the factory workers' position than his colleagues in Manchester, and was

11. Ewart's friend John Kennedy, another mill-owner, wrote articles which provide evidence of these attitudes; see *Memoirs of the Manchester Literary and Philosophical Society*, 1819, pp. 115–37; pp. 430–45.

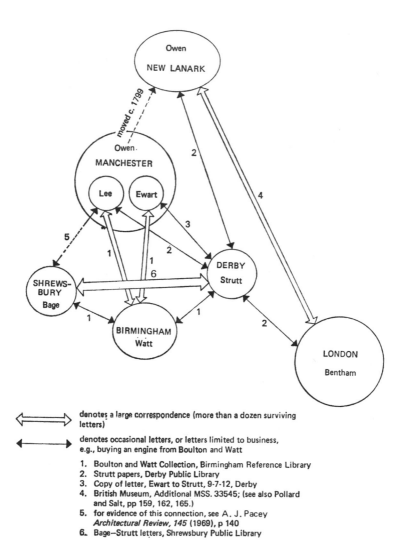

Owen
NEW LANARK

moved c. 1799

Owen.
MANCHESTER

Lee   Ewart

2

4

3

5

1   1   2

6

DERBY
Strutt

SHREWS-
BURY
Bage

1   1

BIRMINGHAM
Watt

2

LONDON

Bentham

⇐====⇒ denotes a large correspondence (more than a dozen surviving letters)

◄───► denotes occasional letters, or letters limited to business, e.g., buying an engine from Boulton and Watt

1. Boulton and Watt Collection, Birmingham Reference Library
2. Strutt papers, Derby Public Library
3. Copy of letter, Ewart to Strutt, 9-7-12, Derby
4. British Museum, Additional MSS. 33545; (see also Pollard and Salt, pp 159, 162, 165.)
5. for evidence of this connection, see A. J. Pacey
   Architectural Review, 145 (1969), p 140
6. Bage–Strutt letters, Shrewsbury Public Library

Figure 37

Relationships between men discussed in chapter eight, illustrated by the flow of correspondence between them during 1790–1820. The diagram can be read as a highly simplified map with New Lanark, near Glasgow, in the north and London in the south-east. The location of surviving letters is indicated by the numbers. No correspondence between Bage and Lee (5) has been found, but Lee knew of Bage's work on iron beams (Pacey, *Architectural Review, 145*). The numerous Bage–Strutt letters are in Shrewsbury Public Library.

optimistic about the current campaign for the reform of Parliament. But his friend Charles Bage was concerned about what the authorities might do if the agitation for reform became too strong. 'I distrust your calculation as to the improving state of Man in Society. In proportion as knowledge is diffused among the lower orders, the fears and vigilance of the government will increase ... and if we will not be kept down, we shall burst out into Revolution ...'[12]

In Manchester, many people thought that revolution was coming in 1819, when an enormous crowd of mill-workers and hand-loom weavers gathered on St Peter's Fields, near the centre of the city, to air their grievances, and to call for the reform of Parliament. The crowd was in fact quite peaceable, but the authorities were so frightened that they called in a local military force to arrest the main speaker, Henry Hunt, and stop the meeting. Soldiers on horseback rode into the crowd with sabres unsheathed, and in what became sarcastically known as the victory of Peterloo, 11 people were killed and about 400 injured.

The year of Peterloo was also the year of the first Factory Act, which attempted to regulate the hours during which children could be employed in the textile mills. Three years before, a Parliamentary committee had gathered evidence. Peter Ewart by now had a cotton-mill of his own, and the committee found that he employed 192 people, of whom 14 were children under ten and 120 were aged between ten and eighteen.[13] George Lee travelled to London to present his views, and found 'a busy meddling Spirit of Legislation afloat'. (15 June 1816.)

There were many delays in preparing legislation on children's employment, but in 1818 it became clear that a bill of some sort would be passed, and the Manchester mill-owners began to organise opposition. Lee's partner, George Philips, was now a member of Parliament, and he played a prominent part in opposing the Bill. Ewart wrote to John Rennie, the engineer, asking him, 'to exert himself *immediately* and strenuously with his friends in Parliament'; Lee asked the younger Watt to do what he could to oppose the Bill, 'the Principle of which is subversive of the Manufactures and if carried into a Law will doubtless be extended to all'. (5 April 1818.)

12. MS. letter, Bage to Strutt, 25 February 1818, Shrewsbury Public Library.
13. *Parliamentary Papers*, 3, 1816, 209, 374–5.

This, then, was the background to the Factory Act of 1819, which was partly the result of the campaign for some regulation of factory conditions which Robert Owen had been conducting since 1815. Owen had left Manchester for Scotland about 1799, where he became a partner in the cotton-mills at New Lanark. In his management of these mills, he showed that the conditions of workers could be substantially improved without the level of profits being adversely affected. At a time when the children of mill-workers often started work at the age of six, Owen provided them with schools and educated them until they were ten. He thought that, ideally, children ought not to start work until they were fourteen, and that the working day should be something less than ten hours. In fact, his workers were putting in a 12-hour day in 1816, and this was fairly general. The Strutts' workers did a 12-hour day in the mills at Belper near Derby, and among a total labour force of 1,500, there were 100 children under ten. These figures, however, do not really indicate which employers had a bad record in the employment of children. The Strutts provided schools for the children who worked in their factories, and took considerable trouble over their welfare.

Opposition to the Factory Act, then, did not necessarily imply a callous attitude to the conditions of children or other work-people, but for men like Ewart and Lee the Act seemed an unnecessary infringement of their liberty. Even William Strutt seems to have felt like that, although he was a friend of Robert Owen, whose agitations had done so much to bring it into being. In 1819, Owen had visited Strutt's son, then a pupil at Manchester College, York, and a little later, Owen stayed at the Strutts' house in Derby.[14]

Despite this friendship, Strutt seems to have agreed with the majority of the 'philosopher-manufacturers' that the Act was unnecessary, because he believed that conditions were already and inevitably improving. It was possibly even thought by Strutt and others that the restrictions introduced by the Factory Act would obstruct such 'natural' improvement and might even leave the factory workers worse off than they were before. Strutt, indeed, was an optimist, and like other well-meaning manufacturers, he could not see what Robert Owen, with his more sensitive imagination, was worrying about. The 18th-century ideal of freedom, applied to an industrial society, would

14. MS. letters, William Strutt to Edward Strutt, Derby Public Library.

tend to give real freedom only to a few, while leading to a cruel and brutalising existence for many. At that time, though, industrial society was still young, and people's experience of it was limited.

The Benthamites

The idea that progress was inevitable and natural in a free society was especially well expressed in the 18th century by Joseph Priestley, the Unitarian minister, educational pioneer and chemist. He held it to be a 'universal maxim, that the more liberty is given to everything which is in a state of growth, the more perfect it will become'; and he thought that 'all things . . . have of late years been in a quicker progress towards perfection than ever'. He also thought that it was the duty of governments to protect 'the lives, liberty or property of the members of the community', but not to intervene in other ways. In judging the actions of a government, there was one great test to be applied: 'The good and happiness of the . . . majority of the members of any state, is the great standard by which every thing relating to that state must finally be determined . . .'.[15]

In 1768, the year when Priestley wrote this, another of his works was read by a young Oxford graduate who had returned to his university to vote in an election. In the small library at Harper's Coffee House he found a pamphlet by Priestley which contained the phrase 'the greatest happiness of the greatest number'. At once he made this his own, seeing it as 'the only rational foundation, of all enactments in legislation and all rules and precepts destined for the direction of human conduct in private life'.[16]

The young man who was so taken up with this principle of 'greatest happiness' was Jeremy Bentham (1748–1832), whose later writings and influence were such that modern authors have described him as 'the philosopher of the Industrial Revolution',[17] and his followers as 'the theorist of the Industrial Revolution'.[18]

15. Priestley, *Essay on Government*, quoted by Willey, *The Eighteenth-Century Background*, Peregrine edn, pp. 187–90.
16. Mack, *Jeremy Bentham*, pp. 102–3.
17. Roberts, *The Whig Party 1807–12*, p. 264.
18. Halévy, *History of the English People in the 19th Century*, I, 1949 edn, p. 586.

But Bentham viewed the industrial revolution from a greater distance than the other men discussed in this chapter. He lived comfortably in London, and had no experience of the enormous factories and the overcrowded workers' housing of Manchester. However, his brother, Samuel Bentham, was a naval architect and shipwright, through whom he knew William Strutt of Derby. So he was able to gain some contact with the world of industry and technology. And the increasing pace of technological change filled him with optimism. It is said that he appeared to grow younger as he aged, so much was he exhilarated by the air of progress that he felt around him. He rejoiced in the multiplying technological and social improvements which he found everywhere.

Bentham had been trained in law, and was an active campaigner for the reform of Britain's antiquated and corrupt legal system. He was also interested in the widespread demand for Parliamentary reform; in 1790 he drew up plans showing how annual elections could be held with a secret ballot. Many of his attitudes suggest a *laissez-faire* approach to economic life, and in other ways too his views were similar to those of other people mentioned here (p. 241). Like them he thought that society developed according to laws of nature, and had a natural structure. He tended to agree, too, that by letting nature take its course – and by letting individuals work for their own self-interest – improvement could be obtained.

But Bentham also made important modifications to the usual *laissez-faire* approach. It seemed to him that if one could understand the laws of nature as they affected society, the art of government could be improved. Instead of leaving 'natural' social development to take its course, governments could use their knowledge to control or improve on what 'nature' was already doing. The guiding principle in all this would be 'the greatest happiness of the greatest number'. This was the test by which the actions of governments, industrialists, landowners and even private individuals could be judged.

'Utilitarian' is the word generally used to describe the philosophy of Bentham and his group, but Bentham himself preferred to say that his criterion was not one of 'utility' but of 'greatest happiness'. In discussing science and what would today be called technology, Bentham said that their purpose should be the increase of human happiness. His attitude can be compared with

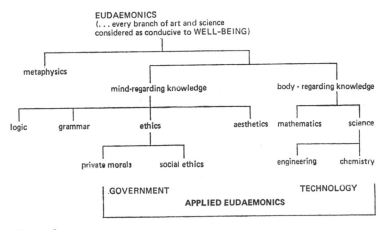

Figure 38
Eudaemonics: an interpretation of Bentham's 'encyclopedical tree'.
(Adapted from Mary Mack, *Jeremy Bentham: an Odyssey of Ideas 1748–1792*, Heinemann, 1962, p. 445)

the views of some of the 17th-century authors discussed in chapter five, who held that knowledge should be used for the welfare of mankind. Bentham was, in fact, strongly influenced by one of the most important of these, Francis Bacon (1561–1626), whose views on the value of science might also be called 'utilitarian'.

Bacon had been a lawyer, and it was probably his writings on the reform of law which first attracted Bentham's attention. But Bacon's views on the organisation of knowledge also interested Bentham, including the idea of an 'encyclopedical tree' which represented the mutual relationships of all the different 'branches' of knowledge. When Bentham set about constructing his own tree of knowledge, he made the trunk stand for a new science he called eudaemonics. This was a science of human impulses and behaviour, which described everything that could lead to human happiness and well-being. The tree had three main branches: a small one which represented metaphysics, and two larger ones representing 'body-regarding' knowledge and 'mind-regarding' knowledge. The body-regarding section consisted of mathematics and the natural sciences, while the mind-regarding branch split into smaller branches representing logic, grammar, ethics and aesthetics.

Making all these subjects grow as branches from the same

eudaemonic stem suggests that all subjects, even mathematics, were to be related to the problem of increasing happiness. But of course, the art of government more than anything else was concerned with this. Government, indeed, was a sort of applied eudaemonics. If legislators neglected to study this science, and to collect information about society, then parliaments ought to remain inactive. A *laissez-faire* policy was better than an ill-informed one. But if the government of a country took the trouble to gain a full knowledge of the society it ruled, then there was nothing it might not do.

Thus the first responsibility of a government was to collect information. For example, it ought to be regularly informed about the size of the population and how fast it was growing. The first census in Britain was taken in 1801, and it was probably no coincidence that Bentham's stepbrother, Charles Abbot, was involved in its organisation. Bentham also called for registers of harvests, food prices, the flow of money, and industrial production. And he thought that, given this information, legislators would be in a position to create 'positive well-being', or programmes of social welfare aimed at abundance for all.

In this respect, 'Bentham's principles contrast vividly with the doctrine of *laissez-faire*. When government had the necessary facts and a trained bureaucracy to interpret and use them, it might regulate industrial production to prevent surpluses, unemployment, and recessions; it might set minimum wages, establish old age pensions and health insurance plans. . . . But Bentham was of course sceptical of what the English government as he knew it might accomplish. In that nest of nepotism and bumbling amateurism, few officials knew as much about the activities of lesser social and economic organizations as the members did themselves. But government ought to know more. Until it did, he counselled, it had best practise *laissez-faire*.'[19]

The moral inventions of Strutt and Owen

If, as Bentham thought, reformers and legislators were really the practitioners of an applied science derived from eudaemonics, then they should be prepared to introduce 'moral inventions'. The devising of a new system of law or taxation would constitute such an invention, or a project for the relief of unemployment. But in the hands of William Strutt and Robert Owen, moral

19. Mack, *Jeremy Bentham*, pp. 296–8.

inventions could become partly technological innovations, including, for example, the design of houses for mill-workers.

The moral invention of which Bentham himself was most proud was his 'Panopticon'. This was initially conceived as a prison whose inmates would be morally reformed by being put to work under constant supervision. This would be arranged by putting a 'keeper's lodge' at the centre of the building 'with a commanding view of every part of the space into which a prisoner can introduce himself . . .'. A building with a circular plan would allow this to be done most effectively. Samuel Bentham worked out the architectural details, and had a model of it made in 1791.

Jeremy Bentham seems to have thought that the architectural form of this circular building would by itself have a beneficial effect, and he spent a long time trying to persuade the authorities to have a prison built to this style in London. In the end, though, nothing was done, and probably the only Panopticon ever built was a cotton-mill of circular plan erected by William Strutt in 1813. This formed part of the complex of factory buildings owned by the Strutt firm at Belper in Derbyshire, and like most of the rest of Strutt's buildings, it had a fireproof structure with brick floor arches. In 1819, Strutt may have been thinking of building another fireproof Panopticon. He was then designing a prison, and had experimented with 'Arches beautiful in appearance, of *common* bricks entirely . . . and as cheap as common Walling – so that all *Houses* may now be made fire proof with scarcely any increase of expense – I shall build the Town Jail of Derby so'.[20]

Another aspect of Strutt's activity in the field of moral invention was his contribution to the building of Derby Infirmary,[21] which was opened in 1810. Strutt seems to have made some kind of improvement to almost every aspect of the domestic arrangements in the Infirmary, but the most important was the system of heating and ventilation which he devised. This depended on the circulation of hot air by convection, distributed in ducts from a stove in the basement.

Strutt had experimented with heating-systems since the early

20. MS. letter in Derby Public Library, William Strutt to Edward Strutt, 2 June 1819.
21. Hacker, *Journal of the Derbyshire Archaeological and Natural History Society*, *80*, 1960, p. 57.

1790s, because some form of heating was needed in the cotton-mills which he designed and built. In 1794, Jeremy Bentham wrote to Strutt reporting on a recent patent for heating by steam;[22] and Bentham also made enquiries in London on Strutt's behalf about copper tubes which were needed for experiments.[23] Samuel Bentham was also interested, and in 1805 sought Strutt's advice about a method for 'drying wood artificially', no doubt in connection with his work in the shipyards.[24]

In 1808, visitors to Bentham's house in London included a Quaker, Joseph Lancaster, who ten years earlier had founded a school which embodied several novel principles. This for Bentham was another 'moral invention', and Lancaster's methods also appealed to the Strutts. They had already organised a Sunday School at Belper where children could learn to read and write. In 1809, William Strutt and his brother Joseph invited Lancaster to their home in Derby, and shortly afterwards began to organise a school on Lancaster's lines. At the same time, William Strutt's friend Charles Bage was planning a similar school in Shrewsbury, which was to be housed in a building he had designed specially for it.

There was something rather grimly utilitarian about Lancaster's schools; one of their features was that they enabled a very large number of pupils – up to a thousand – to be taught by one master. This was arranged by dividing the pupils into groups of ten, each group having its own monitor drawn from among the older pupils. In 1829, the Strutts had two hundred pupils in their 'Lancasterian school', but whether there was really only one master is uncertain.

In 1815, Jeremy Bentham planned a Lancasterian school 'for the use of the middling and the higher ranks of life'. At about the same time, Bentham met Robert Owen and introduced him to Lancaster's ideas. When Lancaster visited Scotland to speak about his schools at public meetings, Owen gave him his support. But privately Owen thought that Lancaster's monitorial system of teaching was no substitute for real education.

Owen's educational ideas were founded on the belief that character was formed by environment. Bad behaviour was the result of bad environment, and education should consist to a

22. Egerton, in *Annals of Science*, 24 (1968), p. 75.
23. MS. letter, J. Bentham to Strutt, 17 July 1794, Derby Public Library.
24. MS. letter, S. Bentham to Strutt, 20 July 1805, Derby Public Library.

large degree in exposing children to a good, interesting and varied environment, by using models, objects collected from the countryside, and music – with almost no use of books among the younger children. The environment of everybody in the community was, of course, as important as the environment of children in school, and could be greatly improved by organising communities as a whole. Owen could experiment along these lines in the mill-workers' village which belonged to the New Lanark cotton-mills near Glasgow, of which he was manager from 1800 to 1824. Thus it was at New Lanark that he tried out his educational ideas in a 'New Institution for the Formation of Character'. This was a 'moral invention' which he planned in 1809, but the building which housed it was only completed in 1816. A graceful, three-storey structure, it was built next to one of the cotton-mills, and was heated, interestingly enough, by a ducted hot air system run from two stoves in the basement. Similar to, but less sophisticated than, Strutt's form of central heating, this system was devised by William Kelly, a technician employed at New Lanark.[25] Jeremy Bentham's support for this and other projects of Owen is shown by the fact that he invested money in the New Lanark mills at this time, so becoming one of Owen's partners.

As already briefly mentioned, the machinery in many early cotton-mills was powered by water-wheels (chapter seven). These mills were necessarily situated where there was water available to drive them, and so were often some distance from any large town. In these circumstances, mill-owners had to build houses in order to attract workers to their factories, and many mill villages developed in country areas as a result.

The village at New Lanark had originated in this way, but although Owen did much to improve the house and community institutions, the village itself was already in existence when he first went there in 1800. Other notable mill villages were at Styal, south of Manchester, and at Belper and Milford in Derbyshire, where the Strutt mills were situated. Styal was laid out by Samuel Greg, the mill-owner with whom Peter Ewart had been in partnership for some years. Greg was a liberal in political outlook, and like Strutt and Owen he was probably interested in Bentham's ideas. Thus in the planning and organisa-

25. Butt (ed.), *Robert Owen, Prince of Cotton Spinners*, pp. 230–35.

tion of all these communities we might expect to find 'moral inventions' along Benthamite lines.

The Strutts' village at Belper is perhaps the best example. Education there was less progressive than at New Lanark, though it was not neglected; but in other respects Belper was certainly as good or better as a place in which to live. The most ingenious feature was the design of the houses, which was almost certainly the product of William Strutt's inventive architectural inclinations. Typically they had (and still have) a living-room with a small kitchen and a cellar or pantry leading off it, and two bedrooms; but there were many variations in plan to allow for different-sized families, different social status, and variations in the layout and slope of the site. Besides providing houses and schools, the Strutts arranged for milk, meat, vegetables and coal to be supplied cheaply; they promoted friendly societies and a savings bank, and they built churches. Everything, it seems, was thought of, and over it all, the Strutts exercised a certain paternalistic authority, maintaining discipline by a system of fines which were deducted from the quarterly payments of gift money made to the mill-workers. Owen evidently inspected and approved the village, no doubt picking up ideas for application in his own schemes; and when William Strutt died in 1830, Owen's regret was deeply felt. He wrote to Strutt's son, Edward:

'I wish we had a dozen such men as your father at the head of our affairs. I fear there is a great lack . . . of such useful knowledge and integrity as he possessed. . . . [He is] one of the most valuable men that the century has produced.'[26]

One more 'moral invention' which needs to be mentioned was Owen's idea for 'Villages of Unity and Co-operation'. This arose after the end of the wars with France in 1815 when returning soldiers and slackening trade led to a lot of unemployment. Owen suggested that unemployed men and their families should be organised into self-sufficient communities in which agriculture and manufacturing would be practised side by side. For a short time the suggestion was taken seriously by the authorities, and a sketch of one of Owen's villages, showing a quadrangle of buildings set in farming country, appeared in a Parliamentary report. But while official interest was limited to the possible effect on unemployment, Owen saw his villages as an

26. MS. letter, Derby Public Library.

ideal way of living, a sort of paradise on earth, and had visions of a new age when everybody would live in communities of this kind.

Owen's villages of unity might be seen as an idealised version of the factory-workers' villages, although another origin will be suggested below. His chance to experiment with the idea came in 1825, when he went to America to join with others in establishing a community called New Harmony. Unfortunately, though, not many people found Owen an easy man to work with, and he returned to Britain, in 1829, sadder and much less wealthy for the experience.

A philanthropic technology?

That there was a large element of idealism in the technological activities of men like Strutt and Owen cannot be in doubt. But from the point of view of this book, such idealism will hardly seem like a spur to technical change, because it had the effect of leading these men away from technological problems, and of causing them to concentrate on social questions. William Strutt, pioneer of 'fireproof' construction in cotton-mills and an expert on water-wheels, came to spend a lot of his time on the less technically demanding problems of designing workers' houses, and on the purely social problem of organising life in the factory communities.

The houses at Belper had features which are certainly of interest to the historian of technology, for instance the very novel cast-iron window frames. But to worry about the number of bedrooms a worker's house should have, or where food should be stored, or even how far from the house the outside lavatory should be sited – none of these seems like an engineering problem of the first order. Yet it is very clear from the highly original plans of the houses at Belper that Strutt gave a great deal of thought to these things.

To exclude all this from a study of technology because no advanced engineering principles were involved would be to fall into a trap set by 20th-century specialisation. For implicit in the modern specialised approach is the view that technology is about 'hardware' and not about society. In fact, every technical innovation has social consequences – almost all technology is concerned with bringing about changes in society – and to train engineers in 20th-century universities as if engineering

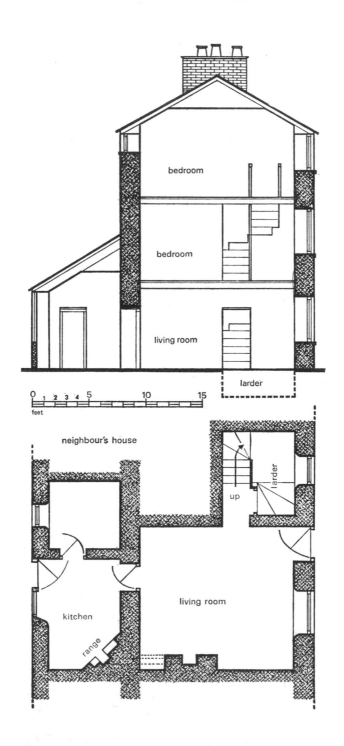

bedroom

bedroom

living room

larder

0   1   2   3   4   5   10   15
feet

neighbour's house

larder

up

living room

kitchen

range

is simply a matter of pipes, electronics, concrete and mathematical calculation seems little short of irresponsible.

The significance of Bentham, Strutt and Owen is that, for all of them, social innovation was as important as technical innovation, and there was no sharp line to be drawn between the two. New techniques in building and in such related fields as central heating were actually necessary if the social innovations were to succeed.

Strutt was probably the most successful practitioner of this mixture of technical and social arts, but, as he once admitted, he did not enjoy writing about his ideas and inventions. It is clear, however, that he was influenced by Bentham, and Bentham certainly did try to explain how practical subjects like mechanics and chemistry were related to social or ethical questions. Eudaemonics was the all-embracing science of human happiness in which both practical and social studies could play a part. From a conventional point of view, William Strutt seems to be a man with wide and unrelated interests, but one could, as an alternative, look on all his inventions and social experiments as part of a unified 'eudaemonic' programme. One could go further and say that what he was trying to do was to transform the industrial technology of his time into a more socially appropriate technology. But one should obviously be cautious about reading too many ideas into the work of a man who left relatively few of his thoughts on paper.

A historical point that remains is the similarity between Benthamite ideas and some of the 17th-century ideas of what was described in chapter five as 'philanthropic' science. During this earlier period, there was great stress on agriculture, chemistry and medicine, because these practical arts could be of direct benefit to mankind; yet at the same time and among the same people, there was a strong interest in educational reform,

Figure 39

Ground-floor plan and section of a terrace house built for the Strutts' employees at Belper, and probably designed by William Strutt in 1795.
(Based on the author's survey of 7 Long Row, Belper; see also M. W. Barley, in *Archaeological Journal*, *118* (1961), pp. 237–9)

population statistics, and other 'social arts'.[27] Bentham studied the works of Francis Bacon, and this accounts for the 17th-century flavour of some of his ideas. But one might also ask whether the educational ideas of Comenius had any influence on Owen's schools, and whether the ideas of Hartlib or Petty were remembered. There is no evidence of any direct connection, but an element of continuity can be traced.

The 17th-century 'philanthropic' science was an ideal which chiefly inspired people of a certain Puritan or nonconformist persuasion. Wherever there were people with similar beliefs in the early 19th century, the memory of 17th-century forbears was sometimes still alive. Nonconformist academies, such as Manchester College, which Strutt's son attended, continued an educational tradition begun at Durham with the college founded under Cromwell. Several of Owen's partners at New Lanark were Quakers; Owen himself, despite his public and controversial opposition to all religion, habitually used Biblical language to describe his idealism, and seems genuinely to have absorbed a great deal of nonconformist thinking, although in secular form.

For example, when his New Institution for the Formation of Character was opened in 1816, Owen gave an 'Address to the Inhabitants of New Lanark' which was later published – and in it, he portrayed the New Institution as a foretaste of the coming millennium. Using the language of the Biblical book, Revelation, he described how 'Old things shall pass away and all shall become new'. He said he did not know 'What ideas individuals may attach to the term Millennium', but he did believe that 'society may be formed so as to exist without crime, without poverty, with health greatly improved, with little, if any, misery, and with intelligence and happiness increased an hundred fold'.[28]

One possible source for some of Owen's ideas about education, the millennium, and workers' communities may perhaps be traced to the ten years he spent in Manchester. Four miles from that town was the Fairfield Moravian Settlement, in which millennialist and educational ideas were certainly discussed,

27. This term is used, as in chapter five, for comparison with 'mechanical arts', 'chemical arts', and other such terms for practical skills and crafts.
28. For this aspect of Owen's thought, see W. H. Oliver, 'Owen in 1817: the Millennialist moment', in *Robert Owen, Prophet of the Poor* (ed. Pollard and Salt).

in which Comenius was revered as a former Moravian leader, and which itself provided a successful example of a self-sufficient working community. It was a talking-point in Manchester in the 1790s, for 'Though established within these twenty years it has the appearance of a little town . . . cotton manufactory forms a principal part of the employment of the inhabitants, including spinning, weaving & c. . . . fine needle-work is carried to a great pitch of perfection, and is chiefly sent to London. There are also in this settlement taylors, shoemakers, bakers, and a sale shop for most articles.' So John Aikin described it in a well-known book on Manchester published in Owen's time there,[29] and Aikin's account and the illustration he provided could well have formed the original of Owen's Villages of Unity and Co-operation. There was even some architectural similarity between the square plans of both sorts of community and the style of the central groups of buildings. But Owen never said that he was thinking of a secularised version of the Moravian settlement, although some contemporary community builders may have been.[30]

Owen, Strutt and Bentham have so far been discussed as if they held similar views about the progress and development of industrial society. But while there were many practical problems on which they could co-operate, the fact is that Owen in some ways differed fundamentally from the others. All these men were optimistic – indeed, the one characteristic shared by all the people mentioned in this chapter was a tremendously optimistic feeling about the future of industrial society. But while Strutt and Bentham were hopeful about *existing* trends, Owen was optimistic about the possibility of creating a radically different, and better, form of industrial order. When he used the language of millennialism to describe this new kind of society, he may have seemed something of a crank; but after reading what he said when describing it in terms of economics, one can begin to see why the term 'socialism' originated in discussions of Owen's ideas.

Owen's views can be explained by returning to the question of Parliamentary reform in which Watt, Lee, Ewart as well as Strutt and Bentham had all been interested. Owen was relatively uninterested in this cause. Political movements seemed to him superficial unless grounded in economic reality. A Parliament in

29. *A Description of the Country from thirty to forty miles round Manchester.*
30. Armytage, *Heavens Below*, pp. 93, 131 n.

which landowners had less power was pointless if the landowners maintained their economic strength and their ability to
influence the price of food. In stressing economic rather than
political reform, Owen had struck a chord which has been
characteristic of most socialists ever since. G. D. H. Cole
remarks that Owen was essentially 'at one with Marx in discerning
the foundations of Socialism in the inherent logic of the economic
order'.[31]

Owen's views can be explained briefly in terms of the idea,
current in his time, that society and all its economic operations
behaved according to laws of nature. If this were true, it should
be possible to devise a set of concepts and principles to describe
society, and in particular, the contemporary growth of industry.
This, we might think, is what Bentham tried to do. But having
formulated a science of society or of economics, ought one to
try to develop a corresponding technology of government,
applying the facts and theories one had arrived at? Owen and
Bentham would have agreed in saying 'Yes', while the
philosopher-manufacturers, like Ewart and Lee (and perhaps
even Strutt), quite definitely said 'No'. Both Owen and Bentham,
while welcoming the new industries, saw that they would lead to
beneficial results only if an applied human science and an
applied economics were added to the applied physical science on
which industrial technology was based. Owen went very much
further with this than Bentham, however. He was 'never for a
moment in doubt about the triumph of the machine and of large-
scale production based upon the new sources and instruments of
power'. He differed from others in his insistence on the need
for controlling and organising these vast new forces. They
'were replacing the individual producer . . . by a collaborative
group of producers, who must work together in designed
harmony in order to achieve a good result. Competition was the
essence of the old order, not of the new. The vital principle of the
new industrialism must be Co-operation.'[32]

The idea which most distinguished Owen from his contemporaries, then, was his view that collective control of the new
forces generated by the industrial revolution was a necessity. This
meant economic control, which was not to be achieved simply by

31. *The Life of Robert Owen*, 3rd edn, p. 11.
32. *The Life of Robert Owen*, 3rd edn, p. 4.

electoral and Parliamentary reform, but by communal and co-operative ownership of the means of production. As will be shown in the next chapter, Owen's conclusions on this matter were reached partly through his observation of current technological change and how it was affecting the work and status of the people employed in the newly-built factories.

The difference between Owen's views here and the opinions of Bentham and Strutt is less important than the fact that all three of these men saw technical progress and social change as part of a single process. They could see how new technology and new kinds of social organisation should be developed in conjunction with one another, and within the limited scope of his factory village Strutt showed what this might mean in practice. This integrated view of technical and human development is perhaps something which needs greater emphasis in the late 20th century.

9

The effects of mechanisation in Europe and Asia: trends in technology between 1810 and 1870

The age of steam transport

In 1807, the first passenger steamship service in the world was inaugurated on the 150-mile run between New York and Albany. To begin with, the boat used was the *Clermont*, which had been designed by the American engineer Robert Fulton, and was driven by a 19-horsepower engine built by Boulton and Watt in England.

Boulton and Watt sold another engine to Fulton in 1811. As time went on, and more steamboats were built, they were faced with the problem of advising boat-builders on the power of the engines needed by particular vessels. Peter Ewart, the engineer discussed in the previous chapter, was experienced in the design of water-wheels, and recognised that the theory of the water-wheel could be applied to the paddle-wheels then used on steamers. In 1817 and again in 1826, he made calculations for Boulton and Watt on this basis, pointing out the inefficiency of current steamers. Much power was lost 'in agitating the water and in tossing it up behind the paddle wheels'. (24 March 1826.)[1]

Shortly after this, William Fairbairn's engineering works in Manchester got the job of constructing a steamboat for the Forth and Clyde Canal. Fairbairn negotiated with Boulton and Watt for an engine, 'through my friend Peter Ewart', and once again Ewart was involved in discussing what engine-power would be needed. Construction of the engine was delayed, however. In the summer of 1830, Ewart reported:

'I yesterday met Fairbairn, who says the Forth & Clyde people are very urgent to have their boat completed. . . . Under the uncertainty of getting engines from [Boulton and Watt], he has

1. Dates refer to MS. letters in the Boulton and Watt Collection.

sounded Stephenson, who appears to be unwilling to contribute any of his . . . powers towards the improvement of Canal navigation, whose speedy anihilation he has so often prognosticated.' (20 August 1820.)

This seems to indicate that Fairbairn had tried to order an engine from Robert Stephenson and Company of Newcastle. This firm had been set up in 1823 by George Stephenson (1781–1848), his son Robert (1803–59) and two friends, primarily to build locomotives for use on the colliery railways of Northumberland and Durham. The steam locomotive, indeed, began its career at much the same time as the steamship, with Trevithick's experimental locomotive of 1803–4, and with the first practical use of locomotives in 1812, on northern colliery railways at Leeds and on Tyneside.

These colliery railways usually covered quite short distances between a mine and a wharf where the coal could be loaded on to boats. Such railways were therefore complementary to the inland waterways – rivers and canals – and did not compete with the boats which used them. But in the 1820s the idea of the main-line railway emerged, and this certainly was a threat to the canals. The Stockton and Darlington Railway of 1821–5 pointed the way, although it was really little more than a colliery railway. The first inter-city main line was built between Liverpool and Manchester during the years 1824–30. This line competed with two waterways, the Bridgewater Canal and the Mersey and Irwell Navigation, and the proprietors of these not only opposed the railway project by representations to Parliament, but in some cases offered physical obstruction to the surveyors working on it. George Stephenson himself was twice involved in these encounters, and the bitterness of this no doubt influenced the reaction Fairbairn met with when he enquired of the Stephensons about a canal boat engine.

Meanwhile, in 1823, the Royal Navy had acquired its first steamboat, and by 1837 there were 27 steamers[2] in naval service. Two years earlier, this development had signalled a rather abrupt change in life for Peter Ewart, who at the age of sixty-seven uprooted himself from Manchester to become the Royal Navy's first Chief Engineer. He was responsible for 'the steam machinery of the British Navy' and for establishing facilities to maintain it. To do this he had to plan workshops and order

2. Smith, *A Short History of Naval and Marine Engineering*, pp. 19, 52.

equipment for installation at Woolwich Dockyard, which became the first naval establishment capable of repairing boilers and engines. Ewart worked there until 1842, when he was killed in an accident at the dockyard.

Not long before Ewart's death, British steamships had enjoyed one of their first victories in naval warfare, and it was noted in an obituary notice of Ewart that they had amply proved their worth.[3] The occasion of this was the war against China of 1840–42. Several steamers were involved, some of them belonging to the East India Company. They were more than a match for the junks sent out to meet them, and their flat-bottomed iron hulls were ideal for penetrating the major rivers of China.

The kind of work Peter Ewart undertook for the Navy contrasts sharply with that of his earlier career in Manchester. Indeed, his interests were altogether so varied as to include almost every aspect of contemporary engineering. His achievement in engineering was small compared with Smeaton's or Watt's, but his career can be usefully studied for the perspectives it provides on technical change at this period. Before he left Manchester, Ewart spent much of his time in the management of cotton mills, but he also designed machine tools – for example, a planing machine (27 October 1829) – and dealt with almost all the technical problems which could arise in the textile industry.

In 1813, Ewart obtained a patent (No. 3648) for a novel type of power loom. This affected plans he had for setting up his own business. He told the younger James Watt: 'I have not yet come to any determination whether to set up a Manufactory of Looms, or an establishment for weaving. . . . I shall be better able to decide when I get the two looms I am at work upon completed'. (12 June 1813.)

Power looms had been in use in the cotton industry since 1784, when the first ones were introduced by Edmund Cartwright, but their mechanical complexity had delayed their widespread adoption. Ewatt's loom would, in principle, have been simpler mechanically. His idea was to have cylinders and pistons built into the structure of the loom, so that its reciprocating action – for example, the to and fro motion of the shuttle – could be produced by the direct application of steam or compressed air in these cylinders. Pistons 'are connected immediately or by

3. James Walker, in the *Civil Engineer and Architect's Journal*, 6, 1843, pp. 102–3.

means of a lever . . . in such a manner that the reciprocating motion of the piston shall produce a corresponding reciprocating motion in the [loom] . . . without the intervention of a rotary motion or wheelwork'. (9 April 1813.)

Ewart's looms are not heard of again, but his interest in textile machinery continued; in 1833 he obtained another patent (No. 6505) for 'Improvements in the spinning machines called mules, whereby they become self-actors'. A 'self-actor' in this context meant an automatic machine, while the spinning mule was an alternative to the Arkwright type of machine and capable of spinning a much finer thread. The mule had been introduced by Samuel Crompton in the 1780s, but at first it was manually operated. To gain any advantage from driving it by power, its very complex cycle of operations had to be automated, or as they said, made self-acting. Some limited success in this was achieved about 1800, but 'the fully automatic self-acting mule did not become a reality until the inventions of Richard Roberts between 1825 and 1830'.[4]

Ewart must have known Richard Roberts (1789–1864), who had settled in Manchester in 1816, and who had rapidly acquired a reputation for the machine tools which he designed and built, as well as for his textile machinery. It was Roberts's expertise as a maker of machine tools which enabled him to succeed with the self-acting mules – and indeed, with power looms also. Ewart and others could design perfectly sound looms or automatic mules, but they could not manufacture them in quantity. The mechanism of these machines was necessarily an intricate combination of many moving parts, all of which had to be accurately made. Given time, a craftsman could make one machine of this type with complete success, but faced with the task of equipping a factory with, say, a hundred mules, the craftsman's methods would be almost totally impracticable. A group of craftsmen could certainly make the hundred machines. But if each machine was made individually in this way, there would be detailed differences between one and another, even though all were to the same design. Thus components would not be interchangeable between one machine and others, and it would be impossible to keep a stock of spare parts which could be used on any one of the hundred machines which happened to break down.

4. Hills, *Power in the Industrial Revolution*, p. 127.

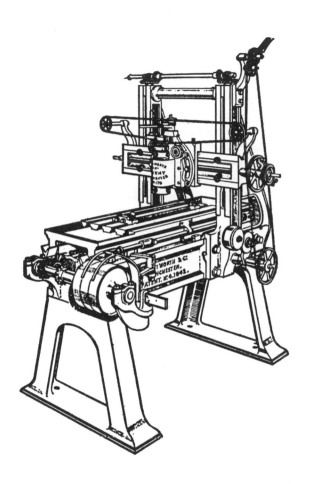

Figure 40

A power-driven, self-acting planing-machine introduced by Whitworth in 1842. The reversing of the workpiece after each stroke was achieved automatically, and there was also an automatic crossfeed.

(Crown copyright, Science Museum, London; reproduction taken from fig. 133 of Aubrey F. Burstall, *A History of Mechanical Engineering*, Faber & Faber, 1963, p. 219)

The answer to this problem was to devise machine tools which could cut pieces of metal accurately to the specified size of the standard components of the mules. This could be done if 'self-acting' machine tools were introduced, because these could effectively be programmed to stop removing metal from a component as soon as a particular size was reached. Then the dimensions of the product would not be left for the craftsman to judge by eye. Richard Roberts's achievement in applying machine tools of this type to the manufacture of spinning machinery was described in 1835 as follows:

'Where many counterparts or similar pieces enter into spinning apparatus, they are all made so perfectly identical in form and size, by the self-acting tools, such as the planing and key-groove cutting machines, that any one of them will at once fit into the position of any of its fellows in the general frame.'[5]

This principle of standardised and interchangeable parts is often regarded as an American innovation of the mid-19th century, but as Musson and Robinson have pointed out, the American pioneers 'were preceded in the application of such methods by certain early British engineering firms' – including that of Richard Roberts.[6]

The 1820s and 30s may be regarded as marking the final major phase in Britain's industrial revolution, and during these two decades, many of the most fundamental technological changes were associated with machine tools in one way or another. For not only did the invention of new types of machine tool make it possible to complete the mechanisation of the textile industry, but the new and more compact types of steam engine used in steamships and locomotives depended on them also.

In the 1820s, some of the best steam engines for ships were made by Maudslay, Sons & Field of Lambeth Marsh, London, a firm which had been founded in 1810 by Henry Maudslay (1771–1831). There, many of the best machine tool engineers of the next two decades received their training while working either as apprentices or assistants. Richard Roberts, in particular, had worked for Maudslay before coming to Manchester. Other associates of Maudslay included Joseph Whitworth, James

5. Ure, *The Philosophy of Manufacturers*, p. 37.
6. Musson and Robinson, *Science and Technology in the Industrial Revolution*, p. 473.

Nasmyth and Joseph Clement.[7] An example of the self-acting machine tools designed by Whitworth is the planing machine illustrated(see fig. 40). Like many of the machines introduced by the Maudslay school, its object was to utilise automatic operation to achieve great precision in the shape and dimensions of the product.

The automatic factory

By 1830, the principle of the self-acting machine was being applied in many sectors of industry. Newcomen's steam engine had been self-acting since its introduction in 1712, in the sense that its steam and water valves were turned on and off automatically in the right sequence. The centrifugal governor used to keep a machine running at constant speed had been applied to windmills in the mid-18th century, and was adapted by Watt for his steam engine in the 1780s. Just before 1800, an example of automatic production had been provided by a series of forty machines installed at Portsmouth Dockyard by Marc Brunel for shaping the wooden pulley-blocks used in ships' rigging. Maudslay worked on these machines as a young man and they strongly influenced his approach. Then, by 1830, other examples of automatic productions were to be seen in self-acting looms and spinning mules.

Commentators on the progress of industry in the 1830s seized on all this as the most significant development of the time. 'Automatic', said Andrew Ure in his *Dictionary of Arts, Manufactures and Mines*, is a term 'I have employed to designate such economic arts as are carried on by self-acting machinery'. Manufacture, in its original sense, meant work carried out by hand. But 'in the vicissitude of language' it had come to mean almost the exact opposite, for the ideal manufacture 'is made by machinery, with little or no aid of the human hand, so that the most perfect manufacture is that which dispenses entirely with manual labour'.[8]

To such a degree had this idea captured Ure's imagination that he made it almost the basic axiom of his *Philosophy of Manufactures*, published in 1835: 'The most perfect manufacture

7. See Rolt, *Tools for the Job*, for an account of the work of these men.
8. *Dictionary*, article 'AUTOMATIC'; 4th edn, I, p. 108.

is that which dispenses entirely with manual labour. . . . The philosophy of manufactures is therefore an exposition of the general principles, on which productive industry should be conducted by self-acting machines.'[9] The ideal factory, therefore, was 'a vast automaton, composed of various mechanical and intellectual organs, acting in uninterrupted concert for the production of a common object, all of them being subordinated to a self-regulated moving force'. That moving force was of course the steam engine, 'the controller-general and mainspring of British industry', and the term 'self-regulated' refers to Ure's notion of the feed-back principle by which the governor on such an engine operated.

It is clear that Ure's vision of an automatic factory resulted from the great impression made upon him by the self-acting machines in the textile mills: 'It is in our modern cotton and flax mills that automatic operations are displayed to most advantage; for there the elemental powers have been made to animate millions of complex organs, imparting to forms of wood, iron, and brass, an intelligent agency. And as the philosophy of the fine arts, poetry, painting, and music, may be best studied in their individual master-pieces, so may the philosophy of manufactures in these its noblest creations.'[10]

But despite the vision of automatic factories which textile mills evoked in Ure, they were in one respect a long way from being automatic. The machines were not usually arranged to give a continuous flow of material through the mill, and goods had to be man-handled a great deal in passing from one process to the next. The need to drive all the machines in a mill from one (or perhaps two) steam engine(s) by means of long rotating shafts, with pulleys and belts, dictated a compact plan for the building, usually in several storeys, and this imposed considerable limitations in devising a layout which would allow for efficient production. But Ure had heard of a series of patents taken out by J. G. Bodmer in 1824 for use in cotton spinning mills. The effect of Bodmer's inventions was to allow the output of one machine to be fed directly into another for the next stage in the process, without human intervention. Thus 'the several organs of a spinning factory are united into one self-acting and self-supplying body – a system most truly *automatic*'.[11] A fully-

9. *Philosophy of Manufacturers*, p. 1.
10. *Philosophy*, p. 1, continued.
11. *Dictionary*, article 'SPINNING', 4th edn, 2, p. 695.

automated factory was not a real possibility in Ure's time, but in these ways he was able to imagine what it would be like. It was, he said, the 'constant aim and tendency of every improvement in machinery to supersede human labour altogether'.

If a particular process could not be completely mechanised, Ure said, it should be organised according to the division of labour, with complex tasks broken down into a series of very simple operations, each of which should be done by a separate worker. Wherever possible, machines or special tools should be introduced to make these elementary operations even simpler, so that less skill was needed. The aim was to diminish the cost of the necessary labour, by 'substituting the industry of women and children for that of men; or that of ordinary labourers, for trained artisans'.[12]

Ure recognised no moral objections to the employment of children, and claimed that they actually enjoyed working in factories: 'the work of these lively elves seemed to resemble a sport'.[13] As for the other workers, he thought that the effect of introducing automatic machines was beneficial, or as he put it, 'philanthropic, as they tend to relieve the workman either from niceties of adjustment, which exhaust his mind and fatigue his eyes, or from painful repetition of effort, which distort and wear out his frame'.[14]

These patronising remarks ignore all question of the satisfaction which a skilled craftsman might have formerly felt in doing his job; they ignore all notions about the positive social value of skilled work and the consequences of its loss. Ure's views are, indeed, a complete contrast to those of his contemporary, Robert Owen, who until 1824 was manager and part-owner of the New Lanark cotton mills. Owen disliked the way in which skilled manual work was being replaced by mechanism; and the division of labour for him meant division of interest, so that every job became totally uninteresting. This was wasteful in human terms, and led to frustration, boredom and crime.

In his proposals for Villages of Unity and Co-operation, Owen envisaged that workers would spend only part of their time in manufacturing. The rest of their working hours would be devoted to agriculture. In this way they could lead a more

12. *Philosophy of Manufacturers*, p. 23.
13. *Philosophy*, p. 301.
14. *Philosophy*, p. 8.

balanced life, and there could be more variety both in work and in environment. As it was, Owen thought, mechanisation was leading to the depreciation of labour, because, from the manufacturers' point of view, men could be regarded merely as alternatives to machines.

Owen's ideas on this subject emerged when he analysed the causes of the unemployment which followed the end of the wars with France in 1815. There was some contraction in trade, and factory-owners sought to make economies in the operation of their plant. 'Men being more expensive machines for producing than mechanical and chemical inventions and discoveries, so extensively brought into action during the war, the men were discharged and the machines were made to supersede them . . . the new power created by new inventions and discoveries was already enormous, and was superseding manual power.'

'The immediate cause of the present distress is the depreciation of human labour. This has been occasioned by the general introduction of mechanism into the manufactures of Europe and America, but principally into those of Britain, where the change was greatly accelerated by the inventions of Arkwright and Watt.' Labour was depreciating in terms of market value as well as in terms of what would today be called job-satisfaction, 'and human labour may now be obtained at a price far less than is absolutely necessary for the subsistence of the individual in ordinary comfort'.[15]

A less damning analysis of the manufacturing system which at the same time was more sensitive than Ure's was given by Charles Babbage in 1832 in his classic work *On the Economy of Machinery and Manufactures*. In many ways, his ideas followed in direct line from those of Adam Smith, so it is not surprising to find that Peter Ewart, the Manchester engineer, gave them his approval.[16] Babbage asked Ewart to look over the draft of some chapters, and Ewart found 'only one part upon which I shall be glad to make a few observations to you'.[17]

15. See Cole, *The Life of Robert Owen*, 3rd edn, pp. 176–9, 225.

16. For Ewart's views on Adam Smith, see pp. 236–7 above.

17. MS. letter, Ewart to Babbage, 18 February 1832; British Museum Additional MSS. 37186, f. 256. I am grateful to Brian Warburton for bringing this to my attention.

Babbage stressed the division of labour in the organisation of industry, and he held that 'Governments ought to interfere as little as possible between workmen and their employers'. However, he did agree that the government should limit the employment of children in factories, arguing that this was a matter of giving protection to the weaker party. He thought that mechanisation in industry was in the interests of both workers and employers, because it increased the wealth of all. But he believed that such common benefits should be made more clearly evident by means of profit-sharing schemes. Through such schemes, employees would gain directly from the prosperity of the firm for which they worked.

Neither Owen nor Babbage said much directly about self-acting machines or the idea of an automatic factory, because both were writing before Ure had given such great stress to these ideas. But Babbage made his own contribution to the development of automatic techniques. In 1824, he consulted Peter Ewart about automatic looms, and in particular about devices which would stop the working of such a loom in the event of a warp thread breaking. Ewart and a friend of his told Babbage that 'If you conclude to take a patent we shall have much pleasure in promoting as far as we can the adoption of your invention . . .'[18]

Babbage's interest in automatic looms extended to work which had been done in France by Jacques de Vaucanson (1709–1782) and J. M. Jacquard (1752–1834). Vaucanson had a reputation for making 'automata': that is, animated clockwork toys, but he had also devised a silk-weaving loom in which the pattern woven into the fabric was produced by the operation of an automatic gadget. In Jacquard's improved version of this loom, the pattern of the cloth was determined by a series of cards with holes in them which were fed into the machine. A group of metal rods were pushed against each card; those that passed through a hole were lifted several inches, and this controlled the re-arrangement of warp threads between each passage of the shuttle.

The device was conceived for use with hand-looms in France, but greater advantage was gained from its application to power-looms in Britain. In addition, it provided Babbage with the idea of punched cards, and his experiments with mechanical com-

18. MS. letter, Ewart to Babbage, 4 March 1824, British Museum Additional MSS. 37183, f. 110.

puters probably owed much to the example of this mechanism. From about 1823, Babbage became deeply involved with a project to construct a computing-machine, and he employed Maudslay's associate Joseph Clement to help him. Clement was expert in the design and construction of machine tools and was especially skilled in any branch of mechanical construction that called for great precision and accuracy.

Since Babbage had so direct an interest in the hardware of automation, it is ironic that the possibility of automated industry was so much more clearly expressed by Andrew Ure, in his book of 1835. In the next three decades, Ure's remarks on self-acting machines influenced several people who wrote on the effects of mechanisation, including most notably Karl Marx.[19]

Where Ure had said that 'manufacture' in its original sense meant work carried out by hand, and had argued that ideally industry would be conducted entirely 'by self-acting machines', Marx drew a similar distinction between manufacture in the old sense and 'modern industry'. 'In the former case, the movements of the instrument of labour proceed from the workers; but in the latter, the movements of the worker are subordinate to those of the machine.' A factory was a 'lifeless mechanism independent of the workmen', who were reduced to being mere appendages to the productive process.[20]

To pursue Marx's ideas on this subject in detail would take the argument out of the period with which this chapter is concerned. But it is worth noting two issues which link the arguments about mechanisation put forward by Owen, Baggage and Ure with the later ideas of Marx. Firstly, all these men could see that mechanisation was necessary if production and wealth were to increase. So there was a sense in which everybody benefited from the increased use of machines, even if it disrupted the established pattern of work for ordinary prople. Where Ure and perhaps Babbage differed from Owen and Marx was over the question of whether workers were being 'exploited' and whether the benefits were being fairly distributed.

19. For the relationship of Ure, Babbage and Marx, see Rosenbloom, 'Men and machines', in *Technology and Culture*, 5 (1964), pp. 491–6.

20. The way in which these comments of Marx's relate to the history of technology can be seen from Klemm, *A History of Western Technology*, pp. 308–14.

The second point emphasised by all these authors was that fewer craftsmen of the old sort were needed in industry, because the skill was now being built into the machines. Ure claimed that working people were glad to avoid the burden of thinking or of taking pains over their work. But Marx pointed out that the way in which machines simplified work 'is used to make workers out of those who are just growing up, who are still immature, *children*, while the worker himself has become a child deprived of all care. Machinery is adapted to the weakness of the human being, in order to turn the weak human being into a machine.'[21]

Industry, as compared with older, craft forms of production, had alienated man from his work, because the worker now had no control over the design or quality of the product of that work, and also because a worker could not use his natural abilities, but was forced to perform uninteresting and degrading tasks.

Among the owners of industry, work was – and is – regarded by many as solely an instrument of production. It was merely the means to the end of manufacturing objects for sale. Its value, therefore, was to be measured in terms of the money value of the objects produced. What was at issue in the points made by Owen and Marx was that work could and should be regarded as having other sorts of value as well – as when it exercised or extended the abilities of the worker, and allowed him to contribute some service or material aid to the people among whom he lived. In earlier parts of this book, some account has been given of older ideas about the value of human labour and skill in the life of society or of an individual. Reference has been made to a religious ideal of work being good in itself and necessary for spiritual discipline and development (chapter one). A secular way of expressing this might be to talk about the ways in which work can be a means of personal fulfilment and satisfaction.

All this makes some kind of sense when one is talking about the work of a craftsman, but factory industry can hardly be reconciled with this point of view. Owen thought that one solution might be to give people more variety in their work. In his projected Villages of Unity, the workers were intended to divide their time between agriculture and manufactures. Things might also improve, he sometimes suggested, if work-people took the management of their labour into their own hands, by organising

21. *Karl Marx – Early Writings* (ed. and trans. Bottomore), p. 170.

production on a co-operative basis. From 1820 onwards, some working men in various parts of the country formed themselves into Owenite groups and tried out co-operative methods in trade and production. In London, the Co-operative & Economic Society was founded in 1821; the London Co-operative Trading Association followed in 1828. The modern Co-operative movement originated much later with the Rochdale 'pioneers' of 1844, and was strongly influenced by these early experiments, though it had no direct connection with Owen.

The Owenite co-operatives and communities were an attempt to ensure that trade and industry were run in the interests of those who did the work. Marx came from the Rhine province of Prussia, and it was natural for him to think about the state control of industry as a way of achieving the same end. In chapter six (above) it was observed that in Saxony and Austria during the 18th century, state control of certain industries was exercised on the basis of 'mercantilist' theories of government and commerce. In Marx's time, Prussia had become the country where mercantilist techniques of state control were most effectively practised. Thus it can be said that German socialism in the late 19th and early 20th centuries was 'the outcome of two conceptions which mutually influenced each other – Prussian Mercantilism, a State philosophy with strong socialist tendencies, and the ideas of Marx and Lassalle'.[22] Mercantilist policies did not usually serve the interests of working people, of course, but socialists could envisage ways in which mercantilist techniques of state control might be used for a different purpose. Such ideas did not occur to Robert Owen because state-run industries on the mercantilist pattern did not exist in England. Thus for him it seemed that co-operatives or community organisation would be the best way of ensuring that industry was run in the workers' interests.

India and the industrial revolution

The 'depreciation of human labour' due to mechanisation, which Owen commented on and Marx analysed, affected skilled workers

22. Bruck, *Social and Economic History of Germany*, p. 48; Ferdinand Lassalle was a leader of German socialism around 1850–64, after Marx had settled in England.

in India as much as in England. Indeed, the effect of the English factories on the textile-workers of India was often more catastrophic than it was for their British counterparts. After 1815, hand-loom weavers in Britain found their earnings steadily reduced as they tried to compete with the power-looms then

Table 2. Import Duties Levied on Indian Goods brought into Britain

Per cent of value of goods

	1812	1824	1832
Cotton Goods			
muslins	27·3%	37·5%	10%
calicoes	71·7	67·5	10
other types	27·3	50	20
Other Manufactures			
cane work	71	50	30
mats	68·3	50	20
lacquered ware	71	62·5	30
silk manufactures	prohibited altogether		20

Source: Dutt, *The Economic History of India under Early British Rule*, 7th edn, p. 294.

being installed in factories. The value of their labour quite literally depreciated, and eventually they were forced to abandon hand-loom work. Among spinners, there were fewer such problems, because the expansion of the industry in Britain was so rapid that displaced hand-spinners could usually find factory work quite quickly. But the cotton-mills in Britain caused a permanent loss of livelihood for many cotton-spinners in India, because, as Andrew Ure rather smugly explained: 'By the aid of mechanical fingers, one Englishman at his mule can turn off daily more yarn and of far finer quality than 200 of the most diligent spinsters of Hindostan.'[23] After the introduction of

23. Ure, *Dictionary*, article 'COTTON MANUFACTURE', 4th edn, Vol. I, p. 529.

the spinning mule in the 1780s, it had been possible for British mills to equal and surpass the quality of Indian cottons. Thus the Indian product slowly lost its European market; indeed, cheap cloth from Lancashire was increasingly sold in India. In Britain, the Indian cotton goods suffered the added disadvantage of having to pay a prohibitive duty – often around 70 per cent of their value – while cloth woven in England could enter India almost duty-free (see table 2). Indian exports of cloth inevitably fell; the Indian textile industry declined, and a contemporary of Ure noted that 'Dacca, which was the Manchester of India, has fallen from a very flourishing town to a very poor and small one'.[24]

For a time, the Indians maintained their superiority in the art of calico printing, and this prolonged the life of some export markets. Even here, though, there was British competition. The Indians' technique of printing on cloth had been copied in Britain; the secret of their dyes and mordants had been discovered; and the British had now perfected machinery which would allow calico printing to be carried out by factory methods. Ure's experience was that 'The printing machinery of great Britain had begun to supersede . . . the cheapest hand labour of India'.[25] Again, however, competition was distorted by the heavy import duties imposed by Britain.

The fortunes of Indian textile workers were in these ways as closely tied to the new factories in Britain as those of English or Scottish workers. As machines were introduced in Britain, workers experienced what is now termed 'technological unemployment'. English workers in this position could seek jobs in the new factories, but the Indians clearly could not. While the depreciation of labour in the British textile industry chiefly meant that independent skilled workers were turned into machine-minders, in India it often meant the complete loss of a livelihood. Britain exported its technological unemployment along with its cloth.

It would be wrong to romanticise the skill and craftsmanship of hand manufacture in the textile industry. Work was tedious and repetitive, and in India especially, workers lived in great poverty. Their poverty was none the less increased when what Marx called 'modern industry' developed in Britain. Moreover,

24. Simkin, *The Traditional Trade of Asia*, p. 288.
25. Ure, *Dictionary*, article 'CALICO PRINTING', pp. 307–8.

the same thing occurred in other trades; in one type of manufacture after another, the 'modern industry' of Britain produced goods which could be sold more cheaply than Indian products both in India's traditional export markets and throughout much of the sub-continent itself. A complete list of Indian handicrafts and industries which suffered in this way would include:[26]

cotton spinning and weaving, silk weaving, dyeing and calico printing;

iron and steel, brass, tool-making, manufacture of agricultural implements;

ship-building;

glass-making.

In no case was the disaster so great as in textiles, where India had declined from being the world's greatest exporter in 1700 to being a net importer in the 1850s. By then, India's imports from Lancashire exceeded its own exports by about eight times. But the collapse of iron- and steel-making in India was also very marked. In the 18th century, iron was made in small charcoal-fired furnaces with the draught supplied by bellows. Water-mills were sometimes used for crushing the ore, as at Dhunpoor, Kumaon and Garhwal, but the bellows were worked manually, sometimes by as many as eight or nine men. The furnaces were certainly inefficient, but produced such a good quality of metal that in the 1790s the British thought of importing it to reduce their dependence on Swedish iron. But by the 1820s and 30s, the British could produce their own high quality iron. Imports from Sweden had fallen, and British iron-masters had become more interested in finding export markets for their own products. Indian iron-making declined rapidly in the face of this competition. Dharampal estimates that in the early 1700s there may have been 10,000 small furnaces being used throughout India.[27] But during the 19th century, as a British historian has noted, 'cheap imported iron and steel goods practically stamped out the

26. Simkin, *The Traditional Trade of Asia*, pp. 246, 287–8; Dharampal, *Indian Science and Technology*.

27. Dharampal, *Indian Science and Technology*, p. LIV.

indigenous industry'.[28] A knowledge of the growth of iron exports from Britain,[29] coupled with comments made by contemporary British travellers in India, makes it possible to chart this decline with some confidence (see fig. 41), even though considerable uncertainty exists about total figures for Indian iron production in the 18th century.

Table 3. Iron and Steel Production in India

Year	Production (*tons of pig iron per year*)	Remarks
before 1800	200,000[a]	very approximate estimate
1849	less than 10,000	estimate; competition from imports now severe; value of imported metal goods was £221,061[d]
1857	negligible[b]	value of imported metal goods was £802,762[d]
1866	negligible[b]	value of imported metal goods was £1,233,387[d]
1900	30,000	estimate based on the amount of ore used
1916–17	147,500[b]	nearly all production was at Jamshedpur works
1921–22	270,000[b]	
1934–35	892,000[b]	
1948	1,487,000[c]	
1958	2,135,000[c]	

Sources:
a. Based on Dharampal, *Indian Science and Technology*, p. LIV.
b. Anstey, *The Economic Development of India*, pp. 27, 253.
c. United Nations, *Statistical yearbooks*.
d. Dutt, *The Economic History of India in the Victorian Age*, pp. 161, 345.

Around 1830, Englishmen in India began to be concerned about what was happening. 'We have destroyed the manufactures of India', exclaimed one man about then, and he went on to suggest that some protection should be given to silk weaving, 'the last of the expiring manufactures of India'. Another observer was alarmed by 'a commercial revolution productive of so much present suffering to numerous classes in India'.[30]

28. Anstey, *The Economic Development of India*, p. 27.
29. Dutt, *The Economic History of India in the Victorian Age*, pp. 161, 345.
30. Quoted by Simkin, *The Traditional Trade of Asia*, p. 287.

In 1843 a Captain Campbell working near Calcutta wrote that in the trade between India and England 'a source of deep injury to the former country arises from England having deprived her of the trade in cotton cloth, the manufacture of which was, but a few years ago, one of the most valuable and extensive of Indian products'. He pointed out that large quantities of English bar iron were being imported by India, 'which to Madras alone

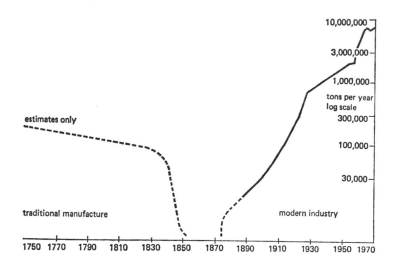

Figure 41
Iron production in India.
(Sources: see table 3)

amounts to 1,000 tons per annum', and suggested that the loss of the cotton trade would be partly compensated if India could 'supply her own wants' in iron.[31]

In fact, several more years were to pass before any 'modern industry' was established in India. The first cotton-mills were built in the 1850s, but it was not until 1875 that a modern iron industry was established. In the interval between the decline of its traditional manufactures in the early 19th century and the

31. Campbell's paper is reproduced in full by Dharampal, *Indian Science and Technology*, pp. 249–63.

first introduction of modern industry thirty or forty years later, India experienced a period of very great poverty. This interval is illustrated for the iron industry in fig. 41. Lack of precision about quantities of iron produced before 1900 is here less important than the matter of timing—the length of the period during which India had no significant iron industry being the most important point. This was a period of more than a generation – long enough for skill and interest in iron-making to be forgotten in many areas, and for the discipline demanded by work in this industry to be lost. Many of the old skills, of course, would not be relevant in the modern industry, but to allow them to disappear before the new form of production was introduced meant starting with a work-force in the new iron-works whose habits of working and level of knowledge were less than they might otherwise have been. The transition from 'manufactures' to 'modern industry' in any country meant abandoning traditional skills, but the relatively gradual and continuous transition which was effected in Europe meant that some knowledge, skill and experience was usefully transferred from one form of industry to the other. In India, the older skills were simply allowed to go to waste, and the new ones had then to be planted in an unnecessarily barren soil.

Most kinds of technical change affect the way people are expected to work, so ideas and idealism concerning the value of work frequently influence the development of technology, or are influenced by it. Robert Owen's comment about the depreciation of labour has already been quoted, and its application to 19th-century India is only too clear. Owen was referring partly to the money-value of work, and the way in which the wages of a skilled worker often decline as mechanisation progresses. But he also shared the view that skilled work could be rewarding and satisfying in itself, and appreciated that in this sense also the value of work might depreciate as mechanisation developed, and workers were turned into machine-minders.

If work is valuable in these two ways for the person who is doing it, it also has a social value, which the experience of India prompts one to consider. This is the potential contribution of an individual's labour and skill to the development of the community or nation to which he belongs. The work by which one earns one's own livelihood also contributes to the kind of livelihood which other people will be able to earn, both now and in the future. Human labour and skill is one of the most potent of all resources for economic development. To have people un- employed or underemployed in 19th-century India, and to throw away their skills uselessly, was to abandon what at that time were the country's richest resources for its own future progress. The continuing tragedy of India in the 1970s is that very large num- bers of its people remain unemployed, and so are unable either to gain the satisfaction of exercising fully their own intelligence and skill, or to contribute to the development of their still im- poverished country.

India, China and Japan

India was not the only country whose textile-workers or whose iron industry was threatened by the rapid progress of mechanisa- tion in Britain. Both in Asia and in Europe, there were other nations whose traditional trades were vulnerable to this kind of competition. From about 1815 onwards there were many cases in Europe where local textile industries were upset by the influx of cheap yarn or cloth from Britain. Some of the worst instances came in the 1840s, when there was very serious hardship among woollen weavers in Silesia and flax spinners in Flanders. In effect, these continental workers were taking 'part of the burden of adjustment ... from Britain's shoulders'.[32] They too were suffering from technological unemployment generated in Britain.

However, European governments could and did set a limit to the disruption of their industries, by the use of tariff barriers which prevented cheap British products from coming in too easily. In Asia, a control of imports from Britain was effected in China and Japan by limiting European trade to certain ports, and by limiting the total volume of imports in some commodities. Neither form of protection was available to India, because it had no real government of its own. Ever since 1712, the centralised rule provided by the Moghul Emperors had been collapsing. There was no unity among local rulers, and there were disputes between Hindus and Moslems. India's external trade, and pro- gressively more of its internal government, fell into the hands of the British East India Company – which naturally had no special interest in protecting Indian manufacturers once these had ceased to find a profitable market in Europe.

32. Landes, *The Unbound Prometheus*, p. 190.

During the 18th and early 19th centuries, Japanese trade with Europe was severely restricted, so traditional manufacturers there were not affected by imports from Europe. But China exported porcelain and silk to Europe, and by the end of the 18th century, its exports of tea were growing rapidly. In 1770, 5·6 million pounds of tea were shipped from Canton to Europe; by 1800 this export had increased to 20 million pounds.[33] The problem was that the Chinese imported very little from Europe in return, and a large proportion of the porcelain, silk and tea had to be paid for in bullion – usually silver. Thus there was a chronic imbalance of trade seriously unfavourable to the Europeans, and this continued until British merchants found that an addiction to opium-smoking was growing in China, and could be encouraged. They arranged for opium poppies to be grown in Bengal, and by 1827, they had succeeded in this trade to the extent that £2,200,000 worth of opium was brought into Canton during the course of twelve months. This reversed the balance of trade so that it now favoured the British, and by the end of the 1820s the Chinese Treasury's silver reserves were being depleted at the rate of over £1,000,000 per annum.

Not unnaturally, the Chinese government attempted to stop the import of opium, which was damaging the health of the people as well as ruining the imperial finances. But their efforts to do this only led to war with Britain and a crushing naval defeat. It was here that the steamships whose engines were maintained by Peter Ewart won the famous victory mentioned earlier in this chapter. The outcome was the 'unequal treaty' of 1842 which gave Britain much greater freedom in its trade with China. A further treaty, signed in 1860, after another military expedition, put virtually the whole Chinese Customs system into Western hands. Lancashire cotton goods and English ironware, it was hoped, would now be freely sold to the Chinese, whose indigenous industries could expect to follow the same fate as India's.

The industrial nations of the West also wished to sell their wares in Japan. After a visit from a United States warship in 1853, the Japanese signed treaties with America, Britain and Russia in 1854, and gave the Americans special privileges in several Japanese ports a little later.

The sharp contrast between the fortunes of China and Japan

33. Simkin, *The Traditional Trade of Asia*, pp. 214–15, 270–75.

after 1854 resulted very largely from the fact that the Chinese imperial government, twice humiliated by Western invasions, grew progressively weaker; while in 1868, Japan acquired a strong and effective government with the Meiji Restoration. China, in fact, was facing an internal crisis as well as external threats. During two centuries of peace and relative prosperity between 1650 and 1840, the Chinese population had more than trebled.[34] Agricultural production also increased, with much land newly brought into cultivation, but it seems that by 1840 the pressure of population on resources was becoming critical. During the 1850s and 60s, the government lost control of vast areas of the country to the T'ai P'ing rebellion, a 'great peasant rising caused by oppression and corruption'.[35] Suppression of this movement was achieved only with great difficulty, and with very great economic disruption. After that, no central government in China again had much authority until after 1949.

India, and then Japan, were the two Asian countries in which modern industry gained its first foothold. The first railway in India was opened in 1852, twenty years sooner than the earliest in Japan, and thirty years before the first in China. The first cotton-mill in India was erected in 1851, about fifteen years in advance of Japan. But despite India's early lead in these two fields, its underlying economic weakness remained. In many European countries, as also in Japan, railway construction gave a vitally important boost to the early stages of industrial growth, since railway-building made demands on such other basic industries as coal-mining, mechanical engineering and steel-making. India, however, was still expected to function as a market for British goods, so although British investment had paid for 24,000 miles of railway in India by 1900, nearly all the locomotives, rolling-stock, rails and bridge girders were imported from England, and the Indian economy did not gain as much stimulus as might otherwise have been expected. With the cotton industry, too, a very rapid growth in the number of factories between the 1850s and 1900 did little to stimulate the growth of supporting engineering industries. The machines in the mills and the large engines which drove them were again mostly imported, and mainly from Britain.

In contrast, the Japanese, responsible for their own industrial

34. Ho Ping-ti, *Studies on the Population of China*, pp. 25, 64.
35. Fitzgerald, *The Birth of Communist China*, p. 44.

progress, and anxious to become self-sufficient, established machine shops and engineering works more quickly than was done in India. During the 1890s, they began 'hasty construction of heavy industry for military needs'. Armament manufactures brought forward the machine-tool industry and shipbuilding, and these led in turn to the establishment of an iron and steel industry.[36] In the textile industry, large cotton spinning mills were established using imported machines, but hand methods continued to be widely used in weaving and in the silk industry. This saved a great deal of capital at a crucial time, and reduced the country's dependence on imported equipment.

So while Japan in 1910 was well on the way to becoming self-sufficient in its basic engineering industries, India had made very little progress in that direction. Meanwhile, the plight of China was much worse. Its traditional manufactures were in decline; it had lost a war with Japan in 1895, and much of the country was being developed as a market for Japanese goods.

Ideas and idealism in the technology of other cultures

Near the beginning of this book can be found the comment that the technical achievements of European civilisation around the year 1100 were somewhat less impressive than those of the contemporary civilisations of the Arabs, the Indians and the Chinese. Europeans learned much from the technical skills and inventions of all these other cultures, and ended by surpassing them all in technological development. So at risk of seeming to digress from the main theme of this book, it has seemed right to sketch very briefly the ultimate fate of some of these other technologies. The brilliance of the Arabs' Islamic civilisations quickly faded, and by the middle of the 19th century the arts of India and China were in a disastrous decline. Only the Japanese, whose ancient culture and technology was learned primarily from China, experienced an industrial development similar to that of the West. The major reasons for the distinctive development of Japan have already been indicated:

1. Japan did not go through any lengthy period when its external trade was under foreign control, but after 1868, the

36. Okita, in *Economic Development with special reference to . . . East Asia*, pp. 376–85.

Japanese took energetic control of their own economic moderni-
sation. India and China had to wait until 1947 and 1949 before
they could do the same.

2. The traditional manufactures of Japan were not eroded by
Western imports, but survived intact until after modern industries
were introduced. Traditional skills were therefore not abandoned
before new ones were learned, and traditional industries contributed an increasing export of finished manufactures during the
first twenty years of Japan's industrial revolution. This was true
particularly of weaving, and of silk, lacquer and pottery manufactures. The traditional industries were essentially labour-
intensive, and absorbed little capital. Their expansion at a time
when capital was in short supply greatly assisted the early development of Japan.[37]

Although these two points can be used to account for much in
the comparative history of India, China and Japan in the 19th
century, they do not explain the different technical development
of these cultures as compared with Europe over the longer period
between 1100 and 1850. One can say without much hesitation
that China in 1100 possessed the most technically sophisticated
civilisation which then existed, and perhaps the most highly
developed that the world had ever known. Why then did the West
develop an industrial technology while China did not?

The answer, surely, must be given in terms of the ideas and
values which are involved in technological change. What seem
most important in this context are differences concerning intellectual and symbolic objectives in technical progress. For example,
there was far more of an intellectual development in the early
practical arts and technology of the West than in those of China.
The crucial period was the Renaissance in 15th-century Europe,
when the scholarly study of Roman technical achievements and
the application of mathematics to engineering provided two
powerful incentives for people from the educated classes to take
an interest in certain kinds of technology. Among the results of
this was the work of Alberti and Agricola, and the large numbers
of books on machines which appeared from the 16th century
onwards (chapters three and five). In China, by contrast, the
literature on engineering was 'distinctly small, perhaps mainly

37. Ranis, in *American Economic Review*, 47 (1957), pp. 594-607.

because the constructions of artisans, however ingenious, were too often regarded as unworthy of the attention of Confucian literati'.[38] If anything, the latter were more interested in agriculture than machines.

In Europe, mathematics was important not only for its immediate practical value, but also in awakening an intellectual interest in the geometrical and mechanical problems of the engineer. The Chinese developed many branches of mathematics to a very high level, but their mathematical interests were never as relevant to practical problems as Euclidean geometry proved to be. Thus some differences between the practical arts of China and those of the West may be explained by reference to earlier differences in mathematics, and in particular to the fact that modern Europe was heir to the geometry of ancient Greece, while China was not.[39]

As to symbolism in technology, this might be far more crucial than would at first appear. Europeans expressed some of their deepest aspirations in monuments which often had a large technical content – the Gothic cathedrals, the Versailles waterworks, the Languedoc Canal. China does not lack comparable monuments, but the aesthetic ideals of its builders were quite different from those of European architects and engineers, and less often led to critical structural problems and experiments. Chinese monuments did not usually 'challenge' nature like those of the West, but very often expressed a feeling that 'man cannot be thought of apart from nature'. Buildings had a horizontal emphasis rather than reaching up to great heights, and there was an air of repose rather than restlessness about them. 'Chinese architecture was always with, not against Nature; it did not spring suddenly out of the ground like European "Gothic" buildings.'[40] Thus, to take a different example, it would not have seemed very appropriate to the Chinese to build a water-garden on top of a waterless eminence, as was done at Versailles. Such a feature would be better at some point where water was naturally available. Collaboration with nature meant that ornamental schemes of this kind less often turned into major engineering works than in Europe.

38. Needham, *Science and Civilization in China*, *4*, part 2, p. 1.
39. Needham, *Science and Civilization in China*, *4*, part 3, pp. xlv, xlvi, 145 note d, 378 etc. See also Needham's article 'Mathematics and science in China and the West', *Sociology of Science* (ed. Barnes), pp. 21–44.
40. *Science and Civilization in China*, *4*, part 3, pp. 60–61.

A different and more important point about the symbolism of technology is that from the 15th and 16th centuries onwards the idea of invention came to have a symbolic value in Europe. New techniques and new machines came to be identified with 'progress', and Europeans saw their great inventions as marking their superiority over ancient Greece and Rome; they were excited by them and by the persons of genius who brought them into existence. But such things did not have the same significance in Chinese culture, and when European mechanical inventions were first brought to China they were not seen as symbols of progress, but were regarded merely as novelties or playthings. Of course, China possessed inventors and engineers of its own. But most of their greatest achievements belonged to an earlier age. Their great skills in iron-smelting, their expertise as bridge-builders, their techniques of flood control and their knowledge of ship design – all seem to have reached their culmination before 1400.

The most clear-cut case of Chinese technical expertise reaching a summit of achievement around 1400 concerns their navy. Under the admiral Cheng Ho, Chinese ships explored the whole of south-east Asia and most of the Indian Ocean. They sailed down the coast of East Africa, and they carried two giraffes back to Peking to illustrate the strange lands they had found in the west. The Chinese and the Arabs at this time effectively divided the sea-borne trade of Asia and Africa between them, and Chinese exports reached African towns like Zimbabwe through Arab trading-posts at Mombasa and Sofala. The Chinese exploration of these distant lands was carried out with some very remarkable ships. The largest of them were 440 feet long and 180 feet at broadest beam. They carried a crew of four or five hundred men, and probably displaced more than 1,000 tons.[41]

These ships protected the trade of Chinese merchants and conducted the Chinese government's diplomatic relations with the rulers of such places as Bengal, Madras, Ceylon and Aden. Naval operations of various kinds were, indeed, a major part of Chinese policy at this time. Between 1403 and 1419 Chinese government shipyards produced 2,149 sea-going vessels of all types, including 94 of the very large vessels just mentioned. But then there was a sudden reversal of policy; after 1419, orders

41. *Science and Civilization in China*, 4, part 3, pp. 480–81.

for new ships ceased almost entirely.[42] During the 1430s, the long voyages in the Indian Ocean were stopped, and the navy was confined to Chinese waters. Thereafter, China never again had a major navy. So when European ships first reached the East Indies soon after 1500, they found no sea power to match their own. And four centuries later, English ships in the Opium War found themselves facing Chinese vessels of only about one-third of the size of the largest 15th-century junks, and with only limited fire-power, while Cheng Ho's squadrons would have dwarfed the English force both in size of vessels and in numbers.

The withdrawal of the Chinese navy in the 1420s and 30s seems to reflect a definite and conscious value-judgement by the current ruling class, and this could have affected other practical arts besides just shipbuilding and navigation. There seems to have been a deliberate turning away from grandiose adventures, and a tendency to feel that the practical arts needed little further development. The ideals and values which led to this decision were those of 'the classical Confucian motif of scholarly austerity', as practised by a class of efficient administrators and scholar-landlords.[43]

The values of this group, more attuned to agriculture than to mechanical technology, and embracing a view of nature more gentle and accepting than that of the West, may very properly be admired. One may easily feel that some parts of their attitudes may be of continuing relevance in the 1970s. But clearly, they left China at a great disadvantage in a world which was rapidly being colonised by the more aggressive and restlessly innovating civilisation of the West. It seems surprising and disconcerting that the Chinese for so long remained oblivious to this growing threat.

In several ways, then, the 15th century seems to mark a watershed in the comparative history of the two most technically progressive civilisations of the world. Up to 1400, Needham claims, China had clear technological superiority. Then during the 15th century the intellectuals of the West became increasingly interested in the engineering arts through the stimulus of the Renaissance; while almost simultaneously Chinese intellectual life was becoming less sympathetic to some forms of technical

42. *Science and Civilization in China, 4*, part 3, p. 479 note f.
43. *Science and Civilization*, p. 524; see also, for example, Fitzgerald, *The Birth of Communist China*, pp. 30–33.

development, and in some fields the practical arts were entering a period of stagnation.

The historian of the future will perhaps be able to give a better perspective on these things than is possible at present. He may suggest, perhaps, 'that technical skills are not good criteria of true civilization, that harmony and balance in a human society are better than restless change and the chimerical search for progress to some undefined goal'.[44] He may also be able to assess the ways in which the values of the East concerning technical change were capable of contributing to the new philosophy of technical development which the West in the 1970s seems so badly to need. One Japanese scientist has expressed his views about this by talking about the need for a post-industrial culture in Japan which would be 'warm and humane, to replace the cold inhuman western import'.[45]

44. Fitzgerald, *The Birth of Communist China*, p. 35.
45. Quoted in the *Guardian*, 24 June 1971.

Part Three

PAST AND FUTURE

Ideas, idealism and some current directions in technical progress

Mid-19th century technology

By 1851, the period of the industrial revolution, as it is conventionally understood, was over. The Great Exhibition held in Hyde Park during that year showed what had been achieved for all the world to see. There was no branch of manufactures in which the British lacked competence. Their steam engines and textile machines were so highly developed that no further innovation of importance could be expected. The potentialities of the machine tools introduced by Maudslay and his school had been widely exploited. And the expansion of the railways during the 1830s and 40s 'brought the British coal, iron, and heavy engineering industries to technical maturity . . . By, let us say, the Exhibition of 1851, Britain had mastered and extended over virtually the whole range of its resources all that the then science and technology had to offer'.[1]

One of the most intelligent of the many commentators on the Great Exhibition was Charles Babbage. His book *The Exposition of 1851* was published in the year of its title. It expressed a view of British prospects which was much less cheerful than might have been expected. The British, Babbage thought, were neglecting the sciences on which their technical achievements were based. In more general ways, though, he was extremely hopeful about the benefits which technical progress would bring, and in one of his earlier works he had expressed himself most eloquently on this subject.

'The productions of Nature', he wrote, 'varied and numerous as they are, may each, in some future day, become the basis of extensive Manufactures, and give life, employment and wealth to millions of Human beings. But the crude treasures perpetually

1. Rostow, *The Stages of Economic Growth*, p. 60.

exposed before our eyes contain within them other and more valuable principles. All these, in their innumerable combinations, which Ages of labour and research can never exhaust, may be destined to furnish, in perpetual succession, the sources of our wealth and of our happiness.'[2]

There was no limit to the growth of science. Indeed, 'the further we advance from the origin of our Knowledge, the larger it becomes, and the greater power it bestows upon its cultivators to add new fields to its dominions. Yet does this continually and rapidly increasing power, instead of giving us any reason to anticipate the exhaustion of so fertile a field, place us at each advance on some higher eminence, from which the mind contemplates the past, and feels irresistibly convinced that the whole already gained bears a constantly diminishing ratio to the still more rapidly expanding horizon of our Knowledge.'

Progress was being made in the study of chemistry, electricity, heat and light; and the science of mathematics, 'having grasped the mightier masses of the Universe, and reduced their wanderings to laws ... is now preparing its fetters for the minutest atoms which Nature has created.' Mathematics, indeed, would 'ultimately govern the whole of the application of Science to the Arts of life'.

During the decades which followed, there was every reason for thinking that Babbage's general view of scientific and technical progress was right. New sciences were emerging – organic chemistry, electromagnetism, thermodynamics – and all of them had enormous potential for practical application. The development of organic chemistry led to the synthesis of the first aniline dye in 1856; azo dyes came in 1863; celluloid in 1868; viscose rayon in 1892 and bakelite in 1909. The birth of thermodynamics as a science was directly stimulated by the improvement of the steam engine from Watt's time onwards, but the establishment of its principles was in turn a stimulus for the invention of a whole family of new engines using hot air or internal combustion as the working principles. Otto's gas engine of 1876 was one of the first. It was used extensively in small factories and for applications where intermittent use made steam engines uneconomic. Before the end of the 1880s, petroleum offered the prospect of an even

2. See Barlow and Babbage in *A Treatise on the Manufacturers and Machinery*, p. 81; compare Babbage, *On the Economy of Machinery and Manufactures*.

more flexible source of power. Daimler made his first petrol engine in 1882, and several experimental motor-cars were being tried out by the end of the decade.

The first practical application of electricity was the telegraph, patented by Cooke and Wheatstone in 1837. Next came electric lighting, at first using carbon arc lamps, and then with the familiar filament lamp in a glass bulb, which was introduced by Edison in 1879. Edison's company opened small power stations in New York and London in 1882, and in 1889 Ferranti's design for Deptford Power Station pioneered the use of alternating current for large-scale supply systems.

While these new, science-based technologies were coming into being, the more conventional branches of engineering were being revolutionised by the introduction of steel and reinforced concrete. Steel became available on an industrial scale in 1859 with the introduction of Bessemer's converter, and was used extensively in railway track. But it was not until C. W. Siemens, Pierre Martin and Gilchrist Thomas had introduced other processes and improvements that the engineering potential of steel was fully realised. This was in the 1880s; reinforced concrete came into regular use in the next decade, largely as a result of French initiative.

After 1850, then, and particularly after about 1870, technical progress was apparently taking a new course, and one which had been in no way foreshadowed during the industrial revolution of Arkwright and Watt. Moreover, this new direction was one which Britain seemed ill-equipped to follow. The United States and many European countries were, by this time, developing their own industries, and it proved to be Germany and America which were best able to take advantage of the new technologies. Many of the pioneers of organic chemistry were Germans, even though it was a British chemist, W. H. Perkin, who made the first aniline dye in 1856. With regard to the internal combustion engine and the first motor-cars, Otto, Benz, Daimler and Diesel are only a few of the many famous German names which could be mentioned.

In both cases, German pre-eminence owed a great deal to the excellence of technical education in Germany. The rapid growth of industrial organic chemistry was partly the result of the teaching and research carried on in German universities. Work on internal combustion engines gained much from the way in which mechanical engineering was taught in the German polytechnics and at the Freiberg Mining Academy. Britain's lack of enterprise with regard to chemistry or to the new engines was largely explicable by its failure, up to that time, to develop any effective technical education. The new technologies were more completely based on science than those of the late-18th-century industrial revolution, and a system of scientific and technical education had become a necessity for any industrial nation.

The full implications of the technical changes which began in the 1870s and 80s were not clear until very much later. Researches in organic chemistry at this time led not only to the introduction of celluloid, rayon and bakelite, but also started a long sequence of discoveries concerning the large molecules out of which such materials are formed; and these discoveries led in turn to a new generation of synthetic materials, beginning with nylon in 1935, and continuing with terylene and polythene just over a decade later.

Radio and electronics developed along a similar time-scale. The possibility of wireless transmission was established by the theories put forward by Maxwell in the 1860s, and by the experiments of Hertz and Marconi around 1890 and 1900. Thus the beginnings of radio, and all that it led to, also belong to this crucial late-19th-century period of discovery and innovation – even though commercial broadcasting did not begin until 1922, and microwave applications, like radar, did not come until after 1940.

These developments in electricity and wireless, chemistry, steel-making and thermodynamics added up to what some people have called the beginnings of 'high technology'[3] and others have described as a 'Second Industrial Revolution'.[4] Patrick Geddes, in 1915, was one of the first to try to interpret this series of innovations. He introduced the terms 'palaeotechnic' and 'neotechnic' to indicate the difference between the traditional technology on which the first industrial revolution had been built, and the new technologies of the late 19th century.[5] Steel and electricity, he

3. e.g. Earl Cook, in *Scientific American*, *224* (September 1971), p. 135.
4. Landes, *The Unbound Prometheus*, p. 235.
5. Geddes, *Cities in Evolution*, quoted by Mumford, *Technics and Civilization*, p. 109. Mumford added the term 'eotechnic' to denote an even earlier phase.

thought, were characteristic of a 'neotechnic' phase of technical development which would eventually supplant entirely the cast-iron and coal-fired plant of 'palaeotechnic' industry.

When Babbage wrote about future technical progress with such optimism in the 1830s, he was standing on the threshold of the neotechnic era. He knew enough about the work being done in chemistry and electricity in his own day to realise its potential importance, though he can hardly have guessed what would be achieved even in the next thirty or forty years. He also realised that technology would be increasingly dependent on science, and he appreciated the seriousness of some of the deficiencies in current British science, especially when compared with work being done on the continent. In all these ways he showed great foresight. But there was one crucial subject where later readers might justly have accused him of wishful thinking; and this was the subject of future sources of power.

The power required to drive all the machinery in British textile-mills in 1834 amounted to between forty and fifty thousand horsepower. Of this, about 15,000 h.p. came from water-wheels and about 30,000 h.p. from steam engines. Steam engines were becoming increasingly important; a French contemporary remarked that to take away all the steam engines in Britain would do the country more harm than to destroy her navy. By 1870 the point was more pertinent than ever. At this date, water-wheels were providing the textile industry with somewhat less energy than before, but steam power had increased ten-fold, and steam engines were developing about 300,000 h.p.[6]

Steam power, indeed, was of central importance to 19th-century industry, and it caught people's imagination in a way that is now difficult fully to understand. Evidence of this is provided by the way in which the engines themselves were embellished by their designers. The columns and entablatures of Greek architecture were adapted to fit the framing of the great engines which powered factories, and the buildings in which they were housed were made the architectural focus of the factory complex, with large round-headed windows and elaborately decorated interiors.

Babbage had portrayed progress in terms of the growth of knowledge. But then he talked about power resources, and referred to doubts about whether 'the weak arm of man' possessed

6. Blaug, in *Economic History Review*, 2nd series, *13* (1960–61), p. 379.

'the physical force requisite to render that knowledge available'. Some people were saying that 'the source of power is not without limit, and the coal mines of the world may ultimately be exhausted'.

It would be premature, he thought, to be alarmed about this, because 'knowledge is Power', and knowledge 'not merely gives to its votaries control over the mental facilities of their species, but it is the generator of physical force'.[7] Knowledge of the expansive power of steam had already made vast new supplies of power available; in the future, new knowledge would become available, about using the tides, or volcanic springs, or other undreamt of sources of power. Thus if power was one thread in the fabric of progress, without which knowledge was of no effect, knowledge in its turn would add new sources of power to that fabric.

During the 1860s, the earlier optimism of Babbage and many of his contemporaries was challenged in a well-argued book on Britain's coal resources written by the economist W. Stanley Jevons.[8] The life of Victorian England depended so heavily on the steam engine, Jevons said, and accessible deposits of coal were relatively so limited, that the nation's material prosperity could not continue to increase for much longer. Even if petroleum proved to be as useful a source of energy as people were then beginning to say, this would not make any difference in the long run, because petroleum was as limited as coal in the total quantities available.

The details of Jevons's argument can be summarised as follows: during the year 1861, nearly 90 million tons of coal had been extracted from British mines, most of it for consumption within Britain. For several years previously, and perhaps since 1820, coal production had been increasing at an annual rate of $3\frac{1}{2}$ per cent. If this rate of increase were to be sustained for another hundred years, coal production would reach 2,600 million tons a year by 1961, and the total quantity of coal mined prior to that date would be over 102,000 million tons. This was clearly impossible, because Britain's total reserves of accessible coal were then estimated to be less than this latter figure. What would happen, said Jevons, was that coal would have to be obtained from progressively deeper and more difficult seams, and so would

7. Barlow and Babbage, *A Treatise on the Manufactures and Machinery*, p. 81.

8. Jevons's book *The Coal Question* was published in 1865.

become increasingly expensive. Consumption would no longer increase by $3\frac{1}{2}$ per cent annually. It would soon become static, and then begin to fall; 'the conclusion is inevitable, that our present happy, progressive condition is a thing of limited duration'.[9]

Jevons was highly regarded in academic circles – he became a professor at Manchester in 1866 – and his book had wide influence.[10] In the year following its publication a Royal Commission was appointed to look into the state of Britain's coal reserves. This body was more complacent than Jevons, and another Royal Commission which examined the same problem in 1901 suggested that his prognostications were totally misleading. Jevons himself had died some years before this second Commission reported, but a new edition of his book was brought out by a friend, A. W. Flux, in order to defend the point which Jevons originally made. Flux showed that the rate of increase in coal production had decreased from the annual $3\frac{1}{2}$ per cent which Jevons quoted to just over 2 per cent. He very reasonably claimed that this vindicated Jevons's view that the $3\frac{1}{2}$ per cent rate could not be kept up indefinitely. Even growth at the 2 per cent rate would, by the year 2000, have used up exactly half of the 141,635 million ton reserves estimated by the most recent Royal Commission. In order to demonstrate the impossibility of sustaining the 2 per cent growth rate, Flux followed Jevons's example, and plotted a graph to illustrate its implications. If this graph is superimposed on one showing the actual production of coal since Flux edited the book, it can be seen that the production figures only follow the 2 per cent growth curve until 1913, after which coal mining began a long period of decline. Jevons's argument had been overtaken by events – by the cessation of British exports of coal during the First World War, and by the long period of depression which followed it.

Jevons's view of the future of technology was a pessimistic one – too pessimistic, as it turned out – yet he combined his gloom predictions with a resolute and almost irrational hopefulness about the future of civilisation as a whole. He asked whether his generation was sensible to allow 'the commerce of this country to rise beyond the point at which we can long maintain

9. Jevons, *The Coal Question*, 1865 edn, p. 215.
10. Bone and Himus, *Coal*, p. 16.

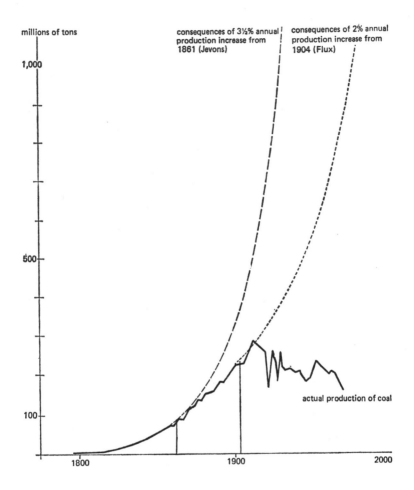

Figure 42

Graphs plotted by Jevons and Flux to illustrate the implications of sustained growth in coal consumption, superimposed on a graph showing actual consumption of coal in Britain.

(Compiled by the author from the frontispiece to W. S. Jevons, *The Coal Question*, 3rd edition [ed. A. W. Flux], Macmillan, 1906, and incorporating more recent statistics)

it'. He answered that 'No part, no function of a nation is independent of the rest, and in fearlessly following our instincts of rapid growth we may rear a fabric of varied civilization, we may develop talents and virtues, and propagate influence which could not have resulted from slow restricted growth, however prolonged'.[11]

Looking at the history of technology in Britain, Jevons went on: 'It is questionable whether a country in any sense free can suffer such a grand movement to begin without suffering it to proceed its own length. One invention, one art, one development of commerce, one amelioration of society follows another almost as effect follows cause. . . .' Coal resources would ultimately be exhausted, and industrial progress would be threatened but if, in the meantime, 'we lavishly and boldly push forward in the creation and distribution of our riches, it is hard to overestimate the pitch of beneficient influence to which we might attain in the present. *But the maintenance of such a position is physically impossible. We have to make the momentous choice between brief greatness and longer continued mediocrity.*'[12]

Jevons had emphasised his belief in the value of economic growth at the beginning of his book by quoting Adam Smith (*The Wealth of Nations*): 'The progressive state is in reality the cheerful and hearty state to all the different orders of society; the stationary is dull; the declining melancholy.' He might have quoted another 18th-century work, Joseph Priestley's *Essay on Government*, where it was said to be a 'universal maxim' that the more liberty which is given 'to everything which is in a state of growth, the more perfect it will become'. Although Jevons had seen the severe limitations to which current patterns of growth would be subject in the future, he still seems to have shared the optimism which had given rise to the *laissez-faire* attitudes of a century earlier (chapter eight).

The 1860s and the 1970s

Any work on history, however academic and apparently objective, is inevitably written from the standpoint of the author's own time and circumstances. This book was written between 1967 and 1972, and was strongly influenced by the public issues of those

11. *The Coal Question*, 1865 edn, pp. 344–6.
12. *The Coal Question*, 1865 edn, pp. 347–9; Jevons's italics.

five years – particularly as they impinged on current and future developments in technology, and as they affected the author in his teaching work at an institute of technology.

Seen from that particular standpoint, Jevons's book on coal resources has a vivid interest and relevance. He was facing much the same dilemma as we have been made to face by more recent problems of technological development and economic growth. But having recognised that growth could not for long continue, Jevons still believed that it should be pursued with all vitality and persistence. What he seems to have thought is that a society which ceases to develop in this way begins to die; that life itself is a forward motion, and so all forms of development are necessary and good; and that there is no 'contentment but in proceeding'.

Jevons felt an immense exhilaration in the expanding, developing society of his time, which he identified with its rapid pace of industrial growth. Babbage, in the passages quoted above, talked with the same feeling about the growth of scientific knowledge, which, he recognised, would lead in turn to further technical and industrial advances.

Babbage and Jevons make an appropriate ending for the historical narrative of this book, not only because they belong to a convenient historical period – the final phase of Britain's industrial revolution – but also because some of their faith in technical progress, and rather more of their conflicting doubts about the future, are still with us a century later. It is the more prosaic pessimism of Jevons that is called to mind most often, especially in current discussions of the 'energy crisis'. For example, similar arguments to those of Jevons are currently being put forward to show that the world's oil reserves will last only for a relatively short period in the future if the consumption of oil continues to expand at the current rate. Even allowing for the new oil-fields that were rapidly being explored and proved in the early 1970s, half the original oil deposits in the whole of the earth's rocks may have been used up by the middle of the 1990s.[13] Nearly all other sources of energy are subject to the same kind of limitation, and although some people hold that technology can solve all the problems of technical progress, and have pointed to the promise of

13. Hubbert, 'The energy resources of the earth', in *Scientific American*, *224* (September 1971), p. 65.

power from thermonuclear fusion, there will be ecological and resource limitations even to this.

One might also take comfort from the graph presented in fig. 42, which appears to show that the worst pessimism of Jevons and Flux was not justified – coal consumption did not continue to increase for long after their time, and present reserves are still quite large. It should be remembered, though, that it took a war and a long period of unemployment and hardship as well as technical change in energy supplies to produce that effect. Are we to wait for a convulsion of similar magnitude to overcome the problem of our diminishing energy and mineral resources?

There are no clear answers to many of these questions, and no escape for us from the kind of forebodings which Jevons expressed. There are other worries as well, concerned with pollution of air and water, and most alarmingly of all, with population. Like Jevons, many people are asking whether present patterns of development can continue for much longer. Their answers are less positive than his, and more full of doubts, because even before the joint threat of energy shortage, environmental destruction and population growth was widely recognised, the direction of current technical advance was being criticised in several quarters.

In the 1930s and 40s, Aldous Huxley and George Orwell were painting horrific pictures of the technology-based society which seemed to be on the way. Orwell remarked that while we would probably all agree 'that machinery is made for man and not man for machinery; in practice any attempt to check the development of the machine appears to us an attack on knowledge and therefore a kind of blasphemy'.[14]

In the late 1950s, when most people in the West were more prosperous than they had been when Orwell was writing, J. K. Galbraith dissected the economic fallacies of 'the affluent society'. He argued that the current form of industrial and technological growth was based on an outdated understanding of what the needs of people in an advanced industrial community really were. It neglected their need for security of employment and income, and for social and public services, while producing more and more material goods, of which there was already a plenty.

14. Orwell, *The Road to Wigan Pier*, Penguin edn, p. 182.

Yet another disturbing problem became apparent when one considered the non-industrialised regions of the world, which produced many of the raw materials needed by the industries of Europe and America. In 1959, C. P. Snow said that the 'main issue' in current technical progress was, 'that the people in the industrialised countries are getting richer, and those in the non-industrialised countries are at best standing still: so that the gap between the industrialised countries and the rest is widening every day. On the world scale, this is the gap between the rich and the poor.'[15]

But despite the contradictions of the affluent society, despite the gloomy image of 1984, despite the depletion of natural resources and damage to the environment, some romanticism of the kind that Babbage and Jevons expressed has persisted. There is among some people a feeling of compulsion about the pursuit of advanced technologies – a sense that man must be continually proving his virility by pioneering on the frontiers of what is only just possible. The Anglo-French supersonic airliner which first flew in 1970 was not built because anybody had demonstrated a need for such aircraft, but because really large supersonic planes had just become a possibility. It was felt that it would be ducking a challenge to choose not to build them. That this attitude also prevailed when men first landed on the moon in 1969 was clearly expressed in comments published at the time, which made this achievement seem comparable to Scott's expedition to the South Pole, or the first successful ascent of Everest in 1953. Granted, the moon flight had scientific objectives as well; but most of them could have been accomplished more cheaply by other means, and the real reason why men landed on the moon was simply that, like Everest, it was there.

One may also compare these feelings about modern technological enterprise with the attitudes of innovators or explorers in any age – of Columbus, sailing into an uncharted Atlantic, or of the cathedral-builders in the 12th and 13th centuries, with their soaring spires and vaults. It is possible to see a moon-rocket as 'like a cathedral ... a symbol of aspirations towards higher things'.[16]

15. Snow, *The Two Cultures*, p. 39.
16. Medawar, *The Hope of Progress*, p. 116.

Despite the military purpose of so much advanced technology – including a large part of the space programme – it is important to recognise the spirit of adventure and exploration with which it is often approached. For some people, every technological possibility is a new continent to be explored, and an opportunity to be pressing forward into a future of undreamt-of excitement.

Thus just as Jevons felt an immense enthusiasm for the technological progress of his own time, while simultaneously being worried about its ultimate destination, so opinion about science and technology in the 1950s and 60s reflected considerable enthusiasm, but also serious misgivings. In the 1950s the enthusiasm predominated, and schools and universities expanded their capacities for scientific and technical education very rapidly. Romantic idealism about the growth of knowledge, coupled with the prospect of high status and salary, led to greatly increased recruiting into science among young people. Many more of them than before opted to study science (but less often technology) at technical colleges and universities, and on qualification many sought employment in the expanding academic, industrial and government-owned research laboratories.

More recently, however, disillusion set in, and there was a reaction in Britain which became known as 'the swing from science'. It showed itself as a growing reluctance among students to study scientific and technical subjects to an advanced level. It began to be noticed in the middle 1960s, and it was later found that the proportion of science students in the sixth forms of English schools fell from 41 per cent in 1962 to 31 per cent in 1967. A similar drop in the popularity of science was observed at the same time in other industrial countries.

This was not as serious a problem as percentage figures suggest, because the total numbers of students were rising very fast. But hopes for economic expansion seemed threatened by a shortage of technically qualified manpower, and an official committee of enquiry was set up. This found defects in the teaching of science in schools, but also reported that for 'many young people science, engineering and technology seem out of touch with human and social affairs. It is significant that biological and medical studies have not suffered the decline of the physical sciences ... The objectivity of science and the purposefulness of technology have become identified, for some, with insensitivity and indifference ... material progress, for many young people, may seem to be irrelevant to current moral issues, if not an affront to widespread poverty and suffering.'[17]

This report was published in 1968, at a time when there was growing unrest in the universities of several countries. Many issues were at stake, but one student leader, prominent in the dramatic upheavals which took place in Paris, complained that university education had become appallingly distorted: 'its only function is to condition students so that they will fit into the economic and social system, as mere puppets, dancing to the tune of technocrats, of men busily organising the misery of the underdeveloped countries and the affluence of the rest.'[18]

The author of these comments was a student of the social sciences; students of science and technology were much less vocal. None the less, most people with any experience of the universities at this time can testify to a growing disenchantment in the science and engineering faculties – a sense of resigned boredom in the way many students pursued their work, with a significant number of the brightest students changing to arts subjects or to medicine after graduation.

It was at first difficult to understand why this reaction against science and technology began when it did. There was 'nothing as obvious as Hiroshima and Nagasaki' in the 'late nineteen-fifties or the early nineteen-sixties to change the public image of science. Nevertheless, the public image does seem to be changing. It seems to be losing some of its power to fire the idealism of the young (which is still, of course, one of the great forces of the universe).'[19]

That was written in 1969, when the swing from science was still a largely inarticulate reaction against the contradictions of the developed, industrial, 'affluent' society – the contradictions of unmet human and personal needs in the most prosperous of countries, and the growing gap between the rich and poor in the world as a whole. Before 1969, there had been few reasoned arguments to be heard about this from the young people who seemed to be rejecting science, except against nuclear weapons. But from about that time, new criticisms of technology began to

17. Council for Scientific Policy, *Enquiry into the Flow of Candidates in Science* . . . (the Dainton report), pp. 79–80.

18. Cohn-Bendit, *Obsolete Communism*, Penguin edn, p. 30.

19. F. R. Jevons, *The Teaching of Science*, pp. 123–8.

be heard. Evidence about the environmental damage caused by industrial development began to gain wide publicity, and complaints were voiced about pollution, aircraft noise, the misuse of fertilisers and pesticides, the dangers of food additives, and many other topics. In February 1971 J. K. Galbraith pointed to current discussions of supersonic aircraft, missiles and road-building, and said:

'I would guess – without knowing – that already last year the discussion of how *not* to have new inventions, how to stop the proliferation of new technology, occupied the American legislature in the ratio of at least 10 to 1 and maybe 50 to 1, over how to promote new technology.'[20]

But at the same time as these piecemeal attacks were being made on individual abuses of technology and on potentially destructive innovations, more far-reaching questions were being asked by people who, like W. Stanley Jevons in the 19th century, have projected current trends into the future, and have shown how temporary present industrial development must necessarily be. The energy resources and food production which would be necessary to support the existing kind of development for more than two or three decades are simply not within man's reach – the position with regard to oil, and energy in general, has already been mentioned. To exploit all the possibilities which do exist for obtaining extra food, fuel, and minerals would damage the natural environment to the point where human life itself would be seriously and adversely affected. These prognostications have come from reputable sources – from a research team at the Massachusetts Institute of Technology,[21] and from respected scientific magazines.[22] They have received widespread publicity in newspapers and journals of more general interest.[23] And they seem to presage an end to the kind of technical progress which has characterised Western civilisation since the time of Babbage and Jevons.

20. *New Scientist*, *49* (February 1971), p. 377.

21. See Meadows and others, *The Limits to Growth*; and Forrester, *World Dynamics*, 1971.

22. *Scientific American*, special issue on energy resources, September 1971; *Ecologist*, special issue on 'a blueprint for survival', January 1972.

23. e.g. *Guardian*, 20 October 1971 and 6 March 1972; *Playboy*, June 1971.

The hope of progress

These developments suggest that ideas about the nature and direction of technical progress have recently fallen into a state of some confusion. It is no longer possible to believe, as Babbage and Jevons did, that the unhindered growth of science and technology will lead to a strengthening of civilisation. Technology, like science, is 'losing some of its power to fire the idealism of the young', because of the inhumanity of some of its applications – and because of the ecological effects of its polluting and destructive misuse.

The reasons for this disillusionment are very largely justified, but the negative and destructive attitude to technology which has resulted is saddening and disturbing. 'It is true that our runaway technology is bringing us towards the brink of disaster . . . [but if] the study of science is abandoned by all except those who are content to be manpower-units, then within a generation, there will be no one competent to analyse and expose the ecological blunders produced by our bureaucratic technology.'[24]

More important, though, there will be no one able to think constructively about what the objectives of future technological development should be; and no one to devise the new technologies which are required, to meet human needs less destructively than at present, or to ease the poverty of the least industrially-developed nations. For all these purposes, it is necessary for us to re-formulate our ideas about the purpose of technology, and recover some idealism in its use. For us to remain just critics would be disastrous, because we can destroy ourselves 'by cynicism and disillusion just as effectively as by bombs'. As C. P. Snow has put it in a novel about the student unrest of 1968, 'what the industrialised world, the whole of the West was waiting for . . . [was] someone who could make its life seem worthwhile'.[25]

Another call for a more positive approach to the problems of modern technology came from Sir Peter Medawar in 1969, in his presidential address to the British Association. He quoted Hobbes to the effect that 'there can be no contentment but in proceeding', and affirmed his belief that human happiness depends on a continuous development in many fields, including science and technology. He declared himself 'all in favour of a

24. Ravetz, *Scientific Knowledge and its Social Problems*, p. 28.
25. Snow, *Last Things*, p. 112.

vigorously critical attitude to technological innovation', but he stressed that 'there is all the difference in the world between informed and energetic criticism and a drooping despondency that offers no remedy for the abuses it bewails. . . . To deride the hope of progress is the ultimate fatuity, the last word in poverty of spirit and meanness of mind.'[26]

In a passage from which the title of this book is taken, T. S. Eliot admonished the present 'wretched generation of enlightened men',

> Betrayed in the mazes of your ingenuities,
> Sold by the proceeds of your proper inventions.[27]

This, indeed, is despondency. But the pessimism which the present author feels, and which his book expresses, does not exclude the hope of progress. The crucial point is that the direction of progress is always a matter of choice. Some pessimism is justified, not because the hope of progress has proved to be fraudulent, but because it lies in another direction from the one which is at present being followed.

The problem, therefore, is to define new directions for technical progress in which there is a promise for the future – to decide on objectives for scientific and technological development which carry more conviction than many existing ones. In this way, we may be able to reaffirm the hope of progress, and again pursue our technical work and scientific interests in a spirit of some idealism.

What are these other possible directions which future technical progress might take? As soon as one ceases to define progress in terms of economic growth, it becomes clear that a rich variety of answers can be given to this question. Human development and its associated technical effort may take many different directions, as the historical narrative of this book has been designed to show. There are many possible 'alternative technologies' related to a wide variety of different social and intellectual objectives.

The point may be emphasised – and the content of the book summarised – by means of a diagram, which shows in very simplified form the direction of technical progress at various dates in the past, and contrasts economic objectives in technical

26. Reported in the *Guardian*, 4 September 1969; reprinted in Medawar, *The Hope of Progress*, pp. 125, 127.
27. Choruses from 'The Rock', III, *Collected Poems 1909–1962*, p. 169.

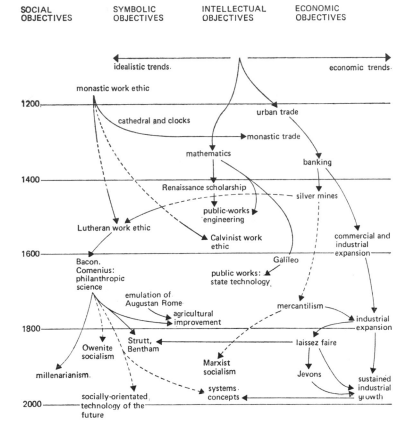

SOCIAL OBJECTIVES SYMBOLIC OBJECTIVES INTELLECTUAL OBJECTIVES ECONOMIC OBJECTIVES

idealistic trends. economic trends.

monastic work ethic

1200

cathedral and clocks

urban trade

monastic trade

mathematics

banking

1400

Renaissance scholarship

silver mines

public-works engineering

Lutheran work ethic

Calvinist work ethic

commercial and industrial expansion

1600

Bacon. Comenius: philanthropic science

public works: state technology

Galileo

emulation of Augustan Rome

agricultural improvement

mercantilism

industrial expansion

1800

Owenite socialism

Strutt, Bentham

laissez faire

millenarianism.

Marxist socialism

Jevons

sustained industrial growth

2000

socially-orientated technology of the future

systems concepts

Figure 43
Directions of technical progress at various dates in the past.

progress with idealistic ones. This is an extended version of a diagram already given in chapter one (fig. 6), where it was explained that technical innovation could be regarded as having an economic objective if it was 'useful' in the ordinary sense of the word, and that its purpose could be regarded as idealistic if its 'usefulness' could be explained only in terms of intellectual, spiritual, or symbolic purposes. Thus cathedrals and astronomical clocks represented an idealistic application of technology, as do moon-rockets in the 20th century. On the other hand, improvements in textile machinery and steam engines usually had an economic objective which could be explained as the production of 'useful' goods and in terms of profits and productivity. In fig. 43, the distinction between economic and idealistic objectives in technology is a little less clear-cut than it was in chapter one, because intellectual and social ideals are now included, and these sometimes lead to innovations of economic usefulness. Thus the attempt to give engineering an improved mathematical basis in the 16th and 17th centuries was a purely intellectual enterprise, but it also made engineering more useful in the economic sphere. Social or humanitarian ideals, such as those of 'philanthropic' science in the 17th century, are often concerned with improving the material condition of mankind, and also therefore lead to strictly economic aims.

It may be thought that other purposes beside economic and idealistic ones should be represented in the diagram. Military objectives in technical progress could well form a class by themselves, though in practice they are often concerned with symbolic objectives such as national prestige, and also with economic ones. Since military technology very largely falls outside the scope of this book, it has seemed preferable not to complicate the diagram by including it.

This method of portraying the varied directions which technical progress has taken in the past is inevitably oversimplified. It does not allow for the mixed motives of much human activity, or for the way in which economic criteria for progress are often used as a common coin for the discussion of divergent, but deeper, aspirations. The industrial technology of China in the 1970s, like that of the West, is intended to promote economic growth. There is the difference, though, that in China there are also well-defined social objectives which many people share, and for which they are willing to work hard, even without personal economic incentives. Money incentives are more important in the West because the more idealistic aspirations of different individuals and groups conflict, and there is no common purpose. The language of economics thus becomes a means for negotiating mutually compatible objectives.

For reasons like this, there is an overlapping intricacy about the objectives of technical progress which the diagram cannot indicate. Despite this, however, the diagram will serve its purpose if it helps to illustrate the wide choice of different directions which technical progress may take.

New objectives in technology

In 1972, the confused and disillusioned state of opinion about the purpose of current technological development is sufficient in itself to provoke thought about what the objectives of future technology should be. Inevitably, many of them will be connected with maintaining the 'standard of living' of people in society, and with human welfare generally. This immediately raises two very urgent problems – the very low standard of living of two-thirds of the world's population, and the way in which the remaining one-third maintains itself by the rapid consumption of irreplaceable natural resources accompanied by considerable environmental damage.

The objectives of future development will have to be related to a different kind of living standard – one which is capable of being sustained in the long term (that is, for several centuries at least) – and one which all people in the world can reasonably hope to share. The present way of life in most Western countries is probably exhausting non-renewable resources too rapidly for it to last for long, and too extravagantly for any of the developing countries to have even a hope of reaching a comparable material level.

The consequences of this for future technology are that agriculture and manufacturing industries must become non-polluting; they must make only marginal use of non-renewable resources; they must not disturb the energy balance of the earth, nor the water and carbon-dioxide cycles. This suggests to the present author – though others may draw different conclusions – that the standard of living we should aim for will be one based more than at present on the things which human skills and creativity can provide with a minimum of material resources. It will be based more on services and less on consumption. If this change of emphasis were achieved, then there might indeed be a hope of continuing progress and development without the dangers which seem to be so pressing at present.

Education and medical care can provide examples of how continuous improvement is possible without any large accompanying drain on material resources, and without environmental damage. At present, of course, there is a tendency in both these fields to use more machines and other material resources. Large hospitals are being built to replace numbers of smaller ones so that a more capital-intensive form of treatment can be provided, using highly expensive equipment. But despite the benefits of the new equipment, these are in some ways retrograde changes. Real achievement in the medical services, as in education, depends less on gadgets than on the skills of nurses or teachers, on their willingness to give time and care to their work, and on personal contact. The ideal in the schools should be classes of ten or a dozen, not classes of thirty, and the ideal in medicine should be an army of doctors and nurses large enough for most sick people to be cared for at home, or in small hospitals in their immediate locality – so that at a time of physical weakness and vulnerability, patients are not suddenly cut off from family and friends.

This kind of development seems desirable from many points of view. Not the least of them is that, at a time when population is growing to crisis-point, and parents must be encouraged to have families with an average of only two, and for a time, less than two children, there will be a great unfulfilled need, among those who would otherwise have had larger families, to give care and affection on a personal level. This need could be partly fulfilled in teaching, medical care and social work, and it provide a positive opportunity for a more human and creative social service than we have at present.

All these suggestions are quite contrary to the current trend. At present, the standard of living is defined largely in terms of material possessions, so wages and salaries have to be high, and they have to rise as economic growth proceeds. This makes it progressively more expensive to employ even the minimum number of teachers, nurses and welfare workers.

In the early 1970s, it is conventional in the British Labour Party to say that health and welfare services can best be improved during conditions of rapid economic growth. The argument is that only growth creates the necessary new finance. There is, of course, truth in this,[28] especially for underdeveloped countries

28. The point about growth being necessary for the improvement of the social services has been put most persuasively by Anthony Crosland, *A Social Democratic Britain*. His argument is based partly on the belief that

which cannot yet afford even a basic medical service for all their people. But in the industrialised countries, where economic growth is now accompanied by the rationalisation of material production and automation in industry, services like education and medicine which cannot be automated tend to experience a disproportionate and often crippling increase in their total labour costs. The new resources released by growth are absorbed almost immediately by higher salaries.

At present, we are faced with the paradoxical situation that there is a growing shortage of people in medical, social and public services, and the quality of these services is deteriorating – but at the same time, rationalised production and automation[29] are producing an almost permanent pool of unemployed and unemployable people. This is partly a class matter; the enlarged body of teachers and social workers suggested here will need education which is at present not readily accessible to the kind of people who are becoming unemployed. The problem is also a result of the fact that wages and salaries have already risen to the point where social services are relatively much more expensive to run than they used to be, and the governments which finance them are under pressure to hold down expenditure and cut taxes.

All these problems are related to the basic contradiction involved in defining the standard of living of already prosperous people in terms of material consumption. Whatever value-judgements we may make individually about the 'affluent society', it seems clear that in the long run it will become inescapably necessary for mankind to devise a way of life which depends much less on non-renewable minerals – oil, uranium and industrial metals – and much more on the resources which nature furnishes in continuous supply – solar energy, water-power, vegetable products, and most particularly, the labour, skill and creativity of human beings.

---

electors in a democratic society will never vote for a reduction in material consumption, even if they get better social services instead. If natural resources become short, though, stark necessity may force electors and politicians to recognise that a satisfying standard of living based on services rather than consumption is a possibility.

29. It seems unlikely that highly mechanised and automated forms of industry will develop to the extent that many people expect, again because of problems about shortages of resources. But since automation by itself leads only to marginal increases in consumption of energy and materials, the question is a complex one.

Human labour and skill – our own resources as individuals – are the only powers we have which increase in the same proportion as our needs and expectations. As the population grows, and material needs with it, so too does the size of the labour-force. And as aspirations for improved living standards develop, so too is it possible for education and technical training to enlarge people's ability to provide for their rising ambitions. The question of how a person's work should be valued and used in the future seems a crucial one, and it is for that reason that some stress has been laid on the 'work ethic' of 12th-century monks and 16th-century miners in the earlier chapters.

The topic has been neglected in recent technical development. We have partly forgotten how to use our own resources as people. Technology has conventionally been a matter of machines and equipment, and its hardware has been used to replace rather than to develop human abilities and potentialities. And now the art of using human potential is sadly lacking in the social services of the industrial countries, and more disturbingly, in the basic industries of many less developed regions. Human labour and skill is the greatest asset of most underdeveloped countries, and the waste that is represented by their persistent unemployment is one of the chief reasons for their impoverishment. As was remarked above in chapter nine, if all the unemployed people of India could be given the jobs they seek, the crushing poverty of that country would be almost immediately relieved. The reason why they are unemployed is partly that the equipment they need to work with has been made too expensive and too elaborate through misunderstandings about the nature of technical progress. Hardware has not been thought of as a means of releasing human potential, but simply in terms of self-contained technical problems. So one objective of technology in the future will be to devise machines and technical procedures which will enable everybody to do work which is personally satisfying, and which will also enable them to make their essential contribution to the material needs and social welfare of the community.

There are some examples in developing countries which provide an insight into how a 'man-centred' technology of this kind might be created. In a few cases, these have been introduced piecemeal by local engineers or expatriates from the West, but in China there has been a consistent policy of devising and using such methods. This policy has been necessary there as a means of saving capital. But it can also help to conserve natural resources and protect the environment, and lessons which may now be learned in China and other developing countries could in the future help the West to find some less profligate way of living. Economists who have studied the problems of developing countries have specified some of the characteristics which this new technology must have. They have described it as 'intermediate' technology because it uses intermediate or low levels of capital investment. Others have talked more generally about 'alternative technologies' – of which 'intermediate' technology might be taken as an example – and these present a variety of hopeful possibilities for the future.[30] But few of those who have commented on these subjects have recognised the changes in the philosophy of technology which their ideas imply – that is, the changes in methods, discipline and general patterns of thinking within technology which the pursuit of different objectives might demand. And this represents a question which can be posed by considering again the relationship between social and political issues on the one hand and technology on the other.

A new discipline: a new technology

It may seem that to discuss the social services in what is supposed to be an account of the future of technology is an irrelevant digression. But to say that would be to find oneself caught in the same narrow categories of thought which have blinkered conventional technology since the time of Galileo – categories which have made it powerful and effective within its limited field, but which have made its progress conflict in so many ways with the deeper and more permanent interests of humanity.

We have, of course, been discussing the overall social objectives out of which more specialised objectives for the different branches of technology will emerge. But even if there were space to discuss particular branches of technology individually, we would still find that the social issues could not be left entirely behind.

30. For 'intermediate' technology, see Schumacher and McRobie, in *Journal of Administration Overseas, 8* (1969). At the time of going to press, publication was expected of two fuller accounts of these issues by E. F. Schumacher (on economic thinking related to intermediate technology) and by David Dickson (on alternative technologies). The author has had no opportunity to consult either of these potentially important books.

Everything a technologist does affects people's lives at some point; and very often his work contributes massively to social change. Technology is a social art, and human as well as mechanical variables should come within its scope.

To recognise that is to find oneself in much the same position as some of the people mentioned earlier in the book, for whom there was no sharp line between technology and social welfare. In the 17th century, for example, Francis Bacon, Hartlib, Comenius and various followers of Paracelsus studied social arts and technical matters side by side. Education, chemistry, languages and agriculture were all related to the overall aim of providing more adequately for human welfare.

Around 1800, William Strutt and Jeremy Bentham also appreciated the essential relationship of the social arts and technology, and while Strutt practised a combination of the two (chapter eight), Bentham attempted to construct an intellectual framework linking them, partly with the aid of ideas borrowed from Bacon. But neither Bacon, nor the Paracelsians, nor even Bentham succeeded in providing a rigorous and intellectually satisfactory discipline for their projected amalgam of technology and welfare. Their efforts were defeated by the far more effective intellectual tools which Galileo and his Italian and French contemporaries provided for science and technology.

In discussing ways of making future technology more sensitive to social and environmental needs, we are really setting out again on this enterprise which failed in the 17th century. The problem is again to build up a new discipline which will allow technology to be used in a properly assessed relationship with human needs and the world of nature. That, at any rate, is one way of explaining why a new discipline is needed in technology. Another argument that leads to the same conclusion arises when we consider the claim which is sometimes made that conventional technology can solve all the problems which it has itself created. 'The deterioration of the environment produced by technology is a technological problem for which technology has found, is finding, and will continue to find solutions.'[31]

This confidence that individual technical solutions can be found for specific technical problems seems an evasion of the larger question of why these problems so regularly occur. People often say that the fault is not with technology but with the

31. Medawar, *The Hope of Progress*, p. 125.

way it is applied. But the two are not separable. Technology is about application. It is not an abstract, unbiased and morally neutral collection of useful skills and knowledge. It also includes ideas about how knowledge may be used, based on pre-suppositions about nature, and how one should study nature and use it, and presuppositions about society, and how technical change and social change are linked. If the practice of technology leads to frequent or dangerous dislocations in the natural environment or in society, then it is perfectly right to suspect that there is something wrong with technology itself, as a discipline – with the ideas it uses or the habits of thought it takes for granted.

> . . . machines will destroy
> what's natural only if
> directed by men who oppose
> a part of themselves to the wholeness
> of their nature.[32]

The trouble with conventional technology as a discipline probably is just that: it does exclude 'wholeness'. It incorporates habits of thought inherited from the mechanical philosophy of the 17th century – from Galileo and his associates and successors. In these men's work, 'the field of research was progressively divided up, and small parts of it were subject to intensive examination . . .'. The accuracy and simplicity of their science was not 'an approach to objective reality but a departure from it', because it was based on a rejection of the wholeness of experience. 'By renouncing a large part of his humanity, a man could achieve godhood . . .' His new power over nature was 'ripped loose from his flesh' and isolated from his being.[33]

Engineers still tend to concentrate on the constructions which they themselves build rather than considering them within a context. They pursue an art whose purpose is to make changes in the natural world and in society. But social and ecological aspects of engineering projects are left to other experts – if they are properly considered at all – and any wholeness of purpose tends to be dissipated. We are lost in the mazes of our ingenuities because, being trained to look at details rather than at wholes, we are confused by the complexity we have created. Our 'knowledge brings us nearer to our ignorance', because we can gain no overall picture of the structure which we ourselves

32. Philip Pacey, in *Poetry Review*, *63* (1972), p. 139.
33. Mumford, *Technics and Civilization*, pp. 50–51.

have made. The new discipline which is needed in technology is therefore a discipline which will concern itself with seeing things whole – with seeing the relationships between our constructions, our environment and ourselves.

If this seems too much to ask, it may help if we examine two recent developments in science and technology. First, there is a particular reaction to the perils created by industrial technology which is 'rapidly creating a new sort of science – critical science'.[34] What this means is that the hazards of pollution and resource-depletion have stimulated some people of scientific competence to pursue careful, rigorous researches into the relationship between technical innovation, nature and society. The ultimate purpose of this kind of science 'is the protection of the welfare of humanity as a part of nature'. Its discipline differs from that of conventional science and technology because 'here the relation of the science to the external world is so fundamentally different'.

'In traditional pure mathematical-experimental natural science, the external world is a passive object to be analysed. . . . In technology, the reactions of the uncontrolled real world on a constructed device must be taken into account, but only as perturbations of an ideal system; the task is to manipulate it or to shield the device from its effects.' But in critical science, the task is 'to achieve a harmonious interaction between man and nature'.

This approach to studying the interactions between man and nature offers some clues as to what the new discipline needed in technology may be like; others can be found in the modern field of research known as 'general systems theory'. Here there is a risk of confusion with the kind of systems theory used in conventional engineering and business management. General systems theory represents a much more far-reaching attempt than this to study 'complexity' and 'wholeness'. It attempts to use such concepts as 'organisation', 'relationship' and 'interaction' to study its subject-matter as a whole, without separating the component parts; 'systems theory is a broad view which far transcends technological problems and demands . . . It heralds a new world view of considerable impact.'[35]

Whether this type of systems theory by itself will provide an adequate basis for the new discipline which is required in

34. Ravetz, *Scientific Knowledge and its Social Problems*, p. 424; other quotations here come from pp. 429–30.
35. von Bertalanffy, *General System Theory*, pp. xi–xii.

technology is uncertain. Taken qualitatively, it can certainly help to clarify problems concerning the interactions of technology and society. Some of its methods are reminiscent of the taxonomic or classificatory schemes which Bentham suggested in the 19th century for a similar purpose – but others take us forward into radically new ways of thinking. Its very emphasis on 'wholes' is by itself a useful corrective.

Like any other field of study, however, systems theory is open to corruption. Where it is used with a mathematical approach, it can be distorted by the illusion that everything in the 'whole' being studied can be weighed and measured. At present, systems theory of this latter kind is used mainly in computer technology, cybernetics and management, where it often seems to be just another way of manipulating people, and where it reinforces existing tendencies to ignore non-measurable human qualities. As one of the pioneers of systems theory has himself admitted, when we contemplate such applications, we might, if we are pessimistic, 'see in the systems movement the arrival of *Brave New World* and *1984*'.[36]

So while it was necessary in the previous section to warn that new objectives in technology would be ineffective if a suitable discipline and methods were lacking, the converse of that warning must be given here. New approaches and techniques must not be allowed to emerge purely under the impetus of their intellectual interest or their commercial potential. The technology of the future needs ideals as well as ideas – objectives as well as an intellectual framework – if the direction of its progress is to be in harmony with the long-term needs of mankind. We may note, though, that the type of approach represented by general systems theory, despite the danger of corruption, is far better equipped than more conventional methods in technology to bring human need into relationship with what nature provides and what man can construct.

In relation to the historical content of this book, sufficient illustration of the probable relevance of general systems theory was given by Ludwig von Bertalanffy, one of its founders, when he traced its antecedents to the 'mystic medicine of Paracelsus',[37] and to the long tradition of thought in Germany which opposed the 17th-century mechanical philosophy. This tradition embraced

36. von Bertalanffy, *General System Theory*, p. 8.
37. von Bertalanffy, *General System Theory*, p. 9 etc.

Leibniz, and later Goethe, but more significantly it included people such as Rudolph Glauber in the 17th century who were closely identified with 'philanthropic' science (chapter five above).

Others who have looked to the history of technology for ideas about its future have turned most often to Francis Bacon,[38] who avoided the mysticism which marred the Paracelsian approach. In the German tradition, and in the work of Bacon also, there was a strong sense of the unity of things, and their inter-relatedness. There was a respect for nature rather than a wish to crudely exploit it; and there were social ideals about the value of technology.

'In this present period, we may find Francis Bacon speaking to us more than Descartes the metaphysician-geometer or Galileo the engineer-cosmologist. As deeply as any of his pietistic . . . forerunners, he felt the love of God's creation, the pity for the sufferings of man, and the striving for innocence, humility and charity.' He felt that knowledge should be 'perfected and governed' in love; and that the fruits of knowledge should be used, not for 'profit, or fame or power . . . but for the benefit and use of life'.[39]

It is with ideals such as this, and with some of the new ideas and disciplines now emerging, that technology will have to be developed if it is truly to serve humanity. To predict more about its future would be unwise; only one thing can be said with certainty: not very far ahead, in perhaps a decade or perhaps a century, the possibilities of the present pattern of technical progress will have been exhausted. But the hope of progress will still be there, for those able to see the variety of new directions which the development of mankind could take. Technology can be remodelled and redirected to serve a different purpose. And although the historical narrative of this book ended with an account of Charles Babbage and Stanley Jevons in the middle of the 19th century, it is intended to direct attention forwards into the future. Its real end-date is the time still to come when the re-formulation of technology begins to happen in a clear and convincing way, because this future opportunity of a renewed idealism in technical progress is what has prompted the book as a description of the ideals of the past.

38. Medawar, 'On the effecting of all things possible', in his book *The Hope of Progress*.

39. Ravetz, *Scientific Knowledge and its Social Problems*, pp. 434–6.

Bibliography

Notes

1. When using this bibliography as a key to books mentioned in the footnotes, take the author's name from the page where the footnote occurs and locate it here by means of the alphabetical sequence. Where a book has two or more authors, look under the name which is given first; where no author can be identified, take the first word in the title quoted.

2. Square brackets [—] indicate the chapter in this book to which particular items in the bibliography are most relevant.

3. *Books recommended for further reading* are marked with an asterisk (*). A book is only shown thus if it is likely to be easily obtainable through a good public library.

4. This is *not* intended to be a comprehensive bibliography of the history of technology, nor does it include all the works used by the author to check small points of detail. It only includes works which are directly quoted in the text, or which have been used *extensively* in the writing of the book.

*Ackerman, James S. *Palladio*, Pelican Books, Harmondsworth, 1966. [chapter 3]
——'ARS SINE SCIENTIA NIHIL EST: Gothic theory of architecture at the Cathedral of Milan', in *Art Bulletin*, *31* (1949), pp. 84-111. [chapter 2]
Adams, F. D. *The Birth and Development of the Geological Sciences*, Baillière, London, 1938; new edn, Dover Books, New York, 1954. [chapter 5]
Agricola, Georgius [George Bauer]. *De re metallica* (translated from the Latin edn of 1556 by Herbert Clark Hoover and Lou Henry Hoover), *Mining Magazine*, 1912; new edn Dover Books, New York, *c.* 1950. [chapter 5]
Aiken, John. *A Description of the Country from thirty to forty miles round Manchester*, London, 1795. [chapter 8]
Aitchison, Leslie. *A History of Metals*, 2 vols., Macdonald & Evans, 1960. [chapter 5]
Alberti, Leone Battista, *De re aedificatoria*, Florence, 1485; trans. James Leoni as *Ten Books on Architecture by Leone Battista Alberti*, London, 1726; facsimile edn, ed. Joseph Rykwert, Tiranti, 1955. [chapter 3]
Allen, J. S. 'The introduction of the Newcomen Engine, 1710-1733', in *Newcomen Society Transactions*, *42* (1969-70), pp. 169-90. [chapter 6]

Andrieu, Michel. *Le pontifical romain au moyen-âge*, vol. *1*, Vatican City, 1938. [chapter 2]

Anstey, Vera. *The Economic Development of India*, Longman, 1952. [chapter 9]

Armytage, W. H. G. *A Social History of Engineering*, Faber, 1961. [chapter 9 and part 3]

——*Heavens Below; Utopian Experiments in England, 1560–1960*, Routledge, 1961. [chapter 8]

Artz, F. B. *The Development of Technical Education in France, 1500–1800*, M.I.T. Press, Cambridge, Massachusetts, 1966. [chapter 6]

Ashton, T. S. *Iron and Steel in the Industrial Revolution*, Manchester University Press, 1963. [chapter 7]

——The Industrial Revolution 1760–1830, Home University Library, 1948; new edn, Oxford University Press paperbacks, 1968. [chapters 3, 6–7]

Atkinson, Frank. *The Great Northern Coalfield 1700–1900*, University Tutorial Press, London, 1968. [chapter 7]

Babbage, Charles. *On the Economy of Machinery and Manufacturers*, London, 1832. [chapter 9 and part 3]

——*The Exposition of 1851*, London, 1851; new impression, Cass, 1968. [part 3]

——*see also* Barlow, Peter, *and* British Museum Additional Manuscripts.

Bacon, Roger. *Opus majus* (trans. Robert B. Burke), 2 vols., Pennsylvania U.P., Philadelphia, 1928. [chapter 2]

Bage, Charles. Bage papers, Shrewsbury Public Library, MS. letter Bage to William Strutt, 25 February 1818, and other correspondence with Strutt. [chapter 8]

Bagrow, Leo. *A History of Cartography* (ed. R. A. Skelton), Watts, 1964. [chapter 2]

Banks, John. *On the Power of Machines*, Kendal, 1803. [chapter 7]

Barley, M. W. 'Industrial monuments at Milford and Belper: Housing', *Archaeological Journal*, *118* (1961), pp. 236–9. [chapter 8]

Barlow, Peter. *A Treatise on the Manufactures and Machinery of Great Britain*, with an introduction by Charles Babbage, London, 1836. [chapter 9 and part 3]

Bateson, Gregory. 'Conscious purpose versus Nature', in David Cooper (ed.), *The Dialectics of Liberation*, Pelican, 1968. [chapter 4]

Bedini, Silvio, and Francis Maddison. 'Mechanical universe: the astrarium of Giovanni de' Dondi', in *Transactions of the American Philosophical Society*, *56* (1966). [chapter 2]

Belidor. *See* Forest de Belidor.

Bell, A. E. *Christian Huygens and the Development of Science in the Seventeenth Century*, Edward Arnold, 1947. [chapter 6]

Benedict, St. *See* Rule of St. Benedict.

Bentham, Jeremy. *See* Strutt papers.

Bentham, Samuel. *See* Strutt papers.

Bergakademie Freiberg Festschrift, 1765–1965, Freiberg, 1965. [chapters 4–6]

*Bertalanffy, Ludwig von. *General System Theory: Foundations, Development*,

Applications, Braziller, New York, 1968; new edn, Allen Lane, The Penguin Press, 1971. [chapter 4 and part 3]

Blaug, M. 'The productivity of capital in the Lancashire cotton industry in the 19th century', in *Economic History Review*, 2nd series, *13* (1960–1961), pp. 358–81. [part 3]

Board of Agriculture Communications. *See: Communications to the Board of Agriculture.*

Boas, Marie. *The Scientific Renaissance 1450–1630*, Collins, 1962. [chapter 3]

Boguslaw, Robert. *The New Utopians: a Study of Systems Design and Social Change*, Prentice Hall, New Jersey, 1965. [part 3]

Bone, W. A., and G. W. Himus. *Coal – its Constitution and Uses*, Longmans, 1936. [part 3]

Booker, P. J. 'Gaspard Monge and his effect on engineering drawing', in *Newcomen Society Transactions, 34* (1961–2), pp. 15–36. [chapters 4 and 7]

Bottomore, T. B. (trans. and ed.) *Karl Marx – Early Writings*, Watts, 1963. [chapter 9]

——and Maximilien Rubel (eds.) *Karl Marx – Selected Writings in Sociology and Social Philosophy*, Watts, 1956; Pelican, 1963. [chapter 9]

Boulton and Watt Collection, Birmingham Reference Library. MSS. letters by George Lee, 18 April 1792, 5 March 1798, and other dates; MSS. letters by Peter Ewart, 9 April 1813 etc. [chapters 7–9]

Branner, Robert. *Burgundian Gothic Architecture*, Zwemmer, 1960. [chapter 1]

——*Gothic Architecture*, Prentice Hall, New York, 1961. [chapter 1]

Braudel, F. P. 'Prices in Europe from 1450 to 1750', in *Cambridge Economic History of Europe*, ed. E. E. Rich and C. H. Wilson, *4*, C.U.P., 1967, pp. 374–486. [chapter 5]

British Museum Additional Manuscripts: 37183 f. 110 and 37186, f. 256 MSS. letters, Peter Ewart to Charles Babbage, 1824 and 1832. [chapter 9]

Brockett, Allan. *Nonconformity in Exeter, 1650–1875*, Manchester U. P., 1962, pp. 59–60, 68. [chapter 4]

*Bronowski, J., and Bruce Mazlish. *The Western Intellectual Tradition*, Hutchinson, 1960; Pelican, 1963. [chapters 7–8]

Brown, R. A., H. M. Colvin, and A. J. Taylor. *The History of the King's Works*, 2 vols., H.M.S.O., 1963 (esp. vol. 1, p. 153). [chapters 1–2]

Brown, R. G. and K. S. Johnston. *Paciolo on Accounting*, McGraw-Hill, New York, 1963. [chapter 3]

Bruck, W. F. *Social and Economic History of Germany from William II to Hitler*, University Press, Cardiff, with O.U.P., 1938. [chapter 9]

Buchanan, N. S. and H. S. Ellis. *Approaches to Economic Development*, Twentieth Century Fund, New York, 1955. [chapter 9; paragraphs on Japan]

Buchanan, Robertson. 'On the shafts of mills', 1808, in *Practical Essays on Mill Work*, 2nd edn, 1823, pp. 252–4. [chapter 7]

Bulferetti, Luigi. *Galileo Galilei nella societa de suo tempo*, Lacaito Editore, Manduria, 1964. [chapters 3–4]

*Burstall, Aubrey F. *A History of Mechanical Engineering*, Faber, 1963. [chapters 2, 7 and 9 and part 3]

Bury, J. B. *The Idea of Progress*, Macmillan, 1932; reprinted Dover Books, New York, 1955. [chapter 2]

Butt, John (ed.) *Robert Owen, Prince of Cotton Spinners: a Symposium*, David & Charles, 1971. [chapter 8]

Butterfield, Herbert. *The Origins of Modern Science*, Bell, 1949; new edn, 1957. [chapter 4]

Byrne, Eugene H. *Genoese Shipping in the 12th and 13th Centuries*, M.I.T. Press, Cambridge, Mass., 1930. [chapter 1]

Cambridge Economic History of Europe, 2 (ed. M. M. Postan and E. E. Rich), C.U.P., 1952; 4 (ed. E. E. Rich and C. H. Wilson), C.U.P., 1967. [chapters 1, 3 and 5]

Cardwell, D. S. L. *From Watt to Clausius: the Rise of Thermodynamics in the Early Industrial Age*, Heinemann, 1971. [chapter 7]

——(ed.) *John Dalton and the Progress of Science*, Manchester U.P., 1968. [chapter 8]

——'The academic study of the history of technology', in *History of Science*, 7 (1968), pp. 118–21. [chapter 7]

Carus Wilson, E. M. 'An industrial revolution of the 13th century', in *Economic History Review*, 1st series, *11* (1941), pp. 39–60. [chapter 1]

*Chambers, J. D., and G. E. Mingay. *The Agricultural Revolution*, Batsford, 1966. [chapter 6]

*Cipolla, Carlo M. *European Culture and Overseas Expansion*, Pelican, 1970 (incorporating Cipolla's earlier works *Clocks and Culture*, Collins, 1967, and *Guns and Sails*, Collins, 1966). [chapters 2, 3, 5, 6]

Clapham, Michael. 'Printing', in C. Singer, E. J. Holmyard, A. R. Hall and T. I. Williams (eds), *A History of Technology*, vol. 3, O.U.P., 1957. [chapter 3]

Cobban, Alfred. *A History of Modern France*, vol. 1, The Old Regime and the Revolution, 1715–1799, Cape, 1962. [chapter 6]

Cohn-Bendit, Gabriel and Daniel. *Obsolete Communism: the Left-Wing Alternative* (trans. Arnold Pomerans), André Deutsch, 1968; Penguin Books, 1969. [part 3]

*Cole, C. W. *Colbert and a Century of French Mercantilism*, 2 vols., Cass, 1964. [chapter 6]

*Cole, G. D. H. *The Life of Robert Owen*, Macmillan, 1930; 3rd edn, 1965. [chapters 8–9]

Communications to the Board of Agriculture, vol. 1, London, 1797.

Cook, Earl. 'The flow of energy in an industrial society', in *Scientific America*, *224* (September 1971).

Coulton, G. G. *Art and the Reformation*, C.U.P., 1958. [chapter 1]

——'The high ancestry of Puritanism', 1905, in *Ten Medieval Studies*, C.U.P., 1930. [chapter 1]

Council for Scientific Policy: *Enquiry into the Flow of Candidates in Science and Technology into Higher Education* (Dainton Report), H.M.S.O., 1968. [part 3]

Crombie, A. C. *Augustine to Galileo: Science in the Middle Ages*, Heinemann, 1957; 2nd edn, Heinemann, 1961. [chapter 1]

——*Robert Grosseteste and the Origins of Experimental Science*, O.U.P., 1953. [chapter 2]

*Cronin, Vincent. *The Florentine Renaissance*, Collins, 1967. [chapter 3]
Crosland, Anthony. *A Social Democratic Britain*, pamphlet, Fabian Society, 1971. [part 3]
Dainton Report. *See* Council for Scientific Policy.
Dalton, Rev. John. *Descriptive Poem Addressed to Two Ladies at their Return from viewing the Mines near Whitehaven*, London, 1755. [chapter 6]
Darby, H. C. *The Domesday Geography of England*, C.U.P., 1952–67: Eastern England, 1952; Midland England, with I. B. Terret, 1954; South-Eastern England, with E. M. J. Campbell, 1962; Northern England, with I. S. Maxwell, 1962; South-Western England, with R. Weldon Finn, 1967. [chapter 1]
Davis, R. H. C. *A History of Medieval Europe*, Longmans, 1957. [chapter 1]
*Deane, Phyllis. *The First Industrial Revolution*, C.U.P., 1965. [chapter 6]
——and W. A. Cole. *British Economic Growth 1688–1959*, C.U.P., 1962, [chapter 7]
Defoe, Daniel. *A Tour through the Whole Island of Great Britain (1724–6)*, Dent, 2 vols., 1962. [chapter 6]
Delius, C. T. *Anleitung zu der Bergbaukunst*, Vienna, 1773, (trans. J. G Schreiber as *Traité sur la science de l'exploitation des mines*, 2 vols., Paris, 1778. [chapters 4 and 6]
Dendy Marshall, C. F. *A History of British Railways down to the year 1830*, O.U.P., 1938. [chapter 9]
——'Some mechanical inventions', in *Newcomen Society Transactions, 16* (1937), pp. 1–26. [chapter 4]
Desaguliers, J. T. *A Course of Experimental Philosophy*, vol. 1, 1734; vol. 2, 1744; 3rd edn, London, 1763. (The atmospheric engine is dealt with in vol. 2.) [chapters 6–7]
Descargues, Pierre. *Dürer*, Heinemann, 1956. [chapter 3]
Descartes, René. *'Principia philosophiae'* and *'Traité de l'homme'*, in *Oeuvres de Descartes* (ed. Adam and Paul Tannery), *8*, Paris, 1905, and *11*, Paris, 1909. [chapter 4]
*Dharampal, Shri. *Indian Science and Technology in the Eighteenth Century*, Impex India, 2–18 Ansari Road, Delhi 6, 1971. [chapters 6 and 9]
*Dickinson, H. W. *A Short History of the Steam Engine*, C.U.P., 1938; new edn. with introduction by A. E. Musson, Cass, 1963. [chapters 4 and 7]
Dijkster uis, E. J. *The Mechanization of the World Picture* (trans. C. Dikshoorn), O.U.P., 1961. [chapter 4]
Donald, M. B. *Elizabethan Copper: the History of the Company of Mines Royal*, Pergamon, 1955. [chapter 5]
Donkin, S. B. 'The Society of Civil Engineers (Smeatonians)', in *Newcomen Society Transactions, 17* (1936–7), pp. 51–64. [chapter 7]
Drake, Stillman. *Discoveries and Opinions of Galileo*, Doubleday, New York, 1957. [chapter 4]
——'Renaissance music and experimental science', in *Journal of the History of Ideas, 31* (1970), esp. pp. 496–7. [chapter 3]
*——and I. E. Drabkin (trans. and ed.). *Galileo Galilei: On Motion and On Mechanics*, Wisconsin U. P., Madison, 1960. [chapter 3]
Dugas, René. *A History of Mechanics* (trans. J. R. Maddox), Routledge, 1957. [chapter 3]

——*Mechanics in the Seventeenth Century* (trans. Freda Jacquot), Neuchâtel, 1958. [chapter 4]

Dunsheath, Percy. *A History of Electrical Engineering*, Faber, 1962. [part 3]

Dutt, Romesh [Ramesachandra Datta]. *The Economic History of India under Early British Rule*, Kegan Paul, 1902; 7th edn, Routledge, 1950. [chapter 9]

——*The Economic History of India in the Victorian Age*, Kegan Paul, 1904; 7th edn, Routledge, 1950. [chapter 9]

Ecologist, [esp.] issue of January 1972, on 'a blueprint for survival'. [part 3]

Edwards, E. L. *Weight-driven Chamber Clocks of the Middle Ages and Renaissance*, Altrincham, 1965. [chapter 2]

Edwards, M. M. *The Growth of the British Cotton Trade, 1780–1815*, Manchester U.P., 1967. [chapter 7]

Egerton, John. *A Catalogue of Books including the Library of John Smeaton which are this day selling*, London, 1794. [chapter 7]

Egerton, Michael C. *The Scientific and Technical Achievements of William Strutt*, unpublished thesis, U.M.I.S.T., Manchester, 1967. [acknowledgements and chapter 8]

——'William Strutt and the application of convection to the heating of buildings', in *Annals of Science, 24* (1968), pp. 73–87. [chapter 8]

Eliot, T. S. *Collected Poems 1909–1962*, Faber, 1963. [part 3]

Ellul, Jacques. *The Technological Society* (trans. John Wilkinson, with an introduction by R. K. Merton), Cape, 1965. [part 3]

Encyclopaedia Britannica, 3rd edn, vol. 17, 1797, article 'Steam', reprinted in John Robison, *A System of Mechanical Philosophy* (with notes by David Brewster), 4 vols. and plates, Edinburgh, 1822. [chapter 7]

Erskine-Hill, Howard. *The Social Milieu of Alexander Pope*, Yale U.P., 1975. [acknowledgements, chapter 6]

——'The medal against time: a study of Pope's Epistle *To Mr. Addison*', in *Journal of the Warburg and Courtauld Institute, 28* (1965), pp. 274–98. [chapter 6]

Ewart, John. *Biographical Sketches of Eminent Characters*, London, 1830. [chapter 8]

Ewart, Peter. 'On the measure of moving force', in *Memoirs of the Manchester Literary and Philosophical Society*, 1813, pp. 105–258. [chapter 8]

——*see also* Boulton and Watt Collection *and* Greg and Ewart partnership agreement *and* British Museum Additional Manuscripts.

Farey, John. *A Treatise on the Steam Engine*, London, 1827. [chapter 7]

Farrar, David M. *The Royal Hungarian Mining Academy: Some Aspects of Technical Education in the 18th century*, unpublished thesis, U.M.I.S.T., Manchester, 1971. [acknowledgements and chapter 6]

Ferguson, Eugene S. *Kinematics of Mechanism from the time of Watt*, United States National Museum, Bulletin 228, Washington, 1962. [chapter 7]

Fiennes, Celia. *Journeys* (ed. Christopher Morris), Crescent Press, 1947. [chapter 6]

Fischer von [or of] Erlach, John Bernard [Johann Bernhard]. *A Plan of Civil and Historical Architecture* (trans. T. Lediard), London, 1737. [chapter 6]

Fitchen, John. *The Construction of the Gothic Cathedrals*, O.U.P., 1961. [chapter 1]

*Fitton, R. S., and A. P. Wadsworth. *The Strutts and the Arkwrights*, Manchester U.P., 1958. [chapters 7–8]

Fitzgerald, C. P. *The Birth of Communist China*, Pelican, 1964. [chapter 9]

Flinn, M. W. *Economic History Review*, series 2, *11*, p. 146. [chapter 7]

Forbes, R. J. 'Metallurgy and technology in the Middle Ages', in *Centaurus, 3* (1953–4), pp. 49–57. [chapter 5]

——'Power' and other articles, in C. Singer, E. J. Holmyard, A. R. Hall and T. I. Williams (eds.), *A History of Technology*, vol. 2, The Mediterranean Civilizations and the Middle Ages, O.U.P., 1956. [chapter 1]

——and E. J. Dijksterhuis. *A History of Science and Technology*, 2 vols., Pelican Books, 1963. [chapter 4]

Forest de Belidor, *Architecture hydraulique*, 4 vols., Paris, 1737–53. [chapter 4]

Forrester, J. W. *World Dynamics*, Wright Allen, Cambridge, Mass., 1971. [part 3]

Frankl, Paul. *The Gothic – Literary Sources and Interpretations*, Princeton U.P., 1960. [chapter 2]

*Fyrth, H. J., and Maurice Goldsmith. *Science, Technology and History*, 4 parts, Cassell, 1965–9 (school textbook with stimulating account of 19th-century technology). [part 3]

Galbraith, J. K. *The Affluent Society*, Hamish Hamilton, 1958, 2nd edn, 1969; Penguin edn, 1970. [part 3]

Galileo Galilei. *Dialogues [Discorsi] concerning Two New Sciences* (trans. Henry Crew and Alfonso de Salvio), Macmillan, 1914; new edn, Dover Books, New York, no date. [chapters 3–4]

——*Opere di Galileo* (ed. Antonio Favaro), Edizione Nationale, Firenze, 1890–1909. [chapter 3]

Geddes, Patrick. *Cities in Evolution*, Williams & Norgate, London, 1915; new edn, Benn, 1968. [part 3]

Geymonat, Ludovico. *Galileo Galilei: a Biography and Inquiry into his philosophy of Science* (trans. Stillman Drake, with a foreword by G. de Santillana), McGraw-Hill, New York, 1965. [chapter 3]

*Gille, Bertrand. *The Renaissance Engineers*, translated from French, Lund Humphries, 1966. [chapters 3 and 5]

*Gimpel, Jean. *The Cathedral Builders* (trans. C. F. Barnes), Evergreen Profile Books, New York, 1961. [chapters 1–2]

Greg and Ewart partnership agreement, Manchester Central Library (archives department), document C5/1/2/2. [chapter 8]

Gregory, Olinthus. *A Treatise of Mechanics*, 2 vols. and plates, London, 1806. [chapter 7]

Guardian, [esp.] issues of 4 September 1969, 20 October 1971 and 6 March 1972. [part 3]

Guericke, Otto von [or de]. *Experimenta nova Magdeburgica de vacuo spatio*, 1672; facsimile edn (with introduction by A. Rosenfeld and O. Zeller), Aalen, 1962. [chapter 4]

Hacker, C. L. 'William Strutt of Derby', in *Journal of the Derbyshire*

Archaeological and Natural History Society, 80 (1960), pp. 49–70. [chapter 8]

Halévy, Elie. *History of the English People in the 19th Century*, vol. 1, England in 1815; vol. 2, The Liberal Awakening (trans. E. I. Watkin and D. I. Barker), Benn, 1924; new edn, 1949. [chapter 8]

*Hall, A. Rupert. *The Scientific Revolution, 1500–1800*, Longmans, 1962. [chapter 4]

——'Engineering and the scientific revolution', in *Technology and Culture*, 2 (1961), pp. 333–41. [chapter 4]

Hamilton, Earl J. *American Treasure and the Price Revolution in Spain, 1501–1650*, Harvard Economic Studies, 1934. [chapter 5]

Harrington, Michael. *The Accidental Century*, 1965; Pelican, 1967. [part 3]

Harris, L. E. 'Land drainage and reclamation', in C. Singer, E. J. Holmyard, A. R. Hall and T. I. Williams (eds.), *A History of Technology*, vol. 3, O.U.P., 1957. [chapter 3]

Hart, I. B. *The Mechanical Investigations of Leonardo da Vinci*, Chapman & Hall, 1925; University of California Press, paperback, 1963. [chapter 3]

Harvey, John. *The Medieval Architect*, Wayland, 1972. [chapter 2]

Haskins, Charles Homer. *The Renaissance of the Twelfth Century*, Harvard U.P., 1927. [chapter 1]

*Henderson, George. *Chartres*, Pelican, 1968. [chapters 1–2]

Henderson, W. O. *Studies in the Economic Policy of Frederick the Great*, Cass, 1963. [chapter 6]

Henry, W. C. 'Biographical notice of the late Peter Ewart', in *Memoirs of the Manchester Literary and Philosophical Society*, 2nd series, 7 (1846), pp. 113–37. [chapter 8]

Héron de Villefosse. *De la richesse minérale*, 3 vols. and atlas, Paris, 1819, vol. 1. [chapter 6]

Hill, Christopher. *Intellectual Origins of the English Revolution*, O.U.P., 1965. [chapter 5]

*Hills, R. L. *Power in the Industrial Revolution*, Manchester U.P., 1970. [chapter 7]

Ho Ping-ti. *Studies on the Population of China 1368–1953*, Harvard U.P., Cambridge, Mass., 1959. [chapter 9]

Hodgkinson, Eaton. 'Account of Ewart's paper', in *Memoirs of the Manchester Literary and Philosophical Society*, 2nd series, 7, pp. 137–56. [chapter 8]

Honey, W. B. *Dresden China*, Faber, 1954. [chapter 6]

Hubbert, M. K. 'The energy resources of the earth', in *Scientific American*, 224 (September 1971). [part 3]

Huizinga, J. *The Waning of the Middle Ages* (trans. F. Hopman), Pelican, 1955. [chapter 2]

Huxley, Aldous. *Brave New World*, Chatto & Windus, 1932. [part 3]

——*Science, Liberty and Peace*, Chatto & Windus, 1947. [part 3]

Irwin, John, and Katharine Brett. *Origins of Chintz*, H.M.S.O., 1970. [chapter 6]

Jensen, Martin. *Civil Engineering around 1700*, Danish Technical Press, Copenhagen, 1969. [chapter 6]

Jevons, F. R. *The Teaching of Science*, Allen & Unwin, 1969. [part 3]

Jevons, W. Stanley. *The Coal Question: an Inquiry concerning the Progress of the Nation, and the Probable Exhaustion of our Coal-Mines*, London and Cambridge, 1865; 2nd edn, London, 1866; 3rd edn (ed. A. W. Flux), Macmillan 1906. [part 3]

Johnson, H. R. and A. W. Skempton, 'William Strutt's cotton mills', in *Newcomen Society Transactions, 30* (1956). [chapter 7; for a closely related article, *see* Skempton, A. W.]

Jungk, Robert. *Brighter than a Thousand Suns* (trans. James Cleugh), Gollancz, 1959; new edn, Pelican, 1960. [chapter 4 and part 3]

*Kearney, Hugh. *Science and Change, 1500–1700*, Weidenfeld & Nicolson, 1971. [chapters 4–5]

*Keller, A. G. *A Theatre of Machines*, Chapman & Hall, 1964. [chapters 2–3]
——'Pneumatics, automata and the vacuum in the work of Aleotti', in *British Journal for the History of Science, 3* (1966–7), pp. 338–47. [chapters 3–4]
——Book review, 'Mechanical Universe' (*see* Bedini, Silvio, and Francis Maddison) in *British Journal for the History of Science, 4* (1968–9), pp. 176–8. [chapter 2]

Kennedy, John. 'The rise and progress of the cotton trade', and 'Effects of the Poor Laws', in *Memoirs of the Manchester Literary and Philosophical Society*, (1819), pp. 115–37 and 430–45. [chapter 8]

Kerker, Milton. 'Science and the steam engine', in *Technology and Culture, 2* (1961), p. 383. [chapter 4]

*Klemm, Friedrich. *A History of Western Technology* (trans. Dorothea Waley Singer), Allen & Unwin, 1959. [chapters 1–6, 9; particularly good on Huygens and Papin, chapter 4]

*Klingender, Francis D. *Art and the Industrial Revolution* (ed. Arthur Elton), Evelyn, Adams & Mackay, 1968; Paladin paperback, 1972. [chapter 6]

*Landes, D. S. *The Unbound Prometheus: Technological Change and Industrial Development in Western Europe from 1750*, C.U.P., 1969. [chapters 6–7, 9 and part 3]

Lanz, P. L., and Augustín de Bétancourt. *Essai sur la composition des machines*, 2nd edn, Paris, 1819. [chapter 7]

Leavis, F. R. (ed.). *Mill on Bentham and Coleridge*, Chatto & Windus, 1950. [chapter 8]

Lee, George. *See* Boulton and Watt Collection.

Leupold, Jacob. *Theatrum machinarum generale*, Leipzig, 1724. The atmospheric engine is dealt with in paras. 202–6. [chapter 6]

Lewis, A. J. *Zinzendorff the Ecumenical Pioneer*, S.C.M., 1962. [chapter 6]

Lewis, M. J. T. *Early Wooden Railways*, Routledge, 1970. [chapters 5–6]

Luckhurst, David. *Monastic Watermills: a Study of the Mills within English Monastic Precincts*, Society for the Protection of Ancient Buildings, London, *c.* 1963. [chapter 1]

Lucretius. *The Nature of the Universe* [*De natura rerum*] (trans. Ronald Latham), Penguin Classics, 1951. [chapter 4]

Macartney, C. A. *The Habsburg Empire 1790–1918*, Weidenfeld & Nicolson, 1968. [chapter 6]

*Mack, Mary. *Jeremy Bentham: an Odyssey of Ideas 1748–1792*, Heinemann, 1962. [chapter 8]

Maddison, Angus. *Economic Growth in Japan and the U.S.S.R.*, Allen & Unwin, 1969. [chapter 9]

Mâle, Emile. *The Gothic Image* (trans. Dora Nussey), Collins, 1961. [chapter 2]

Marczali, Henry. *Hungary in the 18th Century*, C.U.P., 1910. [chapter 6]

Mariotte, Edmé. *Oeuvres*, 2 vols., Paris, 1740. [chapter 4]

——*Traité du mouvement des eaux*, Paris, 1686; trans. J. T. Desaguliers as *Hydrostaticks*, London, 1718. [chapter 4]

Meadows, Donella H., Jorgen Randers, D. L. Meadows and W. W. Behrens. *The Limits to Growth*, Earth Island, London, 1972. [part 3]

*Medawar, P. B. *The Hope of Progress*, Methuen, 1972. [part 3]

Memoirs of the Manchester Literary and Philosophical Society, see Ewart, Peter *and* Hodgkinson, Eaton. [*See also* Henry, W. C. and Kennedy, John]

Merton, R. K. *Science, Technology and Society in 17th Century England*, in *Osiris*, 1938; new edn, Fertig, New York, 1970. [chapter 5]

Mill, John Stuart. Essay on Bentham in F. R. Leavis (ed.), *Mill on Bentham and Coleridge*, Chatto & Windus, 1950. [chapter 4]

Mitchell, B. R., with Deane, Phyllis. *Abstract of British Historical Statistics* C.U.P., 1962. [chapter 7]

Morgan, B. G., *Canonic Design in English Medieval Architecture*, Liverpool U.P., 1961. [chapter 2]

Morison, Elting E. *Men, Machines and Modern Times*, M.I.T. Press, 1966. [chapter 4 and part 3]

Morrison, Philip and Emily (eds.). *Charles Babbage and his Calculating Engines: Selected Writings by Charles Babbage and others*, Dover Books, New York, 1961. [chapter 9]

Mumford, Lewis. *Technics and Civilization*, Routledge, 1946. [chapter 2 and part 3]

Munford, W. A. *William Ewart, M.P.; Portrait of a Radical*, Grafton, 1960. [chapter 8]

Musson, A. E., and Eric Robinson. *Science and Technology in the Industrial Revolution*, Manchester U.P., 1969. [chapters 4, 7–9]

Needham, Joseph. 'Mathematics and science in China and the West', in S. Barry Barnes (ed.), *Sociology of Science*, Penguin Education, 1972.

——and others. *Science and Civilization in China*, vol. 1, Introductory Orientations, C.U.P., 1954; vol. 4, part 2, Mechanical Engineering, C.U.P., 1968; vol. 4, part 3, Civil Engineering and Nautics, C.U.P., 1971. [chapters 6, 9]

Nelson, B. N. *The Idea of Usury*, Princeton U.P., 1949. [chapter 1]

New Scientist, 49 (February 1971) (interview with J. K. Galbraith). [part 3]

Newton, Isaac. *Principia*, 1687; see *Sir Isaac Newton's Mathematical Principles of Natural Philosophy* (trans. Andrew Motte, 1729, and ed. Florian Cajori, 1934), reprinted, University of California Press, 1962. [chapter 7]

Observer, [esp.] issue of 5 March 1972.

Okita, S. 'Choice of technique – Japan's experience', in Kenneth Berrill (ed.), *Economic Development with special reference to East Asia*, Macmillan, 1966. [chapter 9]

Oliver, W. H. 'Owen in 1817: the Millennialist moment', in Sidney Pollard and John Salt (eds.), *Robert Owen, Prophet of the Poor*, Macmillan, 1971. [chapter 8]

Orwell, George. *Nineteen Eighty-Four*, Secker & Warburg, 1949. [part 3]

——*The Road to Wigan Pier*, Secker & Warburg, 1937; Penguin, 1964. [acknowledgements and part 3]

Owen, Robert. *See* Strutt papers.

Pacey, A. J. Book review: 'Science and civilisation in China' (*see* Needham, Joseph) in *British Journal for the History of Science, 6* (1972–3), pp. 210–212. [chapter 6]

——'The earliest cast iron beams', in *Architectural Review, 145* (1969), p. 140. [chapters 7–8]

Pacey, Philip. 'A Gathering' (poem), in *Poetry Review*, vol. 63, no. 2 (summer 1972). [part 3]

Palladio, Andrea. *The Four Books of Architecture* (trans. Isaac Ware), 1738; reprinted Dover Books, New York, 1965. [chapter 3]

Panofsky, Erwin. *Abbot Suger on the Abbey Church of St. Denis*, Princeton U.P., 1946. [chapters 1–2]

——*Gothic Architecture and Scholasticism*, Meridian Books, New York, 1951. [chapters 1–2]

——'Artist, scientist, genius', in *The Renaissance: Six Essays*, Metropolitan Museum of Art, New York, 1962. [chapter 3]

Parent, Antoine. *Essais et recherches de mathématique et de physique*, 2nd edn., 3 vols., Paris, 1713 (esp. the analysis of Descartes' philosophy, in vol. 1, 2nd sequence of page numbering, pp. 1–472). [chapter 4]

——'Sur la plus grande perfection possible des machines dont un fluide est la force mouvante', in *Histoire et Mémoires de l'Académie Royale des Sciences*, Paris, 1704; 2nd edn, Paris, 1722; *Mémoires*, pp. 323–36. [chapter 4]

Parliamentary Papers. 1816, *3* (*Report: On children employed in manufactories*), pp. 209, 374–5. [chapter 8]

*Parsons, W. B. *Engineers and Engineering in the Renaissance*, Williams & Wilkins, Baltimore, 1939; new edn, (ed. R. S. Woodbury), M.I.T. Press, 1967. [chapter 3]

Partington, J. R. *A History of Chemistry*, vol. 2, Macmillan, 1961. [chapter 5]

Patterson, R. 'Spinning and weaving', in C. Singer, E. J. Holmyard, A. R. Hall and T. I. Williams (eds.), *A History of Technology*, vol. 2, O.U.P., 1956.

Pevsner, Nikolaus. *An Outline of European Architecture*, Pelican, 1943; 5th edn, 1957. [chapters 1–2]

*——*Pioneers of Modern Design*, Pelican, 1960. [chapters 6 and 7; part 3]

——*The Buildings of England: County Durham*, Pelican, 1953. [chapter 1]

Pierre de Maricourt [Petrus Peregrinus]. 'Letter on the magnet' [*Epistola*] (trans. Brother Arnold, with an introduction by Brother Potamian), in *Electrical World, 43* (1904), pp. 514–15, 562, 598–601. [chapter 2]

Ping-ti Ho. *See* Ho Ping-ti.

Pirenne, Henri. *A History of Europe from the Invasions to the XVI Century*, (trans. Bernard Miall), Allen & Unwin, 1939. [chapter 5]

Plato. *Timaeus* (trans. and ed. H. D. P. Lee), Penguin Classics, 1965. [chapter 2]

Playboy, issue of June 1971. [part 3]

Pollard, Sidney, and John Salt (eds.). *Robert Owen, Prophet of the Poor*, Macmillan, 1971. [chapter 8]

Pope, Alexander. *The Poems of Alexander Pope* (ed. John Everett Butt), Methuen and Yale U.P., Twickenham edn., 1939–61. [chapter 6]

Praeger, F. D., 'Brunelleschi's inventions', in *Osiris*, *9* (1950), pp. 457–554. [chapter 3]

Prentice, Archibald. *Historical Sketches*, Manchester, 1851. [chapter 8]

Price, D. J. de Solla. *On the Origin of Clockwork*, in Contributions from the Museum of History and Technology, United States National Museum; Smithsonian Institution, Washington, 1959, pp. 81–112.

Price, L. L. *A Short History of Political Economy in England*, Methuen, 14th edn, 1931. [chapter 8]

Prony. *See* Riche de Prony.

Raistrick, Arthur. 'The steam engine on Tyneside, 1715–1778', in *Newcomen Society Transactions*, *17* (1936–7), pp. 131–63. [chapter 7]

Ranis, Gustav. 'Factor proportion in Japanese economic development', in *American Economic Review*, *47* (1957), pp. 594–607. [chapter 9]

Rattansi, P. M. 'Paracelsus and the Puritan Revolution', in *Ambix*, *11* (1963), pp. 24–32. [chapter 5]

*Ravetz, J. R. *Scientific Knowledge and its Social Problems*, O.U.P., 1971. [acknowledgements and chapters 4–5 and part 3]

Read, Donald. *Peterloo, the 'Massacre' and its Background*, Manchester U.P., 1958. [chapter 8]

Reuleaux, Franz. *The Kinematics of Machinery* (trans. A. B. W. Kennedy), London, 1876; new edn, Dover Books, New York, 1963. [chapter 7]

Riche de Prony. *Nouvelle architecture hydraulique*, 2 vols., Paris, 1790–96. [chapter 7]

Robb, Nesca A. *Neoplatonism of the Italian Renaissance*, Allen & Unwin, 1935. [chapter 3]

Roberts, Michael. *The Whig Party, 1807–12*, Macmillan, 1939. [chapter 8]

Robinson, Eric: and Douglas McKie. *Partners in Science: Letters of James Watt and Joseph Black*, Constable, 1970. [chapter 8]

——and A. E. Musson. *James Watt and the Steam Revolution*, Adams & Dart, 1969. [chapter 7]

Robison, John. *A System of Mechanical Philosophy* (with notes by David Brewster), 4 vols. and plates, Edinburgh, 1822. [chapter 7]

Rolt, L. T. C. *George and Robert Stephenson: the Railway Revolution*, Longmans, 1960. [chapter 9]

*——*Thomas Newcomen: the Prehistory of the Steam Engine*, David & Charles, 1963. [chapters 4 and 6]

*——*Tools for the Job: a Short History of Machine Tools*, Batsford, 1965. [chapter 9]

Roover, Raymond de. 'A Florentine firm of cloth manufacturers', in *Speculum*, *16* (1941), pp. 1–33. [chapter 3]

Rosenbloom, R. S. 'Men and machines', in *Technology and Culture*, *5* (1964), pp. 489–511. [chapter 9]

Rostow, W. W., *The Stages of Economic Growth*, C.U.P., 1960. [parts 1 and 3]

Rouse, Hunter, and Simon Ince. *History of Hydraulics*, Dover Books, New York, 1963. [chapter 4]

Rule of St. Benedict, The (ed. and trans. Justin McCann), Burns Oates, 1952. [chapter 1]

Salzman, L. F. *English Industries of the Middle Ages*, O.U.P., 1923. [chapter 1]

Scholes, Percy A. *The Oxford Companion to Music*, 9th edn., O.U.P., 1955. [chapter 5]

Schubert, H. R. *A History of the British Iron and Steel Industry from c. 450 B.C. to A.D. 1775*, Routledge, 1957. [chapters 1 and 7]

Schumacher, E. F., and George McRobie. 'Intermediate technology and its administrative applications', in *Journal of Administration Overseas, 8* (1969), pp. 89–96 [part 3]

Schwiebert, E. G. *Luther and his Times: the Reformation from a New Perspective*, Concordia Publishing House, St. Louis, Missouri, 1950. [chapter 5]

Scientific American, [esp.] issue of September 1971 on energy resources, esp. pp. 37–144. [part 3]

*Simkin, C. G. F. *The Traditional Trade of Asia*, O.U.P., 1968. [chapters 6 and 9]

*Simson, Otto von. *The Gothic Cathedral*, Routledge, 1956; 2nd edn, Bollingen, New York, 1962. [chapters 1–3]

*Singer, C., E. J. Holmyard, A. R. Hall and T. I. Williams (eds). *A History of Technology*, 5 vols., O.U.P., 1954–9. [chapters 1–9]

Skempton, A. W., and H. R. Johnson. 'The first iron frames', in *Architectural Review, 131* (1962), pp. 175–86. [chapter 7]

Smeaton, John. *Experimental Enquiry* [papers previously published in the *Philosophical Transactions of the Royal Society*, 1759, 1776 and 1782] London, 1796. [chapter 7]

——*Miscellaneous Papers* [includes articles on astronomy and a new edn of *Experimental Enquiry*], London, 1814. [chapter 7]

——*A Narrative of the Building of the Edystone Lighthouse*, London, 1793. [chapter 7]

——*Reports of the Late John Smeaton, F.R.S.*, 3 vols., London, 1812; 2nd edn, 2 vols., London, 1837. [chapter 7]

Smiles, Samuel. *Lives of the Engineers*, 3 vols., London, 1861; new edn, 5 vols., London, 1874; David & Charles edn, 1968. [chapter 7; on Smeaton, *see* vol. 2 of the 1874 edn]

Smith, Adam. *An Inquiry into the Nature and Causes of the Wealth of Nations*, London, 1776; books I–III (ed. Andrew Skinner), Pelican, 1970. [chapters 7–8]

*Smith, C. T. *An Historical Geography of Western Europe before 1800*, Longman, 1967. [chapters 1, 3, 5, 6]

Smith, E. C. *A Short History of Naval and Marine Engineering*, C.U.P., 1937. [chapter 9]

Snow, C. P. *Last Things* (novel), Macmillan, 1970. [part 3]

——*The Two Cultures and the Scientific Revolution* (Rede Lecture, 1959), pamphlet, C.U.P., 1959. [part 3]

Strauss, E. *Sir William Petty, Portrait of a Genius*, The Bodley Head, 1954. [chapter 4]

Strutt, William. Strutt papers, Derby Public Library. MSS. letters to William Strutt from Jeremy Bentham (17 July 1794), Samuel Bentham (20 8 July 1805) and others. Letters from William Strutt to Edward Strutt (20 June 1819 and other dates). Letter from Robert Owen to Edward Strutt (1830). Unpublished *Memoir* of William Strutt. [chapter 8]

Switzer, Stephen. *An Introduction to a General System of Hydrostaticks and Hydraulicks*, 2 vols., London, 1729. (The atmospheric engine is discussed in vol. II, book iii.) [chapter 6]

Syson, Leslie. *British Water Mills*, Batsford, 1965. [chapter 1]

Talbot, G. R., and A. J. Pacey. 'Antecedents of thermodynamics in the work of Guillaume Amontons', in *Centaurus, 16* (1971), pp. 20–40. [chapter 4]

Tawney, R. H. *Religion and the Rise of Capitalism*, Murray, 1926; Pelican edn, 1964. [chapter 5]

Taylor, E. G. R., and M. W. Richey. *The Geometrical Seaman: a Book of Early Nautical Instruments*, Hollis & Carter, 1962. [chapter 2]

Thorndyke, Lynn. *A History of Magic and Experimental Science*, 8 vols., Columbia, New York, 1925–58. [chapter 2]

——*The Sphere of Sacrobosco*, Chicago U.P., 1949. [chapter 2]

Timoshenko, S. P. *History of the Strength of Materials*, McGraw-Hill, New York, 1953. [chapter 4]

*Trevor-Roper, Hugh. *Religion, the Reformation and Social Change*, Macmillan, 1967. [chapter 5]

——*The Rise of Christian Europe*, Thames & Hudson, 1965. [chapters 1 and 3]

Triewald, Marten. *Beskrifring om eld-och luftmachin vid Dannemora grufvor*, Stockholm, 1734; English translation published as *Marten Triewald's Short Description of the Atmospheric Engine*, Newcomen Society Extra Publications, Cambridge, 1928. [chapter 6]

United Nations: *Statistical Yearbook*, New York, 1971 and earlier years. [chapter 9]

Ure, Andrew. *Dictionary of Arts, Manufactures and Mines*, 1st edn, London, 1839; 4th edn, 2 vols., London, 1853. [chapter 9]

——*The Philosophy of Manufactures*, London, 1835. [chapter 9]

Usher, A. P. 'Machines and mechanisms', in C. Singer, E. J. Holmyard, A. R. Hall and T. I. Williams (eds.), *A History of Technology*, O.U.P., 1957, vol. 3, pp. 324–46. [chapter 4]

Vignes, B. J. M. in *Saint Bernard et son temps*, Association Bourguignonne des sociétés savantes, Dijon, 1928, vol. 1, pp. 259 and following.

Villard de Honnecourt. *Album de Villard de Honnecourt* (ed. J. B. A. Lassus), Paris, 1858. [chapter 2]

Villefosse. *See* Héron de Villefosse.

Vitruvius. *De architectura* (trans. Frank Granger), Heinemann, 1931. [chapters 2–3]

Waite, A. E. (ed.) *The Hermetical and Alchemical Works of Paracelsus*, 2 vols., London, 1894. [chapter 5]

Walker, James. 'Obituary notice of Peter Ewart', in the *Civil Engineer and Architect's Journal*, 6 (1843), pp. 102–3. [chapters 8–9]

Webster, Charles. *Samuel Hartlib and the Advancement of Learning*. C.U.P.,
   1970. [chapter 5]
——'Decimalization under Cromwell', in *Nature, 229* (1971), p. 463.
   [chapter 5]
——'Henry Power's experimental philosophy', in *Ambix* (Journal of the
   Society for the study of Alchemy and Early Chemistry), *14* (1967), pp.
   150–78.
Webster, John. *Academiarum examen*, London, 1654; also *The Saint's
   Guide*, London, 1654. [chapter 5]
Weidler, J. F. *Tractatus de machinis hydraulicis*, Wittenberg, 1728; 2nd edn,
   1735, section iv. [chapter 6]
Willan, T. S. *River Navigation in England, 1600–1750*, O.U.P., 1936.
   [chapter 6]
*Willey, Basil. *The Eighteenth-Century Background*, Chatto & Windus, 1940;
   Peregrine Books edn, 1962. [chapters 7–8]
Williams, Watkin. *Saint Bernard of Clairvaux*, Manchester U.P., 1935.
   [chapter 1]
Williamson, F. 'George Sorocold of Derby; a pioneer of water supply', in
   Derbyshire Archaeological and Natural History Journal (1936), p. 43.
   [chapter 6]
Wilson. P. N. 'The water-wheels of John Smeaton', in *Newcomen Society
   Transactions, 30* (1955–7), pp. 25–48. [chapter 7]
*Wittkower, Rudolf. *Architectural Principles in the Age of Humanism*,
   3rd edn., Tiranti, 1962. [chapter 3]
Wolf, A. *A History of Science, Technology and Philosophy in the 16th and
   17th Centuries*, 2 vols., Allen & Unwin; 2nd edn, 1950–52. [chapter 4]

Index